The Rainy Season

Jill Robinson

Berringden Books

ISBN 978 0 9546400 3 3

Printed in England by Booksprint

This book is dedicated to all women and girls who have had to fight for an education, or are still fighting for their right to receive an education, and to all children brought up in families affected by domestic violence and/or alcoholism.

Since the 1960s, the time to which this memoir refers, various organisations have been set up to assist with matters relating to domestic violence and alcoholism.

For women affected by domestic violence:
White Ribbon Campaign 01422 886545
Refuge 0808 2000 247

For those concerned about alcoholism:
Alcoholics Anonymous 0800 9177 650
Al-Anon (support for relatives of alcoholics) 020 7403 0888
For advice on any matter a good place to start is
the local Citizens' Advice Bureau.

The author gratefully acknowledges the assistance of
Pat Neal, Chris Ratcliffe and Tom Robinson

Chapter 1

The marriage of Dotey Rapson and Jack Sanders took place on July 15th – St. Swithin's Day – 1959, at Tiverton Register Office. That summer was notably dry, and the old adage about rain on St. Swithin's Day being followed by a further forty days and forty nights of rain did not apply. Rather, the marriage heralded ten years of tears, as quickly became apparent to Jess, the couple's eight-year-old daughter, who soon came to reflect that a mere forty rainy days and nights would have seemed like being let off for good behaviour. Jess did not attend her parents' wedding, being unaware that it was taking place. She was at home with her brother, six year old Peter. They had been left in the care of Aunt Gladys, who had travelled down to Devon from her home in Bournemouth. The children had not been at all pleased when Dotey told them that she was going away for a few days, and Aunt Gladys would be looking after them.

"Where are you going?" Peter had asked.

"Why are you going away?" enquired Jess, anxiously. All that Dotey would tell them was that she was going for a short trip 'on business.' This sounded suspicious to Jess, since Dotey did not have a job outside the home, and previous 'business trips' had taken her mother only as far as Exeter on the teatime train, always returning on the last train of the evening. She had never before left the children overnight, let alone for three days. Meanwhile, Peter began complaining about Aunt Gladys' 'high chews'.

"Her hide shoes?" asked Dotey, mishearing him.

"He means the way she eats her food," explained Jess. Aunt Gladys had a tendency to chew her food very thoroughly, with what the children considered to be an exaggerated jaw movement. For her part, Jess disliked the way Aunt Gladys always overcooked jam tarts, baking the jam with the pastry, so the jam often burnt. Dotey cooked the pastry cases first and then added the jam, and Jess much preferred this method. It seemed quite unfair of Dotey to go away without her children, why couldn't she take them on this 'business trip'? Three whole days in the care of Aunt Gladys sounded more like a punishment than anything else; yet they had not been naughty…

However, somehow or other, the children managed to survive Aunt Gladys' ministrations, and on the fourth day Dotey returned, Aunt Gladys went home, and everything seemed to be as normal. It was not until the following Saturday night, when Jess asked her usual bath-time question, "Is Daddy coming tomorrow?" that she had any inkling that things were about to change.

"Yes, your real, true Daddy is coming tomorrow," was Dotey's strangely worded reply.

"You've married him, then?" Jess was astonished at this development.

"Yes, we were married the other day, and went to Torquay on honeymoon, but I couldn't leave you children for long, and of course Daddy had to get back to his Store."

"But will Daddy be coming to live with us, now you are married?"

"Yes, he is coming to live with us for good."

For good – just how hollow this soon seemed.

Jess had realised for some time that other children's parents were usually married to each other, and generally lived under the same roof. When she had asked her mother why their own family was different, Dotey had explained that Daddy was obliged to live in Exeter because his Store, the agricultural merchant's business, was there; he could visit his family only on Sundays since that was the one day of the week the Store was closed. This explanation for their domestic arrangements had never quite satisfied Jess, who knew that other children's fathers thought nothing of travelling the fifteen miles to Exeter and back every day, there was a regular train service and anyway, Daddy had a car. And now this unexpected turn of events, this surprising secret marriage, apparently did not seem as if it could have anything to do with managerial changes at the Store, because Daddy had returned to work there. Jess hoped that her mother would tell her what was going on, but suspected that she would not. Dotey played a very close hand so far as her personal arrangements were concerned, and more than anything else, she detested being questioned, always employing the 'need to know' principle; and in her opinion, Jess did not need to know very much at all.

Dotey deliberately neglected to tell her daughter the real reason for the sudden change in their living arrangements, which was that before embarking on marriage to Dotey, Jack had been obliged to wait all these years until the death of his first wife, of whose existence Jess was unaware.

At the time of his second marriage, Jack was already sixty years old, with a grown-up son, and he did not particularly relish the prospect of being suddenly saddled with two young children. However, with his first wife recently dead after a long illness, he required someone to look after him, so he considered his options and decided to marry his long-term mistress rather than pay a housekeeper. Accordingly, he arranged to move up the Exe valley to live with his second family; he had finally run out of excuses not to.

Jack was paying the price for coveting his neighbour's wife almost twenty years previously, during the war. Albert from next door was serving in Egypt, leaving his wife, Dotey, coping with a sick mother and a couple of unruly evacuees. Jack was envious of Albert since he was on active service; at the outbreak of war Jack himself had volunteered, but was refused because he was a married man in his forties with an invalid wife to care for.

Jack's war had been the Great War of 1914-18, when he had lied about his age to the recruiting officer and no-one had bothered to check that the strapping lad was in fact only fifteen years old. The official policy at the time was that soldiers should not be sent overseas to fight until they were nineteen, but this seems to have been routinely disregarded when Jack enlisted in the Devonshire Regiment, and by the time he was celebrating his nineteenth birthday the war was into its final year. As it turned out, volunteering in 1914 may well have saved Jack's life, since had he waited to be conscripted he would in all likelihood have been sent to the Western Front. As it was, he went first to India, to Madras, now Chennai, (the only place on the sub-continent to have been bombarded by the Germans) where Jack contracted malaria, a disease from which he was to suffer recurrent bouts all his life. He was involved with the transfer of Indian nationalist prisoners, those who had rebelled against British colonial rule, to the Andaman Islands; later he saw service in Palestine, fighting the Turks. (In the 1960s, his children would sometimes hear Jack singing a doleful song about bivouacking in the desert, waiting for 'Johnny

Turk' to put an end to him.) Jack was in Palestine at the time T.E Lawrence ("Lawrence of Arabia") was there, and claimed to have once met him. Jack's battalion was disbanded in August 1918 and he came under the command of the Essex Regiment, seeing action at the Battle of Megiddo in September 1918. He ended the war near Beirut, and was discharged in April 1919 after 4 ½ years of service.

Now, at the outbreak of war again in 1939 Jack felt he was more than ready for another go at the 'Jerries'. But it was the younger men who were required to serve overseas, and Jack's contribution to the war effort was confined to the Home Guard and a certain amount of black-marketeering. In later years he was fond of recounting how he had come across a police checkpoint when returning from Dartmoor with a contraband sheep carcass in the boot of his car. Asking the officers what was the matter, they replied that a prisoner had escaped from the jail, and that they were under orders to search every vehicle leaving the moor. Jack, always able to talk his way out of a tight spot, obligingly invited the officers to inspect the boot of his small Vauxhall, since they would be certain to find the escapee hidden there. The policemen laughed and waved him on.

On a more law-abiding note, Jack contributed whole-heartedly to the "Dig for Victory" campaign; he kept a magnificent kitchen garden, and wooed his neighbour Dotey with runner beans and raspberries. One night he walked her home from a village committee meeting, and to her surprise, kissed her on her doorstep. And so the affair began, one of thousands of war-time liaisons taking place under the threat of a German invasion. Dotey's mother had recently died, and her homesick evacuees had returned to London; in the Spring of 1942 Exeter was suffering the Baedeker Raids (whereby historic cities with no military significance were attacked by the Germans in revenge for the Allied bombing of Lubeck) and so was no safer than the East End. ("Exeter was a jewel; we have destroyed it", crowed Hitler.) Dotey, grieving and alone, succumbed to the charms of her predatory horticultural neighbour. The air-raid shelter at the bottom of the garden, shared between the two households, served as a secret trysting place.

Jack had been born in 1899 into a large family, consisting of four boys and four girls, not at all unusual in late Victorian/early

Edwardian times. He left school at the then customary age of twelve. Half a century later, he would always insist to his daughter that formal education was quite unnecessary, since what counted was time spent at the 'university of life', from which he had graduated in spectacular style following his military service. Jack had of course been much more fortunate than many of his contemporaries, who had not survived the war to graduate from anywhere. After demobilisation, the still teenage Jack was seeking work. Eventually an opportunity arose for him and his brothers to run an Agricultural Merchants store in Tudor Street. Jess remembered it in the 1960s as a rambling pink-washed building, full of various sacks of fertiliser, grain and seed potatoes, and inhabited by a large family of cats, whose pinkish coloured fur seemed to have evolved to blend in with their surroundings. These cats were not to be petted, since they were feral animals, whose job was to keep the rodent population under control.

Jack was far from being an astute businessman; he liked the good life, and would spend any profit from the Store at Newton Abbot and Haldon Races, or in the local pubs. By the time of his marriage to Dotey the business was already beginning to suffer from a lack of investment, as well as price competition from larger enterprises, and Jack was well on the way to becoming an alcoholic. The race-going and drinking continued. Jack's business may have been in decline, but he maintained his accustomed self-indulgent way of life, despite his new family responsibilities.

Chapter 2

Dotey always thought of life as being divided into two distinct epochs; the seemingly carefree days she had enjoyed 'before the war' and the very different years that followed. She was born in Plymouth in 1910, at the end of the Edwardian era, the only child of comfortably-off parents. Her father, George Annear, was in the Post Office Telecommunications service, and had been posted to the remote Connemara Coast of Ireland at the outbreak of the Great War, to work on the Marconi Signal station. Some of little Dorothy's earliest memories were of Clifden in the far West; the wild sea, the rugged coast, the donkey carts, the devout Catholic housemaid kneeling before the dusty grate to impose ashes on her forehead at the beginning of Lent; and it was here that she acquired the pet name by which she came to be known for ever afterwards – Dotey, an Irish term of endearment, a convenient shorthand for Dorothy.

In later life, Dotey hoped she would have the opportunity to make a return visit to Clifden, but lacking the means, she never did. Her daughter Jess eventually went there with her own family in 1992, to find the Marconi station long gone; instead there was a monument to aviation pioneers Alcock and Brown, who had landed their plane there. By the time of that first transatlantic flight in 1919, Dotey and her family had already left Ireland. Her father had been sent to Haverfordwest in Wales towards the end of the war, and was still there when the Armistice was declared. Eight-year-old Dotey took part in the celebrations, joining the parade dressed as Britannia, clutching her little trident, with her bright auburn hair gleaming in the firelight. She was thoroughly enjoying the fun until she heard someone in the crowd remarking that it was a pity they were going to burn that pretty little red-haired girl on the bonfire. After an anxious few minutes, Dotey was relieved to discover that child sacrifice was not after all intended to form part of the Armistice festivities.

The family returned to Devon, and were in Plymouth for the historic 1919 General Election, in which Nancy Astor became the first woman Member of Parliament to take her seat. Nine year old Dotey joined in with singing "Vote, vote, vote for Nancy Astor!" and there was a sense of history being made. Sinn Fein MP Constance Markievicz had been the first woman elected, but she had declined to take her seat. Women over thirty had recently been given the vote, but it would be another nine years until women were able to vote at the age of twenty-one, as men did.

George's work took later him to Exeter. Dotey was very bright, and her parents were advised that she should try for a scholarship to attend one of the city's leading schools for girls. This suggestion horrified Dotey, who had absolutely no wish to go to the trouble of sitting an exam simply for the privilege of being labelled a 'scholarship kid' by those whose parents were wealthy enough to pay the fees. Her father also vetoed the idea, saying that he was well able to pay for his daughter's education, and that it would be quite wrong for her to take one of the limited scholarship places, which he considered should go to girls from poor families.

Dotey left school with no qualifications, since not only did school-work not interest her, but there was no real pressure on girls of her class to succeed academically. Her father got her a job as a telephonist, and she spent a few happy years operating the manual switchboard. In those days, callers had to contact the operator in order to place calls, and the telephonists often occupied quiet moments eavesdropping on the conversations of unsuspecting subscribers. It once gave Dotey great satisfaction to cause a deafening ringing noise to sound in the ear of a former boyfriend, whom she overheard inviting a friend of hers on a date. "But what about Dotey?" Muriel had demurred. The boyfriend had passed some derogatory remark about Dotey Annear, and received a sore ear by way of comeuppance.

Dotey, as recalled by her younger cousin Barbara many years later, enjoyed being the rather spoiled only child, having lots of lovely clothes, plenty of jewellery, a choice of boyfriends (often college boys from St. Luke's), and a great deal of fun. Barbara remembered with admiration her lively auburn-haired elder cousin, who went to tea-dances and house parties and revelled in the excitement of the 'flapper' era. When she was 24, Dotey married Albert Rapson, whom she had met at a tennis club, with little Barbara as her bridesmaid. Albert had been a shop assistant in an ironmongery business, but Dotey's father soon managed to get him a better position as an engineer with the Post Office. The newly-weds moved into a rented house in the village of Alphington, on the outskirts of Exeter. They were able to completely furnish their new home from the best store in the city, all for £100. Dotey of course gave up her job, since women were not expected to continue working after they married. (Many occupations, including the Civil Service and teaching, operated a marriage bar, meaning that married women were not permitted to work.)

For five years, until the outbreak of World War Two, Dotey and Albert lived a sociable and carefree life. They had no children. Dotey later told Jess that she had not then wanted any, being "too selfish." Her great friend from their telephonist days, Phyllis, now a mother of two small children, reminded her that children would be a comfort in her old age; but old age seemed a long way off, and at the time, Dotey did not heed Phyl's advice. (Sadly, both Phyl's children pre-deceased her, dying in middle age and leaving no children of their own, while their mother lived into her nineties; whereas Dotey, who went on to become a mother of four, did not survive long enough to meet any of her four grandchildren.) However, in 1930s Exeter, Dotey and Albert could drive down to the coast whenever they felt like a trip, attend tennis parties and other social gatherings, and generally please themselves, until the outbreak of war in 1939 changed everything.

Chapter 3

When war was declared, Dotey's untroubled life came to an abrupt end. With the imminent threat of German bombs raining down on London two young bothers arrived as evacuees from the East End. To Dotey's horror, Don and Billy were found to be crawling with lice and stitched into newspaper vests for the winter. Dotey had to cut them free, bath and delouse them, then buy them new underwear and pyjamas. (Her experience was by no means uncommon; a report by the National Federation of Women's Institutes, "Town Children through Country Eyes", detailing the responses of 1,700 WIs, made for shocking reading. Vermin, skin diseases and bed-wetting among evacuee children were distressingly common.) Dotey's evacuees, with no indoor bathroom at home, were unused to being bathed, and were terrified of the water, believing they would drown. Their Cockney accents were so pronounced that the Devonians could not understand them; neither could the boys understand the locals. Dotey's introduction to childcare had been dramatic, her comfortable middle-class existence colliding with the stark reality of East End poverty the day that Don and Billy crossed the threshold. Appalled by their messy eating habits and the way they gesticulated awkwardly when holding cutlery, she tried to teach them what she considered to be proper table manners. However, for such disadvantaged children they seemed to be astonishingly well connected, frequently referring to visits from the Major or even the General. Dotey found this puzzling, until the boys' father arrived for a visit, dressed in his Salvation Army uniform, waving his cutlery throughout the meal and talking with his mouth full about the General.

Once everyone had got over their culture shock, Dotey became extremely fond of Don and Billy, and was sorry when they went back to London. Exeter suffered badly in the Baedecker Raids of April 1942, so was no safer than London for evacuees, many of whom were in any case extremely homesick. Dotey, now relieved of child-caring responsibilities, was often on fire-watching duties. She found she was missing Don and Billy, and began to reappraise her ideas as to the possibility of having children of her own. Meanwhile,

Albert had been conscripted into the Navy and was serving as a radio operator. He came home on leave in 1944, and Dotey's first child. Terence, was born in May 1945, shortly after VE Day. Dotey's labour was protracted and she was eventually given chloroform, so that a forceps delivery could be performed. Like her mother before her, and her daughter later on, Dotey suffered with cephalo-pelvic disproportion, in that her pelvis would not expand sufficiently to deliver a baby comfortably. As a result, Terry was slightly disabled during the birth process, but this was not discovered until he began to crawl, when it was apparent that his right leg trailed behind the left. Dotey delayed her second pregnancy because of anxiety about further difficulties. Jeff was born in 1949, and fortunately his birth was more straightforward.

Despite their outward appearance as a happy family, Dotey and Albert had been unable to settle back into their pre-war way of life, since far too much had changed for both of them in the intervening years. Dotey was still grieving for her mother, Olive, who had died in the County Asylum during the war. She had been suffering with a mental illness, supposedly brought on by the change of life, and had tried to cut her wrists. At the time, it was actually a criminal offence to attempt suicide, and offenders were either imprisoned or certified insane. Olive had duly been certified, and incarcerated in the dreaded Digby Hospital outside Exeter. Her death was a terrible blow to an already stressed Dotey, coming at the time of the Exeter blitz. Then shortly after the war her father, George, was sent by the Post Office to Bournemouth, where his last task before retirement was to be the supervision of the installation of a new telephone system. Accommodation was arranged for him with a divorced lady hairdresser, the redoubtable Gladys. She immediately made it her mission to cure her widowed lodger's stomach ulcer before the installation of the new telephone system was complete. This she achieved by means of a relentless diet of egg custard. George then felt obliged to propose to her, and upon his retirement, he announced that he would be remaining in Bournemouth.

Dotey felt she had now lost both her parents within the space of a few years. No sooner had the war ended then she had found herself with a disabled baby to care for, and later on, Jeff turned out to be a lively toddler, requiring constant vigilance. Once, Dotey received a phone call from the owner of the market garden opposite, informing her that there was a child at the open bedroom window, perched precariously on the sill. Dotey had put Jeff down for a sleep in his cot, but he had just discovered how to climb. On another occasion, Dotey was unable to find Jeff even with the door and window securely shut; after a thorough search, he was eventually located, asleep in the airing cupboard.

The Rapson marriage, which had been severely damaged by war-time separation, was falling apart, with Dotey and Albert leading almost separate lives. After the war ended, Dotey had continued her relationship with next-door neighbour Jack, while Albert was heavily involved with the local operatic society. When she became pregnant for the third time, in June 1950, Dotey was convinced that the baby was not Albert's, but was the result of an expedition she and Jack had made in his car to a secluded part of Stoke Woods. She kept the news from her husband, in order to gain time to work something out with Jack. They disagreed about what to do; he thought it was time the whole matter was brought out into the open, while Dotey, sensing disaster, wanted to keep things quiet for as long as possible. Matters came to a head one evening, as Dotey and Albert were washing the dishes after their evening meal. Their two little boys were asleep upstairs. There came a commotion at the back door, and Jack appeared with his sick wife in tow.

"Dotey's going to have a baby, and I'm the father!"

Albert's reaction was typical of his era and class. "I'll ruin you, if it's the last thing I do!" However, nothing could happen immediately, since inconveniently, Albert was at the time the Chairman of the local branch of the Loyal Order of Moose, and Dotey was of course Chairman's Lady. Nobody wanted a scandal to surface during Albert's period of office, so divorce proceedings were put on hold until after the couple's ceremonial duties were complete. Dotey was able to spend a final Christmas with her young sons: Terry was completing his first term at school, and had learned a new Christmas carol, which he sang to his mother on the way home. Dotey found his rendition of *Away in a Manger* heartbreaking, her little boy was naturally looking forward to Christmas and was completely oblivious as to the upheaval which was to follow. Albert then made his wife a final offer; she could remain at home with him and their two boys if she agreed to give up the new baby as soon as it was born and place it in an orphanage, since he was not prepared to raise another man's child. Otherwise, she would have to leave. It was a harsh choice, and almost inexplicably, Dotey declined to give up her lover's baby, thereby sacrificing her two boys, her marriage, her home and comfortable lifestyle. The divorce came at tremendous personal cost to herself, since as the 'guilty' party in the days before 'no-fault' divorce, she was obliged to sign an affidavit chronicling her relationship with Jack, with no detail spared, including the fact that her third child had been conceived in the back of a Vauxhall car as a result of the illicit Stoke Woods tryst. So one morning, five-year old Terry and toddler Jeff awoke to find their mother gone. Terry was distressed and mystified. No-one would tell him what had happened, indeed, as he told Jess years later, the impression he was given, when he asked where his mother was, was that it was 'none of his business'. Albert engaged a local woman known as Auntie Dar to come every day to look after the boys. What eighteen month old Jeff made of the situation can scarcely be imagined.

However, despite Dotey's tremendous sacrifice, it soon emerged that Jack was not prepared to give up anything. He remained at home with his wife, who refused to divorce him, telling Dotey that to run off and set up home with her would be 'bad for business.' He had already been obliged under a court order to make financial restitution to Albert for 'deprivation of conjugal rights', and had been drummed out of the Loyal Order of Moose for seducing a fellow member's wife. Jack considered that he had been punished enough. So bizarrely, Jack stayed on as Albert's next door neighbour, seeing more of Dotey's sons than she now did, since Albert had formally obtained custody of the boys. This was common practice at the time, where the person deemed to be the 'guilty party' lost the children of the marriage. Under the terms of the divorce decree, the boys were permitted to visit their mother for two weeks during the summer holidays, and on Boxing Day. Jack, of course, saw the boys frequently, as the neighbouring families went about their daily business. To them, he was still 'Uncle Jack', but the shared part of the garden was out of bounds.

It was many years before Jess came to realise with dismay that she had been the unwitting cause of all this disruption and heartache, affecting seven people in two families. She felt tremendous guilt that her mother had been obliged to give up so much, and later to endure so much, simply for her sake. Teenage Jess felt that she owed it to Dotey to prove to her that she had made the right decision all those years ago. If Dotey was not happy, as was increasingly often the case, then the blame could ultimately be laid at Jess's feet, and maybe the orphanage would have been the best solution after all; so Jess resolved to try to do and be everything her mother wanted, seeking never to provide Dotey with any excuse for regretting her decision to keep her daughter. In doing so, she made a rod for her own back, since she was a very ordinary girl, while Dotey turned out to be an exacting mother, so far as her only daughter was concerned. Jess quickly came to realise that she could never become the daughter her mother wished for, no matter how hard she tried, and feared that Dotey might consider that she, Jess, had not really been worth the sacrifice – after all, she was not pretty or graceful, nor especially musically talented; in fact she was overweight, shy and clumsy, much to her mother's obvious disappointment. However, Jess was blessed with the gift of perseverance, and she never stopped trying to please the woman who had refused to give her up. If she made a mistake, as often happened, much to Dotey's exasperation, Jess made a mental note to try never to repeat that particular error. She strove to control her clumsiness, although she never really succeeded, and the father of her elder son was still chiding her about this annoying aspect of her behaviour twenty years later. Jess tried hard to accomplish the tasks her mother set her without dropping or spilling anything, but such effort took time, leading to Dotey sighing with exasperation. ("Really Jess, whatever can be taking you so long? I could jump over your head!") When Jess ventured to explain that she was taking her time because she was trying to do things carefully, Dotey often misinterpreted this as Jess going slowly in order to vex her, so that in the end she, Dotey would have to do whatever it was. And so Jess fetched and carried and ran errands for her mother, and learned to bite her tongue, nodding meekly when she really wanted to reply, or 'answer back' as it was then known. Jess realised at a young age that the only way to have a successful relationship with Dotey was through absolute unquestioning compliance, and so Jess complied.

Sometimes Jess asked her mother "Do you love me, Mummy?" knowing that Dotey's reply would invariably be "Of course I do – when you're good." The importance of good behaviour was stressed at every opportunity, while the words "I'm disappointed in you," stung Jess to the quick.

Dotey stuck to her 'need to know' policy and never told Jess any detail of the circumstances of her conception. When a teenage Jess, attempting to work out why her parents had not married until she was aged eight and Peter was six, tried to broach the subject, Dotey told her that it was none of her business. Many years later, Jeff found Dotey's divorce affidavit among his father's papers. He in his turn kept the relevant information from Jess, fearing that telling her would result in Jess thinking less of her mother. When Jeff eventually decided in 2014 to disclose the details of the Stoke Woods car assignation which had resulted in Jess, his sister assured him that she would not stand in judgement of their mother, since after all, Jess herself had made plenty of mistakes in life. All Jess had ever wanted to know was the truth, which had been assiduously kept from her. Jess laughed, remembering travelling as a child in the back of the old Vauxhall, which turned out to have had such a colourful career, involving black market sheep carcasses and adulterous trysts; she could even recall the registration number. Jeff commented dryly that she might like to draw some consolation from the fact that the car had been equipped with leather seats, a detail which Jess had in fact forgotten; she had at least been conceived in some comfort.

Her mother's inconsistency puzzled Jess, she always demanded the truth but never reciprocated; she insisted that Jess study hard when she had clearly despised school-work; she obliged Jess to stay at home and complete seemingly unending household tasks, when Dotey herself had enjoyed a childhood and adolescence of indulgence and gaiety; she dressed Jess and styled her hair in as unbecoming a manner as possible, when, according to Cousin Barbara, Dotey had always been attired in the latest fashions. At least Jack was openly hypocritical: "Do as I say, my girl, not as I do!" Dotey decreed that Jess should have nothing whatever to do with boys, must never marry, but should become a school-mistress. In short, Jess's life was to be the exact opposite of her mother's, and Dotey was determined to ensure that Jess complied. Jess was obliged to share a bedroom with her mother as a teenager, and Dotey would not let Jess go to sleep until she had received a satisfactory report of her daughter's doings for the day, down to the tiniest detail, so Jess felt she had no choice but to obey in every particular.

Chapter 4

Upon leaving Alphington in early 1951, the pregnant Dotey had been banished to the village of East Budleigh to await her baby's birth, and Jess appeared, ten days late, in mid-March. For her confinement, Dotey had returned to Poltimore House Nursing Home, where Jeff had been born, and her daughter was delivered by the splendidly named Dr. Fortescue Ffoulkes. Jack visited soon afterwards, and declared that the baby looked 'Japanese'. Jess was a healthy weight and had evidently become a little squashed during the birth process, but she soon filled out and acquired a rosy colour. Dotey announced her intention of naming her new daughter Jacqueline, as a compliment to him, but Jack declared that she would never learn to spell such a fanciful name; this was to be the first of very many occasions when he would underestimate his daughter's potential ability. He wanted to call the baby Jessie after his late mother, but Dotey thought this sounded too old-fashioned, so they eventually decided upon Jess. When Dotey went to register Jess's birth, she gave the baby's father's name as Albert Roy Rapson, telephone sales engineer. The delayed divorce was yet to be finalised, so Dotey and Albert were still married. The presumption of legitimacy in English law ensured that any child born to a married woman was deemed to have been fathered by her husband, so Dotey's perjury went unchallenged, until a bemused Jess eventually discovered her birth certificate twenty-one years later, while sorting out papers after her mother's death, and did not know what to think. It seemed she had a legal father and a different natural father; but how could she find out which one was her actual father?

Dotey was extremely lonely living at East Budleigh; it was too far away for her Exeter friends to visit very often, and the Plymouth relatives were so disgusted at her behaviour in running off and leaving two small sons that they shunned her. It was not until Barbara's wedding in 1953, when her loyal young cousin insisted that she be invited, that Dotey was re-admitted to the extended family. When Jess was born, Dotey expected Jack to come and live with her and the baby, but he was adamant that he could not leave the Store, his sick wife and his son, since to set up home in a love-nest would create a scandal and badly affect the Store's business. Dotey's father George was in a position to assist his daughter financially, and found Dotey a flat off the Topsham Road in Exeter, which was more convenient for Dotey's friends to visit; but it was very small, and by early 1952 Dotey was again pregnant, so another move was essential. George then took a house for the family in the village of Silverton, high up above the Exe Valley. It was there that Dotey's fourth and final child, Peter, was born in October 1952. Dotey had decided upon a home birth, but the baby was enormous, weighing more than the ten pounds upper limit of the midwife's spring balance scales, and petite Dotey once again had a struggle giving birth. She was by now aged almost 43, and the birth of three children within just over three years had taken its toll on her health.

Jess's earliest memory was sitting up in her pram by a chilly, partly open window, chewing on a 'Biccipeg' rusk, which young children used to be given to assist with teething. However, Jess had no memory of a time before Peter was born - it seemed as though her brother, nineteen months younger herself, had always been there. Peter was a beautiful child, winning the 'Bonny Baby' contest in June 1953 at the village Coronation celebrations, with his head-full of golden curls, fair skin and gorgeous smile. By contrast, plump Jess had unremarkable straight brown hair, and would never in her life win any beauty competition.

Even though she had now given him a son, Jack still refused to live with Dotey. His wife would not divorce him, which was the only way their marriage could be ended, since the 'guilty party' at that time had no right to divorce; any proceedings had to be initiated by the wronged spouse. Jack was still relying on the excuse that he could not risk further scandal while it remained impossible for him to marry Dotey. So, with the temporary rental agreement at Silverton about to expire, a seven year lease was arranged on a four storey Victorian villa on the outskirts of Tiverton.

Dotey initially protested that the house was much too large, and would be very difficult to heat; there were two huge rooms downstairs, with enormously high ceilings. On the first floor there were three bedrooms, a bathroom and separate lavatory, and up a further flight of stairs were three additional large attic bedrooms. The house was heated by means of coal fires, so it was necessary to carry coal-scuttles and ash buckets up and down flights of stairs. At first, Dotey could not find the kitchen, but discovered that it was located in a sort of lean-to conservatory attached to the living room, on the north-facing side of the house, with a sink at the far end and an electric cooker point half way along. There was space for a small utility cupboard, which it was just about possible to squeeze past in order to reach the sink. It would be freezing cold in winter, and stiflingly hot in summer; in fact it was hard to imagine a room less suited to the storage and preparation of food. However, Dotey eventually agreed to take the house on account of the magnificent view, looking across the valley to the woods and hills beyond; she also liked the extensive gardens which would become wonderful playgrounds for the children. The shrubbery at the front was perfect for 'hide-and-seek', the back lawn was ideal for the children's swing.

In the 1870s, when The Close had been built, the houses had been run with the assistance of a number of servants. The basement was now fitted out as a self-contained flat, containing a butler's pantry complete with a set of bells. The servants being long gone, Dotey had to manage with the help of a twice-weekly cleaning lady (a dignified Scotswoman, Mrs. MacDougall,) and a war-wounded ex-soldier gardener on Fridays. Even so, the house presented a huge amount of work for Dotey, especially the coal fire in the living room, which she always struggled to ignite. Dotey seemed to spend hours on her knees trying to get the fire to catch, by means of a sheet of newspaper held across the fireplace, trying to draw air into the grate. Often as not, she would resort to a final desperate act of sprinkling paraffin onto the coals to get the fire started. The coal had to be carted up from the cellar, and the overflowing ash pan taken out each morning. Winter was an ordeal, and in order to enter the conservatory kitchen during the cold weather it was necessary to don coat, scarf, boots and hat. Whenever the kitchen door was opened a howling draught of cold air would sweep into the living room where the children were huddled around the fire, sheltered to only a limited extent by a screen placed between the fire and the door. It was not uncommon for Jess to find her toothbrush frozen stiff, since the only heating upstairs was provided by a couple of small paraffin stoves placed in the bathroom and lavatory, in a not always successful attempt to prevent the pipes from freezing. The bedroom fires were never lit except in cases of illness, since unheated bedrooms were then considered healthier. Intricate frost patterns formed on the inside of the sash windows, as condensation froze on the icy panes.

The Close was over a mile from the town centre, at the top of a steep hill; Dotey had no car, and there were no buses, but fortunately, most tradesmen delivered. Laundry, meat, paraffin and groceries arrived by van, while newspapers and green-groceries came by bike. Coal came by lorry and was tipped straight down the coal-hole into the cellar. The milk-float came daily. Dotey brought her two pre-school children to live in the Close in 1954. They were to remain there for fourteen years, joined in due course by Jack. Jess later remembered the five years before Jack's arrival as being almost idyllic. Despite the inconvenience, the cold, and remoteness from the town, the children were happy. They had plenty of room to play, in the house, the gardens, and the fields beyond. Jess had a big bedroom, so there was plenty of space for her dolls, books and toys. The Close was a private road, so ideal for riding tricycles and bikes, while the shrubbery was great for dens and climbing trees. While Dotey often longed for somewhere more convenient, Jess and Peter were very happy with their surroundings.

Chapter 5

Although she had been an indulged only child herself, Dotey was a very strict mother, who believed the adage 'Spare the rod and spoil the child.' When Jess and Peter fought as toddlers, Dotey fought back; if they pinched or bit one another, she pinched or bit them. There was a special stick kept in the corner of the living-room, and a glance from Dotey in that direction would be enough to stop bad behaviour. The worst sin was telling lies, which Dotey abhorred. The children were slapped or sent to their rooms if they misbehaved, and Jess could recall only a very few occasions when Dotey had thought it necessary to actually give them the stick. Being sent to her bedroom was not too much of a hardship, for Jess had plenty to occupy her there; it was the manner in which she was dismissed that hurt her more than the actual punishment. Often she would be banished without understanding the reason; if she asked why she was being sent upstairs, her mother would reply coldly that the very fact that she did not realise what she had done wrong only made it worse! Jess would then rack her brains trying to recall what her misdemeanour might have been. Usually, it turned out to be something caused by sheer carelessness rather than malice, for Jess was never a deliberately naughty child. She might have forgotten to wipe her feet as she came in from the garden, or perhaps have left the hot tap running by mistake. Dotey would not tolerate thoughtlessness; she was constantly impressing upon Jess how hard her life was, how she, as a single mother, had to 'work her fingers to the bone', or even 'work like a black', (a common enough expression in those pre-politically correct days), for the sake of her children, "Yet this is how you repay me!" with muddy footprints in the hall or hot water wasted. Consideration for other people was a lesson of prime importance, but Jess was rather a day-dreamer, which exasperated Dotey, who wanted her daughter constantly alert, attentive and ready to run errands. "Jump to it, Jess! I need you to fetch my hanky from upstairs. Your little legs are younger than mine!"

A continuing form of psychological punishment was the threat of boarding school. Jess was terrified of being sent to such an establishment; she had read school stories where the girls slept in large dormitories, getting up to all kinds of mischief, and she knew that she would not care for that at all. She liked being quietly at home with Peter and Dotey, with Jack visiting only on Sundays, and knew she would never cope with being sent away. In her innocence, she did not realise that boarding school was expensive and quite beyond her mother's means, so the oft-repeated threat was actually quite empty. Jess believed that those girls who were sent away to school must have been so naughty that their mothers no longer wanted them living at home; she had somehow confused boarding with approved schools, believing them to be the ultimate form of punishment.

It was Dotey's custom to always take an hour's rest in the afternoons, even during school holidays, when the children were at home. They were under strict instructions not to disturb her, and to amuse themselves without mishap, while she lay on her bed or the settee, with the 'Daily Mail' and a few boiled sweets. If it was Mrs. MacDougall's day to clean, she would often have her daughter Jeannie with her, and she would then offer to take all the children to Peoples' Park, where they enjoyed playing on the swings and the witches' hat. Once, Jess and Peter stood in the bandstand and sang the popular song 'Granada', which could be heard on the radio a great deal about that time, much to the amusement of other park users. On other occasions when Mrs. MacDougall was looking after them they walked out into the countryside as far as the Wishing Tree, passing on the way a brick-built barn, which backed onto the road. The children always knocked on the shuttered barn window, as this was 'Mr. Nobody's' house' and no-one ever answered; however, one day, to their great surprise, a ruddy-faced farm hand threw back the shutters. "Mr. Nobody!" shrieked all the children in delight. The farm worker good-naturedly joined in the fun – "Yes, that's me, and this is my house!"

The Wishing Tree, an ancient sycamore, stood in the middle of the road at the junction of Tidcombe Lane and Newts Hill, and was reputed to have magical properties. If you ran around it three times and made a wish, this was supposed to come true. Of course, you were not meant to tell anyone what you had wished for, since this would mean that your wish could not be granted. Once, when Peter was very young, he forgot this rule, and loudly proclaimed that he wished for an ice-cream. All at once an ice-cream van appeared in the distance, heading in their direction. The children jumped up and down, screaming with excitement, but the van drove straight past them and turned down the lane to its next scheduled stop, which was perhaps just as well, since no-one had any money with them.

Jess and Peter were generally polite and well-behaved children, and people would comment on this, praising Dotey as a good mother, which indeed she was, judging by the standards of the day. There was still an idea prevalent at the time that children 'should be seen and not heard'. Jess and Peter were therefore forbidden to interrupt grown-ups' conversations for any reason whatsoever. This often meant standing still for protracted periods while Dotey chatted to people she met in the town. There was no question of fidgeting, whining or asking 'can we go now?' However, Jess often became anxious that she would need to use the toilet before her mother had finished her conversation and they could finally return home. Dotey did not encourage the use of public conveniences, wherein she considered diseases lurked, and preferred Jess to wait. But sometimes Jess was desperate, and did not feel that she would last the ascent of Canal Hill without a comfort stop. Dotey would then produce a penny coin for the public toilets at Lowman Green, with instructions that Jess should on no account sit on the seat, but that she should carefully hover above it.

When they were still quite young, the children were permitted to ride their bicycles in the quiet drive, but not onto the main road. Dotey was anxious about the tradesmen's vehicles, which were continually coming and going; but then one of the neighbours helpfully put up a sign at the end of the drive, which read 'Caution Children!' in big red letters. This caused much amusement, and people would remark to Jess that she was really was such a caution, the authorities had even been obliged to put up warning notices about her... Jess was puzzled, as she did not know this meaning of the word, simply thinking it meant 'Take Care.' The children were instructed never to speak to strangers, who might be wicked escaped prisoners on the run from Dartmoor, nor to accept sweets from anyone they did not know, and absolutely never to accept a lift from any unknown driver. Once Jess was walking home from school in the pouring rain when a car pulled up and the driver offered her a lift. She did not recognise the elderly gentleman as one of her mother's acquaintances, so she declined politely and walked on. Dotey said later that it would have been perfectly all right for her to come home in old Mr. Vickery's car, but she was pleased that Jess had heeded her words and erred on the side of caution.

Like all mothers, Dotey's main concern was for the health and well-being of her children, and she was continually worrying about them catching colds in the ill-heated and draughty house. If she herself had a cold, she would tie a large folded handkerchief over the lower half of her face, so that Jess and Peter should not catch her germs. Jess referred to this as 'Mummy Bandit'. However, despite Dotey's care, the children caught frequent colds, which always turned to catarrh, or 'hung on', for weeks in the freezing house, so that the children had streaming noses every winter. They were dosed with cod-liver oil and vitamin tablets and various proprietary medicines; Vick was applied to their chests, and something known as 'Tickly-tacks' rubbed on their sore noses. Coughs were treated with what Jess considered to be a vile-tasting substance called 'Gees Linctus', or sometimes with pleasanter-flavoured 'Owbridges', while any child off its food was given Lucozade, now known as a sports drink, but which Dotey kept exclusively for the sickroom. Jess also remembered a kaolin and mustard poultice being made up and applied to draw out infection.

Bedtime was strictly adhered to, the children had to be tucked up with the lights out by seven o'clock. They were forbidden to get out of bed for any reason whatsoever. Once when Jess was very young she had a nightmare and woke to find that all the bedclothes had fallen onto the floor. She struggled unsuccessfully in the dark to retrieve them, and eventually called for her mother. Dotey told Jess off in brusque tines, since she did not care to be disturbed of an evening, so Jess was reluctant to call her mother again when she got into difficulties in the dark. However, the same thing happened after a nightmare a few months later, when Aunt Gladys was staying. Jess called out in distress, and Aunt Gladys immediately came and sorted out the bedclothes, tucking her in with kind words, while Dotey clicked her tongue and muttered about the necessity of not spoiling attention-seeking children. It was then agreed that Jess could have a low night-light, so that she could see to readjust her bedclothes should she have another nightmare.

The 7 pm bedtime did not suit Jess, who often could not sleep, it was too early to settle, and anyway, there was often so much noise outside. Depending on which way the wind was blowing, Jess could either hear Blundell's School band practising a mile away to the East, or the Sea-Scouts, blowing bugles in their hut by the canal in the opposite direction. Sometimes the noise was so loud it almost seemed as if the combined bands were marching up the garden path. Occasionally Dotey would play the piano downstairs, she always opened with a song entitled *Rendezvous* ("King George 5th's favourite tune!") followed by a piece by Franz Lehar; but Jess preferred the 'Destiny Waltz' or the 'Song of India', and she especially liked to hear a selection from 'Kismet'. Jess would read with a torch under the covers until she finally felt tired enough to sleep.

Dotey rationed the children's confectionery intake to two sweets per day, eaten after lunch. She insisted that they eat up all their greens, and did not allow them to become at all 'faddy' about food. Once, Jess developed a rash and an aversion to light, so Dotey sent for the doctor, suspecting measles. It was not the usual GP who came, but a locum, a rather grand retired doctor who remembered the days a decade earlier, before the National Health Service, when people had thought twice before calling out the doctor. This superior gentleman declared that Jess's rash was the result of her eating too many sweets and insufficient cabbage. Jess was lying on the settee, feeling extremely unwell, but even in her poorly state she was aware that the doctor was receiving the sharp end of her mother's tongue as he retreated down the hall. The following day, with Jess no better, their family doctor came and diagnosed measles.

Peter's health was an especial worry, since he was subject to bouts of croup, a condition which resulted in severe breathing difficulties. The attacks always seemed to come at night, and Jess would awaken to hear a loud barking cough and a commotion in the bathroom. It was all very distressing. Jess always tried to help her mother manage these attacks as best she could. Traditionally, the treatment for a 'croupy' child involved holding him over a basin of streaming water, while at the same time keeping an umbrella overhead to contain the steam. This was intended to open up the blocked airways. Jess would be in charge of replenishing the kettle, while Dotey held poor Peter firmly over the steaming basin, under the umbrella. Children did in fact die as a result of croup-related breathing failure; but thankfully, Peter eventually outgrew the condition.

On the whole, in between Peter's croup attacks and Jess's episodes of thoughtlessness, the little family lived happily. Dotey read them a story aloud every night, so the children quickly learned to read. They tuned in to "Listen With Mother" every day, singing along with the nursery rhymes. Dotey took them for walks along the canal bank, looking at the resident swans and moorhens, and to a nearby lane to admire the profusion of violets and primroses every Spring. In summer, they visited a local wood to pick beech-leaves for Dotey's *art deco* wall-vases. There were trips to the seaside by train in school holidays, and occasional visits to the circus or the pantomime in Exeter. They took improving periodicals, such as "The Children's Newspaper", and "Look and Learn", while comic strip papers such a "The Beano" were forbidden. Jack came to lunch on Sundays, and would make an attempt to play with the children, telling Jess to hold his hands and stand on his feet while he danced, so that she moved around rather like a toy doll; while Peter received a football to kick around in the garden. Jack always returned to Exeter in the evening in order to 'open up the store' the following day; and since Dotey had impressed upon the children that they should never lie or be deceitful, because their sins would always find them out, the children believed everything their parents told them.

Chapter 6

Dotey had always been close to her father, George. Before her marriage to Jack, she had taken Jess and Peter to visit their grandfather and Aunt Gladys in Bournemouth on a number of occasions, and Jess's earliest memory of the seaside was of Mudeford beach. She had been delighted to discover that the blue bucket and spade she had noticed on arriving at Grandi George and Aunty Gladys' house was actually for her, while the red one was for Peter. (On first seeing these items on the sideboard, Jess had supposed that they must belong to Grandi and Aunt Gladys; but what a co-incidence that their favourite colours were the same as hers and Peter's...) The children ran through Fishermen's' Walk, admiring the coloured lights in the trees, and listened to the band playing the 'Dam Busters March' and the theme to '633 Squadron'. However, Grandi George was not very well, and when Aunt Gladys drove them all to Poole Harbour, he stayed in the car. George died later that year, from a stroke he suffered while playing golf, and Dotey felt his loss keenly. Her father left her a generous legacy, so Dotey bought a baby grand piano and could now afford private education for her children. This she believed to be in their best interests, since she was anxious to avoid them picking up Devonshire accents, which she was sure would happen if she sent them to the local council school.

Westfield was a small, private establishment, occupying the spare rooms in the large house of the proprietor, Mrs. Winters. The class to which Jess was assigned consisted of five boys plus herself as the only girl. Right from the start she was bullied unmercifully by one of the boys, the son of a local town councillor. The other four were too afraid of Jake to say or do anything. Each morning, the teacher would set work for the children to get on with, while she went to see to the school lunch, and it was while the class was left completely unsupervised that Jake would seize his opportunity to bully Jess. He made nasty remarks about Jess's size, her shape, her haircut, her voice, her clothes, her singing or anything else which caught his attention. Jess tried her best to ignore him but she was deeply hurt by Jake's vitriol, which continued day after day, week after week, and term after term. She could not say anything to the teacher, because that would be 'telling', and she knew that Jake had a cruel punishment for those who were 'tell-tales' – he would whisper menacingly, "I'm getting up a gang against you at dinner time." This meant that all the other children were forbidden to associate with the victim, who was to be left completely alone for the duration of the lunch-hour while everyone else trailed around with Jake. Such was the force of Jake's personality, even as a six year old, that none of the other pupils dared to stand up to him.

Jess wept bitterly at home, telling Dotey about this daily torture, but Dotey merely replied stoutly that "Sticks and stones may break my bones, but names can never hurt me," an old adage with which young Jess found it hard to agree.

"He's jealous of you and you must learn to rise above it," said Dotey, and of course, she was right. Jake was the brightest boy in the class, but Jess, the only girl, was equally as clever, and it annoyed Jake when she scored higher than he did in a test, or managed to learn one of the more difficult times tables before he had mastered it. Each child who recited a multiplication table correctly from memory received a gold star, to be stuck on a wall-chart for all to see, and Jess's chart already had a few more gold stars than Jake's. Eventually, Jake knew that drastic action was called for, so he pulled Jess's chair away from under her, just as she was returning to her desk after sharpening her pencil. Jess crashed heavily to the floor, landing in an undignified heap, exposing plump white thighs and navy-blue knickers; her screams brought the teacher rushing in from the kitchen. She castigated the boys for not taking better care of the only little girl in the class; however, appealing to any sense of chivalry had no effect whatever on Jake, although some of the other boys looked rather abashed.

Jess then went on to further annoy Jake by finishing the sum book before he did; in a classic 'Hare and Tortoise' race, Jake completed the last page, and rushed to the front to have his work marked. The other boys were cheering, until it was discovered that he had made two mistakes. Jake at first tried to argue with the teacher that he had in fact put the correct answers and that she had misread them, but she would not accept this, so Jake angrily ran back to his seat to do his corrections. Meanwhile, Jess was steadily ploughing through the final page of sums, and went to have it marked. She had everything right first time; a gold star was hers, plus of course an extra playtime of vilification at the hands of Jake and his cohorts. Jess tried not to let the relentless bullying get to her; however, she was naturally a sensitive child and found it hard having to play by herself or join the younger children in Peter's nursery class who did not really want her, while her own classmates, incited by Jake, joined in with jeering and taunting her across the playground. The only possible way to mollify Jake would be for Jess to do worse than him at her lessons, and this was a sacrifice Jess was unwilling to make. She might not be pretty or good at games, but at least she was clever and hard-working, and she was not prepared to concede this advantage.

As well as the three 'R's, the lessons at Westfield included gardening and deportment. The first enabled Mrs. Winters to get her extensive flower and kitchen gardens weeded at no cost, while the second was considered essential for the girls, who were made to parade around the school hall dressed in navy-blue bloomers and white Aertex T shirts, each with a book balanced on her head. Jess could never successfully manage a complete circuit of the hall, as her book always fell off half-way; the teacher said she must be descended from the Roundheads. Everything about her was round, it seemed; her face, her plump body, her short legs, and even her head. The haircut Dotey insisted on Jess wearing kept her hair extremely short, in a pudding basin style with a full fringe, accentuating the roundness of her face. Other girls had more feminine hairstyles, and Jess longed to be allowed to grow her hair, but Dotey was adamant that long hair would always be getting in Jess's eyes, and would lead to her becoming short sighted.

"I could have plaits, or a pony tail, or bunches," ventured Jess. Other girls managed to keep their hair out of their eyes by adopting these styles. However, Dotey insisted that she knew best; Jess was after all only a little girl who should know better than to answer back to her mother, said Dotey, issuing her sternest warning look. And so Jess was silenced and forced to endure the unflattering hairstyle.

One day a visiting dignitary arrived to open the school fair, and a splendid bouquet was to be presented to his wife. The prettiest girl in the school, Ruth from the kindergarten class, had been chosen for this honour, but at the very last minute she burst into tears. The headmistress looked wildly around for another little girl to perform this important task, and her eyes fell on Jess. Grabbing Jess by her solid arms, she thrust the enormous bouquet into them, and propelled her across the room towards the visiting dignitary's wife.

"Give these flowers to that lady in the hat over there!" she commanded. Jess was somewhat startled, but dutifully obeyed, and everybody sighed with relief. Jess may not be decorative, but she was at least reliable.

Jess was asked to deputise for pretty little Ruth once again one day in the cloakroom when she and Sammy Wroote were putting on their gym shoes – or daps and they are known in Devon – and Sammy told her he was going to marry Ruth Wilcox when he grew up, but just in case he didn't, could he marry Jess instead? Jess was too kind to take offence at this, and simply said they were a bit young to be worrying about such matters at the age of six…

Every year at Westfield, the Headmistress insisted that the pupils enter a competition run by 'Winnie Wilts', a company which manufactured rice pudding. Peter and Jess disliked rice pudding but were obliged to eat their way through several tins-full in order for Dotey to have sufficient labels to send with their competition entries. Dotey complained that Mrs. Winters must have shares in 'Winnie Wilts.' They never won a prize. Mrs. Winters also obliged each family to raise money for the PDSA through their 'Busy Bee' club. Jess preferred supporting sick animals to eating sickly rice pudding. She continued to be very unhappy at Westfield. It really was no fun being the only girl in the class, Jess had no friends so felt very isolated, and begged Dotey to send her to the local council school. Dotey was horrified at the thought of what effect being in a class of forty-plus pupils might have on Jess, after the sheltered environment of Westfield. However, she realised that Jess's continued unhappiness might begin to affect her school work, so considered sending her to the local Convent, where at least there would be many other girls of a similar age to Jess.

"But we're not Catholic!" exclaimed Jess.

"Neither are lots of the pupils," replied her mother. Besides

Westfield, the Convent was the only other local private school option for Tiverton girls, although some older girls travelled to Maynard's school in Exeter. However, Jess got her way, since Dotey's inheritance from her late father was gone and she could no longer afford the fees for Westfield. Her new husband Jack was also very much against private education, especially for girls, so Dotey reluctantly decided that Jess could after all go to Heathcoat Juniors, which luckily had a vacancy in her age-group. Jess was overjoyed. The Westfield Headmistress pleaded with Dotey not to remove Jess, since her school was in imminent danger of closing; some of the boys, including Jake, were about to go to the preparatory department of the nearby Blundell's public school, and numbers at Westfield were diminishing fast. Jess imagined that many parents might want a better standard of pupil supervision than that offered by teachers who left the classroom in order to cook the lunch.

There were indeed lots of girls in Jess's Heathcoat class and she suddenly found herself with the novel experience of having plenty of friends to play with, which was wonderful. She never developed the dreaded Devonshire accent, although, as if in fulfilment of Dotey's prophesy, Peter did when he joined Heathcoats the term after Jess, following the closure of Westfield. By this time, Jess was eight and Peter six, and the recent and unexpected arrival of Jack in the household meant that they very soon had far more serious matters to be concerned about than the way they spoke.

Chapter 7

Jack arrived to live with his Tiverton family in the summer of 1959, and for a short time, everything seemed to go well. He brought with him, amongst an assortment of other odd things, an old croquet set, and set up the hoops on the back lawn. The children enjoyed swinging the mallets, trying to knock the coloured wooden balls through the hoops. Jack set about transforming the kitchen garden into a productive allotment, with all manner of fruit and vegetables. He bought a white rabbit and made a hutch and a large wire enclosure for his use. The children were also delighted with the new swing their father put up for them on the lawn. The summer was very warm, with a record-breaking spell of good weather and Jess (who was always sent to bed early, notwithstanding the heat or the fact that it was the summer holidays) was often much too uncomfortable to go to sleep. She could hear birds singing their evening songs, and the sounds of gardening below her window, so would cautiously leave her bed and peep between the curtains, taking great care not to be seen, since discovery would immediately invite her mother's wrath. Once in bed, the children were meant to stay there. On those long summer evenings Jess could see Dotey weeding the flower beds and clipping the lawn edges, while Jack tended the kitchen garden, his bald head covered with a large white hanky knotted at the four corners, to keep off the evening midges.

During the school holidays, the family took a caravan for a week at Exmouth; it was the smallest caravan on the site and had no mod cons. The party included Noddy the budgie, who twittered happily from his cage, placed in the window where he could enjoy a sea view. Jack stayed only for the weekend, before going back to work, explaining that he did not want to have to close the Store for the whole week. He returned to the caravan each evening, staying overnight. The weather continued very hot and dry, and since their small caravan did not have running water it was necessary for bucketfuls to be fetched from inconveniently located standpipes. Dotey was obliged to do this several times each day, with help from the children. The best way was to take the empty bucket to the uphill standpipe in order to get fresh water, and the kitchen slop bucket to the downhill drain to empty waste water, so that liquid need never be carried uphill. It would be well into the evening before Jack arrived back at the caravan park so of course, he was no help at all with this task. The children would be in their bunks by the time their parents went across to the site clubhouse for a drink. Noddy would also have settled down, his cage covered over with a tea-towel for the night.

Back in Tiverton, with the children returning to school for the autumn term, Jack was having difficulty adjusting to living with Jess and Peter. Although they were on the whole well-behaved, they had the natural exuberance of all young children, and Jack found this extremely wearing when he arrived home from Exeter after work, so the children would be packed off to their bedrooms and out of his way very early. Dotey was continually reminding Jess and Peter that Daddy was very tired after his long day, and wanted to rest, so all noise must be kept to a minimum. Jess was forbidden to practise her recorder after Daddy came home, since he could not tolerate the shrill noise. A bed-time ritual developed, with Jack relaxing in his chair before the fire, reading the 'Express and Echo', when the children came in to say goodnight. Jack would incline the top of his bald head for Jess to kiss, while Peter would shake hands with his father and proffer a large empty whisky bottle. Jack had to turn out his pockets, in search of sixpences. These were tipped into the bottle, which was then replaced on the top of a cupboard. The money was not intended for the children but was a means of saving for Jack's expenses.

Jess noticed that her tired father always seemed to gain his second wind in time to go out to the pub for a late evening drink. Just as it was taking Jack some time to adjust to life with young children, so it was also quite a while before his family were used to having Jack living with them, after so many years without a man around the house. What Jess noticed most about the new arrangement was the noise her father created. Although intolerant of any sound made by his children, he was by far the noisiest member of the household. As soon as he got up in the morning, he could be heard singing or whistling, often songs from his army days. Frequently, he would have a violent attack of coughing, since he smoked heavily, preferring the strongest brands of cigarette. Clattering downstairs from his attic bedroom, Jack would be carrying a covered enamel bucket, since the first-floor toilet facilities were too far away for his night-time comfort. The singing and whistling would continue in the lavatory as he emptied the pail, after which he would climb back upstairs to complete his morning ritual. This often involved an impromptu game of 'hunt the lost collar stud', accompanied by clomping noises and exclamations. "Damn! Where's the ruddy thing gone?"

Having finally cleared out the phlegm, dressed and ready to face the day, it was Jack's custom in fine weather to lean out of his bedroom window, which faced onto the drive at the front of the house, in order to serenade the neighbours and tradesmen. He had a pleasant baritone voice, and his varied repertoire ranged from Great War songs to grand opera; from 'The Quartermaster's Stores' to 'Il Pagliacci', also including several music-hall and popular numbers. He would frequently interrupt his recital in order to converse with passers-by, enquiring after the health of their relatives, or commenting on the weather prospects for the day. Jess liked to hear him sing, it was actually one of the few things that she did like about her father.

"Vesti la giubba e la faccia in farina. La gente paga e rider vuole qua. Ridi, Pagliaccio, sui tuo amore infranto, ridi del dioi, che t'avvelena il cor".

Which Jack translated as: *"On with the motley, the paint and the powder. I laugh, Ha-ha, ha-ha!* Morning, Fern, and how's Arthur today? Better? That's good!"

The hour after tea was the worst time, for Jack claimed he was a martyr to his 'nervous dyspepsia', frequently belching so loudly that he could be heard several rooms away. Dotey would always reprove him, especially when the belch was accompanied by loud farting, but Jack maintained that he could not help it, and it was 'better out than in' since it relieved what he termed his 'exquisite pain'. In an attempt to alleviate his digestive difficulties, Jack would often go for a walk around the room, perambulating from one end to the other, accompanied by a running commentary. ("I'm at the end of the drive now; just passing Lime Tree Cottages; crossing over the stream; almost at Punchard's Farm…")

"Why not go out for a walk?" asked his exasperated wife.

"No need, I'm almost at the Wishing Tree!" Jack would exclaim, continuing his heavy measured pacing around the ottoman, as far as the hall door, then back to the fire again, before doing yet another circuit, whistling softly as he went. He would break off to announce that he was now passing Bingwell Farm on the homeward leg, never of course having left the living room. Dotey would complain that he was wearing out the carpet, while Jess, in the room above, found that she was unable to study or get to sleep. Finally, having expelled all excess wind one way or another, Jack would declare that he was feeling much better, and announce his intention of popping down to the local for a quick one. Was Dotey coming with him? The front door would slam, the car engine rev, and all would be quiet for a few hours. If Dotey had accompanied her husband, they would usually be home soon after closing time, but if Jack had gone on his own to the Constitutional Club, it was often very late when he returned. The steward had a habit of moving the regulars into the back room after hours for a 'private party'.

When Jack eventually arrived home, Jess would be aware of the sound of her father fumbling with his door key; he always seemed to have difficulty locating the lock, and often it took him several attempts to gain entry. He would then be heard crashing through the front door, slamming it behind him, while groping noisily for the light switch, cursing and muttering all the while. After lurching down the hallway, Jack would fall into the living room, startling the sleeping budgie, whom he would loudly greet like a long-lost friend. "Hello, Nod-bod, what do you know?" The budgie would twitter a reply, while Jack switched on the wireless and tuned into Radio Luxembourg, a station which broadcast late into the night. After listening to some pop music, with the volume at full blast, finally there would be a resonant belch, the wireless would be turned off, and Jack would be heard stumbling upstairs to perform his night-time ablutions. Next would come a loud knock on Dotey's bedroom door, accompanied by stage whispers of "Dotey, are you awake?" to which there was generally no response. Jess marvelled that her mother could sleep through all this, while she herself, in the next room, was obliged to endure the complete performance. Sometimes Jack would open Dotey's door uninvited, and stand in the doorway while his wife chastised him for his noise and lateness. Jess could not help but be aware of the murmuring of these resentful conversations, which eventually ended with Jack retreating to the bathroom to collect his night bucket; the clatter of the enamel pail against the attic banisters usually heralded the last of the evening's disturbances. A few more belches, the creak of bed-springs, and peace would finally descend.

At the weekend, Jack liked to listen to the wireless with the sound turned up full volume; this was excruciating when reception was even slightly distorted, as was usually the case. There was always a fearful whistle on both the Home Service and the Light Programme, so Jack tried festooning the aerial wire around the living-room in various directions, in an effort to improve the reception, although this never seemed to help much. The whistle became even louder when Jack was trying to catch something important, such as the football results. Jack religiously checked his pools coupon every Saturday teatime, but he never seemed to get the predicted results, resulting in sighs and shouts and snorts of exasperation and disgust. Finally, the coupon would be screwed up and thrown in the fire. "If that last lot had drawn I'd have won a bloody tenner!" Jack swore a good deal, which alarmed Jess, who was unused to hearing bad language in their neighbourhood. Her mother told her she must never, ever copy him, and that while it might be all right for men to use bad language, little girls must not do so under any circumstances. Sometime she reprimanded Jack, but he of course took no notice beyond telling the children that they should always "Do as I say, not as I do." Smoking was a mug's game, football pools were a waste of money, and God helped those who helped themselves. On the subject of drink, Jack was strangely silent. He was well on the way to becoming a full-blown alcoholic, progress no doubt hastened by the strain of suddenly having to care for a young family; however, the children did not realise this.

Dotey made every excuse for Jack, short of saying that he was 'tired and emotional'; she explained to Jess that he worked long hours at the Store to earn sufficient money to keep his family, and he must on no account be annoyed or disturbed in any way. Yet he appeared to have absolutely no compunction about annoying or disturbing the rest of the family. It seemed to Jess completely unfair that earning money apparently bestowed upon men the right to behave so badly, although she dared not say as much, knowing that any such comment would earn her a slap for 'cheeking her elders', or 'answering back', both of which were of course strictly forbidden. She remembered wistfully the peaceful years with Dotey and Peter and herself living quietly and comfortably together, regretting that those days were now gone for ever. Every move she made now must first be preceded by consideration for Jack; she must not run or call out, since Jack was always talking about the necessity for a young lady to move decorously and speak with a well-modulated voice, whatever that was. Jess was still only eight years old, but it was quite clear to her that Jack did not want a child, but rather a small well-behaved adult.

Chapter 8

For the first few months after her marriage, Dotey frequently accompanied her husband on his evening jaunts to a local inn. Previously, if she had had to go out in the evening, she had always left the children in the care of a babysitter, often Annie MacDougall, the cleaning lady's eldest daughter. Jack, however, flatly refused to pay for a babysitter, insisting that 'a great girl of eight', such as Jess, was perfectly capable of looking after herself and six-year-old Peter. Jack himself, as the second child of a large family, had often been called upon to mind his younger siblings at a similar age during the Edwardian era. In any case, as he pointed out to Dotey, the children should be asleep by the time their parents left for the pub, and would therefore be quite unaware that they were home alone, so there was absolutely nothing to be concerned about.

But Jess knew exactly when her parents went out; she always woke up when the front door slammed shut and the car engine revved into life. And once awake, she was afraid to go back to sleep. She worried that there would be a car crash, and that her parents might never come home, so she got into the habit of creeping out onto the dark landing and waiting for the car to turn into the drive. She would then scuttle back to bed and feign sleep when her mother looked in on her. Once, the telephone rang in the hall, and Jess went down to answer it. It was someone from Dotey's dramatic society, and the caller seemed surprised when Jess informed her that her mother was out. She told Dotey the following day that Mrs. Dart had rung, and Dotey said sharply that Jess should never answer the phone at night. "The ringing woke me up," said Jess, although she had not actually been asleep, but keeping vigil on the landing. This was long before the days of answering machines, and unanswered telephones rang out until the caller eventually hung up. Jack proposed a solution to the problem, by taking the receiver off the hook and putting it on the hall floor, so that any caller would hear the engaged tone and not be able to get through. However, the phone receiver made a loud humming noise when off the hook, which resonated throughout the house, so that Jess could not sleep even if she had wanted to. An exasperated

Jack's next ploy was to attempt to muffle the sound, by means of wrapping the receiver in the hood from an old raincoat. This worked better, but Jess still hated it when her parents went out. On hearing the door slam, she would creep onto the landing and peer over the banisters into the hall below. If she saw the telephone receiver still on the hook, she would sigh with relief, since this indicated that her mother was still in the house. If on the other hand, she saw the receiver lying on the floor, swathed in its hood, she knew that Dotey had also gone out, and that she and Peter were home alone. This thought frequently terrified her. What if there should be burglars? Or Peter might have an attack of croup! Jess doubted that she would be able to cope single-handed with the steaming kettles and other paraphernalia required at such times. What if the chimney caught fire? This had happened twice during the family's occupancy of the house; once they had put the fire out with salt, while on the second occasion their neighbour had called out the fire brigade, which had annoyed Dotey, who said Major Eyre had been much too officious, 'taking too much upon himself'. Dotey had been using the salt again, which usually did the trick.

No wonder that Jess decided it was not safe to sleep until her parents returned. When she confided to her mother her anxieties about burglars, croup and chimney fires, Dotey tried to reassure Jess, telling her that she always let the fire die down and checked that the fire-guard was in place before she left the house, and always made certain to lock the front door, so the children were quite safe. As for croup, it was now some time since Peter's last attack, and he seemed to have grown out of it. Dotey would then promise to bring some beer-mats home from the pub for Jess's collection, which Jess did not think was very much of a consolation. She had never wanted to collect beer-mats anyway. Meanwhile, Jack was exasperated beyond words by Jess's objections. In his eyes, she was just a selfish, whining child, wishing to deny her parents the simple pleasure of going for a well-deserved drink. So Jess soon came to realise that it was useless to express her worries. When left as the guardian of the house, she would put on her dressing gown and take up a position opposite the landing window to await her parents' return two or three hours later. As soon as she saw the headlights and heard the familiar rumble of her father's old Vauxhall turning into the drive, she would dash back to her room. She was always glad when it was Sunday, since the pubs closed half an hour earlier, at ten o'clock. With the statutory twenty minutes drinking-up time, her parents should be home by half-past.

However, one Sunday night in late October, Jack and Dotey failed to return home after closing time. Jess became so cold sitting on the landing that she went back to bed and dozed for a while. She woke at the sound of a car, but it was not the Vauxhall, so she resumed her vigil. The telephone receiver was still lying on the hall floor. Jess crept downstairs to check the time by the living room clock. It was twenty minutes to twelve! She was terribly worried, imagining that her parents must have been killed or injured in a car crash. Uncertain what to do, she looked in the telephone directory for the number of the hotel where she knew her parents often drank. Trembling with fear and the cold, she dialled the number. A man's voice answered.

"Good evening," began Jess, with chattering teeth, "Is that the Hartnoll Hotel? I am so sorry to disturb you, but I wonder if Mr. and Mrs. Sanders were in the bar tonight?"

"Yes, they were here," replied the landlord, "but they left over an hour ago."

Jess gasped, and the landlord immediately became concerned. "You're not on your own, are you?" he asked.

"Well, my little brother's here too, but he's asleep," cried Jess. The landlord asked how old she was, and on hearing she was aged eight, said he would ring the police, to find out if there had been any accidents. Jess gave him her address and telephone number, and replaced the receiver. She very much hoped that her parents would reappear before the man had a chance to ring back, but they did not. Towards midnight the landlord of the Hartnoll Hotel rang to say that he had checked with the police and the hospital, but there had been no accidents reported, and that a policewoman would be coming to look after the children until Jack and Dotey returned.

Jess thanked him, and settled down to await the arrival of the policewoman, but just then Jack's car was heard finally drawing up outside. Jess flung open the front door, and rushed down the front steps to greet her startled parents.

"Mummy and Daddy, you're safe!" she cried, tears of relief

streaming down her face. "I've been so worried, and so has Mr. Hartnoll Hotel, and the police are on their way, but she won't be needed now – and he checked with the hospital..."

"Go back to bed at once, Jess," said Dotey in icy tones. "We are indeed quite safe, as you can see." Jess trotted obediently up to her room, too pleased and relieved at the safe return of her parents to notice their anger.

The following morning brought misery to Jess, more than anything she could have ever imagined. Her father refused to speak to her, and left the room immediately she came in. "I can't be in the same room as her, Dotey! Keep her out of my sight!" But it was Dotey's grim countenance which upset Jess the most. Peter was of course totally mystified, since he had heard nothing of the midnight drama.

"What's Jess done?" he asked. Neither Jack nor Dotey would answer. Jess knew that she was in the wrong, but was not sure exactly why. She had only been worried for her parents' safety, but this was obviously not right at all.

"I'm sorry," she said nervously.

"She's sorry!" Jack shouted sarcastically from the kitchen. "How can I ever show my face down the Hartnoll again after what she's done? I'm going out, Dotey; I don't want to be in the same house with her."

Eventually, Dotey announced that she and Jack were now expecting a summons for neglecting their children, they would have to go to court, and would get into a great deal of trouble; who knows, they might even be sent to prison. The authorities would take Jess and Peter away and put them in an orphanage **and it would all be Jess's fault**. After visiting the Hartnoll, they had simply gone to a friend's house for coffee and stayed later than intended. Parents were entitled to some time to themselves, but no, selfish Jess wanted to deny them even an hour's pleasure!

On hearing this, Jess was heart-broken, since of course it had never been her intention to get her parents into trouble. However, as it turned out, the devastating orphanage scenario never came to pass; the police took no action, not even bothering to send the promised policewoman, so Jack and Dotey got away with child neglect. However, Dotey was careful never to leave the children alone again. If Jack begrudged the money to pay a babysitter, she stayed home. She eventually forgave her eight year old daughter, even telling Jess some months later that it was a relief to be able to stay in quietly instead of having to accompany Jack to the pub every night; but Jack never forgave Jess and Jess knew that he never would. The lesson Jess took from that dreadful night was that her parents' love was conditional on her behaving exactly as they wanted; any deviation from the prescribed path, however well-intentioned, would be punished, ultimately by being sent to the orphanage. It was a hard lesson for an eight-year-old, but Jess learned it well. So began the rainy season of perpetual tears, blighting the remainder of Jess's childhood. Continually scared of doing wrong and upsetting her parents, she sobbed in secret.

Chapter 9

After the Hartnoll episode Jess tried to be very good, since bad behaviour in any shape or form was not to be tolerated, yet she found it difficult to be the daughter she knew her parents really wanted. Dotey and Jack continually tried to impress upon her the correct way for her to behave; little girls should speak only when spoken to, they must always be available to assist with household chores, they must not pull faces when asked to do anything, but should comply cheerfully, and they must not rush out to play as boys did without first checking that their mothers could spare them. Then there were those mystifying rules relating to dress and appearance, whereby girls must always refer to their undergarments as panties, not pants, which were apparently worn only by boys, and never as 'knickers', a word which was 'common'. Girls' clothing must always be fastened with the buttons on the left, while boys' used the buttons on the right; and girls must part their hair in the centre or on the right, not on the left, as boys did. Above all, girls must not be tomboys. Dotey, petite and attractive, often found it necessary to reproach her clumsy daughter.

"Really, Jess, you're like a crab going to Ireland!" was one of her oft-used expressions. Walking through the town, a series of commands would ring out: "Shoulders back, Jess! Head up! Look where you are going! Watch out for that mess! Pick your feet up! Tch, dear me, why must you be so ungainly! Single file, let these people pass – Jess, don't strake!" This last instruction used a dialect word – Dotey detested people who straggled across the footpath thereby preventing other pavement users from passing. In an attempt to encourage her daughter to move more gracefully Dotey enrolled Jess in the Daphne Brain School of Dance, but Jess could master only the first of the five basic ballet positions, and her short legs meant she could never manage to get her foot up onto the barre without a great deal of undignified heaving. Dancing was not to be her thing, and when cast in a performance of "Little Miss Muffet" she found herself in the back row of the spiders, wearing a horrid black itchy costume rather than a pretty pink tutu which of course was the ambition of all little ballet dancers.

Saturday was Jess's designated bath-night, and Dotey always insisted on supervising, since she did not consider that Jess could not be trusted to dry herself properly. As Jess clambered out of the water, her mother handed her the towel, invariably accompanied by exasperated sighing. "What a lump you are, Jess! Really, you're built like the side of a house! Tsk, so hefty! I do hope you'll fine down a bit as you get older…" Yet it was Dotey who laced Jess's tea with unnecessary sugar, declaring that in her opinion, unsweetened tasted like poison, even though Jess found tea more refreshing without sugar; and Dotey who insisted on clean plates at meal-times, reminding the children that they were lucky not to be enduring rationing as had been the case during the recently ended war. Jess quickly came to realise that no-one would ever admire her for her looks, and so her deeds must be the reason people commended her. She must therefore try always to be as good as possible, helpful to Dotey, hard-working at school and polite to all.

Now aged sixty, second-time-around father Jack quickly became resentful of the demands modern children placed upon their parents, which had not been the case when he was young, in the Edwardian era. There were many aspects of the children's behaviour he found extremely annoying, reproving Peter for coming to the dining table one day wearing jeans, insisting that these were work clothes, and that Peter must change before the meal. ("Don't 'ee dare come to the dinner table wearing a boiler-suit!") Jess once arrived at the Sunday lunch table with wet hair, since she had been caught in a sudden downpour on her way home from Sunday School without an umbrella; neither she nor Dotey possessed a hair-dryer, so she had given her hair a vigorous towelling, but it was still quite damp. Jack made her leave the table until her hair was completely dry. Jack also objected to the manner in which Jess drank; coming in one very hot day, Jess poured herself a glass of water, and quickly gulped it down. Her father complained that she was extremely unladylike. Every time Jess had a drink, she was aware of Jack, his head cocked, listening intently for any sound which might escape her throat. This of course made her extremely self-conscious, so that she tended to swallow even more loudly than usual. Jack then tried to train her to tip up her cup at a more acute angle, and allow the drink to slip silently down her throat, but when she attempted this, the liquid went up her nose, making her splutter all over the table. "Sorry, I'm really sorry!" Jess gasped in fright. Dotey begged Jack to leave her alone but he insisted she try again.

"Dotey, she's got to learn! Sip it slowly, girl!" Jess tried henceforth to avoid drinking anything in front of her father, no matter how thirsty she might be. It seemed unfair that men could apparently gulp, belch and even fart to their hearts' content, while girls must always take care to be decorous and never ostentatious in everything they did.

One fine Saturday evening there was heard a sudden dreadful noise of loud gun-fire quite close by. Jack at once ordered everyone to lie flat on the floor in Jess's room at the back of the house, overlooking the valley. There was a lull, and Jack crept cautiously to the window, peering over the sill to see if he could make out what was going on. Outside, birds were singing their evening songs and traffic appeared to be proceeding normally along Blundell's Road. Pam, the young woman from No. 1, knocked at the door, asking to come in. "I've come for some reassurance," she pleaded, but none was forthcoming. Just then, the gun-fire began again, so Pam quickly lay down on the floor beside Dotey and the children, while Jack resumed his vigil.

"We're under attack! Maybe the Russians have invaded! This could be World War Three! Keep down, everyone! Stay away from the window!" Dotey then suggested ringing the Police, since there had been no air-raid warning siren. Jack went to phone and returned, smiling sheepishly.

"All right, it's only Blundell's School holding a military tattoo. Apparently it was advertised in the local papers..."

Everyone sighed with relief and scrambled to their feet. "Dad, can we go and watch?" asked Peter.

Dotey demurred. "It's really not suitable for Jess, and anyway, she's just had a bath. Peter can go if he wants to."

"It's a warm evening, she'll not take any harm," said Jack. But Dotey would not relent. Jess resented the fact that boys were allowed to have so much more fun, the more so when Peter returned from the unexpected trip, having had a wonderful time. She shed a few tears, but her mother assured her that such an event was really quite unsuitable for girls, and promised her a different treat, when something more appropriate presented itself. She must be patient and not expect to get her own way all the time. This was a lesson which every little girl should learn early in life and was good preparation for coping with the many disappointments which the future would inevitably bring.

Jess noticed that boys were allowed more freedom than girls, had more treats than girls, and were required to perform fewer household chores. Peter had to help Jack clean the shoes and gather vegetables from the garden only on Sunday mornings; Jess meanwhile was required to be continually available to assist Dotey with all manner of household tasks – washing, shopping, running errands, doing dishes… It was clear to her that boys were valued more than girls; indeed it was common to overhear a new mother commenting proudly "I always saw myself as the mother of boys," or "Give me lads any time, you know they aren't going to get into trouble!" This puzzled Jess, since at school the boys were naughtier than the girls, and the local paper reported on crimes usually committed by men. Jess had no idea that 'getting into trouble' meant an unmarried girl having a baby, the secret dread of any family with daughters growing up in those days before legal abortion.

Chapter 10

Heathcoat Junior School, to which the children were sent after leaving Westfield private school, was at the time housed next to the textile factory, in the Westexe area of the Tiverton. The West Country had a long tradition of woollen textile manufacture, and the factory had been founded in the nineteenth century by John Heathcoat, who had brought his business from Leicestershire to Tiverton in order to escape the Luddite Riots. These disturbances, widespread throughout the Midlands and the North of England at the start of the Industrial Revolution, were caused by hand-loom weavers destroying factory machinery, which they believed would result in them becoming redundant. John Heathcoat had therefore sought safety in the less militant South West. His factory became the major employer in Tiverton, and his descendants founded a school for the children of the factory workers next to the main building. A branch of the River Exe had been diverted in order to serve the factory; this stream, known as the Leat, ran through the school grounds. The lavatories were situated in a building on the opposite bank, and the school euphemism for going to the toilet was "Please Miss, may I go across the bridge?" This was always an interesting excursion, since one never knew what colour the Leat would be running; it could be red, purple, yellow, pink, green or blue, depending on what dye was being used in the factory that day. Sometimes it was full of colourful foam, while on non-dyeing days it was just a disappointing muddy brown. After passing through the factory and school premises, the Leat rejoined the main river beside a triangular patch of grass, known as the Green, where the children were allowed to play in summer. Although the Green was bounded on two sides by the River Exe and the Leat, Jess did not hear of anyone drowning, or even falling in the river, during the years she was there; it is unlikely that a school playground would be sited there now.

Jess much preferred Heathcoats to Westfield. She was put in a class of 42 pupils, and soon had lots of friends to play with. She joined in with the skipping and other traditional games still commonly seen at the time, such as 'Red Letter', 'What's the time Mr. Wolfie?' and 'Grandmother's Footsteps.' There were any number of variations of 'It', and very occasionally, if the boys were to be included, 'Kiss Chase'. However, Jess found herself at a disadvantage when the girls skipped in time with TV advertisement jingles, since her family did not possess a television set and consequently these jingles were unknown to her. She was similarly disadvantaged in 'Red Letter' where girls moved forward when a letter which was included in their name was called out. Jess had of course only three different letters in her name J, E and S, and even worse, she had no middle name! Everyone else possessed a middle name, but Jess was too honest to assume a fanciful extra name, such as Esmeralda.

Jess was pleased to discover that at Heathcoats she was no longer the fattest child in the class, and of course she was delighted not to be the only girl. Despite Dotey's anxieties as to whether she would be able to 'keep up' in a learning environment so different from that to which she had been accustomed, she found that she was academically ahead of many of her classmates, having thoroughly learned her all multiplication tables at Westfield. Her written work was good, and she was put in the top set for English. The teacher, Miss Bowden, was a charming young woman, whose class of eight-year-olds adored her. She did not disappear mid-lesson to cook the school lunches, and she was keen to develop artwork, to brighten up the rather dingy brown-painted classroom.

"She won't last very long in teaching!" declared Dotey.

"But she's a wonderful teacher!" exclaimed Jess, upset to think that anything could happen to beloved Miss Bowden.

"She's also very pretty," said Dotey. "I imagine she'll be leaving to get married before long. I spotted an engagement ring on her finger at the Parents evening."

"But teachers don't have to leave when they get married these days, do they?" cried Jess. The law had changed, so that married women were no longer barred from professions such as the civil service or teaching.

"Women teachers usually do; if not when they marry, then certainly when a baby arrives." Dotey chose her words with care; a baby arriving sounded rather like a parcel being sent through the post, and

Dotey had no wish to enlighten Jess as to the origin of babies, not at age eight; or indeed ever.

Dotey's words were indeed prophetic, since by the time Peter reached Miss Bowden's class the following year she had become Mrs. Foot, and duly announced to her pupils that she would be leaving soon because there was to be a little addition to the Foot family. This was the sum total of the sex education the children received at Heathcoats.

All the girls at Heathcoats were taught to sew, which was definitely not Jess's strong point. Miss Paine, the sewing instructress, commented on how awkwardly Jess held the needle, and how grubby her sewing quickly became. The girls were set the task of each making an embroidered tray-cloth, demonstrating a variety of stitches. Jess just about managed slipped stitch and chain stitch, but her cross-stitch was far from neat, and herringbone defeated her altogether. Then a strip of ric-rac braid had to sewn near the top, and all the hems over-sewn with blanket stitch. Jess suspected that someone was stealing the needle from her sewing box. Miss Paine became so annoyed with Jess for repeatedly losing her needle that she ordered her to bring one from home. Dotey found a spare needle, but that went missing as well. In exasperation, Dotey purchased the largest darning needle she could find, which made such enormous holes in the cotton cloth that Jess could see the floor through them. Then Miss Paine came to inspect the Jess's handiwork.

"Aagh! Just look at this little girl, trying to sew with this enormous needle! It's like using a crow-bar! It's meant for mending thick socks, not embroidery; you'll spoil the material. Get a proper needle from the store cupboard!"

So Jess received another needle, and took her sewing home with her to prevent further theft. Her mother watched her clumsy attempts to complete the line of blanket stitch, and remarked that Jess looked like a cow handling a musket...

After Jess left Miss Bowden's class, Heathcoat Junior School moved around the corner to premises vacated by the Secondary Modern, which had been given a new building on the edge of the town. The Juniors could at last leave behind the factory, the colourfully foaming Leat and the outside lavatories. The new premises overlooked

Westexe Recreational ground, and had a separate canteen building and a classroom for pupils with special needs, which even boasted a kiln for pottery. Jess's teacher this year was Mr. Champion, who was strict but fair, and who encouraged all his pupils to do their best. He was keen on them entering competitions, and accordingly, the pupils were asked to write an essay on Superstitions. As Dotey's daughter, Jess excelled at this. Her mother was extremely superstitious, discreetly spitting on seeing a white a horse ("Bring first luck to me") and asking "How's the wife, Jim?" on sight of a lone magpie. The first day of the month brought "Pinch and a Punch" and the incantation "White Rabbits", while pinches of spilled salt were tossed over the shoulder to appease the devil. Ladders were to be avoided, hawthorn was never to be brought into the house, and it was unlucky to sweep or wash on New Year's Day – "it sweeps/washes one of the family away". Dotey had dozens of these strictures, and Jess found it quite difficult to remember them all, so writing the essay served as an 'aide memoir'. Mr. Champion liked it, and sent it off to be judged, but Jess heard no more. Possibly the competition was won by an essayist with a mother more superstitious even than Dotey.

The next competition was to come up with an easy way to remember the new colour codes for electrical wiring. The old red, green and black wires were being abandoned in favour of brown for positive, blue for negative with a twisted yellow and green earth cable. Jess wrote "Brown says 'yes', blue says 'no', yellow and green to earth both go." Mr. Champion thought this was very good and duly sent it off, but Jess was not even commended. However, the jingle stayed with her all her life and she used it to instruct her own sons in the correct way to wire an electrical item.

The final competition was to find as many words as possible from the name of the soft drink product 'Suncrush', with a product label to be included. Jess found a dozen, and submitted her list, but again she heard nothing at all. Jack said he wondered whether the results were rigged, it seemed strange that Jess did not merit a mention for effort.

By now the eleven-plus examination was only a year away, and Jess was aware how important it was to pass for the Grammar School. All the parents set great store by it, but Dotey reassured Jess that she really had nothing to fear.

"You've got the brains and the application, so you don't need to worry!" declared Dotey, "I had the brains, but I was lazy; I know you'll do so much better."

Many parents promised their children extravagant rewards, such as new bicycles, if they passed the 11+, and Dotey said that Jess could have a wrist-watch, something she had never before possessed. On the day of the exam, Jack dropped Jess off at the new Secondary Modern school where the exam was to be held. It was an all day affair, with Intelligence tests, as well as English and Maths papers. There were also some general knowledge questions, including "Give the correct name for a one-humped camel." Jess thought it might be a dromedary, although she was not quite sure if that had one hump or two; eventually she decided that Bactrian camels were the ones with two humps. She was conscious that she should not waste too much time pondering over one question. It was a long day, and by three o'clock she felt tired and relieved that it was all over. Her mother had walked through the town and the park to meet her. Dotey was quite certain Jess would pass, after all, she always had her nose in a book, and thanks to Dotey's steadfast refusal to get a television set, Jess did not have any opportunity to waste her time watching what her mother considered to be rubbishy programmes.

Jess did indeed pass, and received a small Timex wrist-watch as a reward. To her surprise, Peter was also given a wrist-watch, a large second-hand one. Jack said that it was unfair to give Jess something, but not Peter, who had not yet had the opportunity to sit the exam. Dotey was cross, since she had not been consulted on the matter; she thought Peter ought to have been made to wait for a present until he too passed the 11+. However, she could hardly take the watch away from Peter, who was already wearing it.

Meanwhile, Jess had been voted Head Girl of the Junior school, and among her duties was the customary visit to the newly elected Mayor in the Town Hall in May. Peter had already performed this task the preceding year, on behalf of the Infant department, when the Mayor-Elect had actually been the first Labour Mayor in Tiverton! Jack and Dotey agreed this was such a come-down. However, by the time Jess's turn arrived, the Mayor was again a Conservative and normality had been restored. The Head Boy, Nicholas, and Jess had composed a welcoming speech, which they learned by heart to recite in unison; they were told that at the end of the speech, it was common practice to request a half holiday. Instead of boldly asking for a holiday, Jess thought it would sound rather more polite if they added the words, "If you think we deserve it." For some reason, this greatly amused the assembled civic dignitaries and clergy, and the request was duly granted. A picture of everyone laughing appeared in the Tiverton Gazette, and Dotey proudly ordered a black-and-white print to add to the family album, which already included pictures of Peter's Mayoral visit and her own Dramatic Society performances.

Chapter 11

After having two sons, Dotey had been delighted to give birth to a daughter. She looked forward to sending her to classes for ballet dancing and piano playing, the activities she herself had enjoyed as a child, and to buying her lots of pretty clothes. However, plump, awkward Jess soon proved to be a disappointment; people sometimes commented on the length of her eye-lashes – 'you could sweep the floor with them' – but that was really because there was nothing else about her appearance that anyone could find to praise. In contrast, little Peter had long golden curls, which people always said were 'wasted on a boy', while Jess's hair was dark and straight and kept very short. Jess was constantly teased at school about her size and shape; however, when she had told her mother about this, Dotey replied firmly that Jess was not actually fat, simply 'well-covered' and 'big-boned.' This contradicted her own oft-expressed bath-time opinion of Jess's size; but according to Dotey, it was one thing for a mother to comment on her daughter's appearance and quite another for outsiders to do so.

Jess's dancing career had come to an abrupt end after the "Little Miss Muppet" show, since it was clear to all that she would never make a dancer and that the money spent on ballet lessons was quite wasted. Also, it was at that time that she and Peter developed whooping cough, so Jess was not fit to dance. Peter, sitting in Dotey's lap in the audience, had actually been coughing throughout the 'Little Miss Muppet' performance, and Dr. Foster arrived immediately they returned home; Dotey expressed surprise, since she had not sent for him; however, it turned out that the doctor's wife had also been in the audience, and recognising the characteristic 'whoop' of Peter's cough, had reported back to her husband, who had kindly come round at once...

When it came to playing the piano Jess fared rather better, although she always struggled to learn the pieces set by the teacher. Jess had already taught herself the descant recorder before the arrival of her sensitive father, who detested the instrument, and she enjoyed playing in Heathcoats recorder band. She could also pick out tunes by ear on the piano, and once she had learned three chords in the key of D major she discovered that she could play almost any simple tune. In contrast, she did not find it easy to read music or to master the correct fingering. However, by dint of much practising of the set pieces, which drove the rest of the household to distraction, she passed her Grade 1 piano exam. Jess was relieved to have passed at all, since the music exams were held at the house of a local dentist, and the candidates were obliged to share the waiting room with the dental patients. Through one door could be heard the sound of the tinkling piano, while from the other came the whining of the dentist's drill. Jess, sitting alone, clutching her music case and feeling terribly nervous, thought she might cheerfully opt instead for a filling if the surgery door opened first. However, the music room door opened, the previous candidate emerged, and Jess was called in. She struggled with the sight-reading, conscious throughout that the people in the waiting-room could hear every note she was playing, but managed the set pieces fairly well. The results were not announced that day, but were sent on later. When they arrived, to her relief, Jess had passed with Merit, although Dotey was rather disappointed that Jess had not achieved a Distinction, as had Dr. Foster's daughter, who had lessons with the same piano teacher. Jess then went on to sit her Music Theory exam; thankfully, this was held not at the dentists, but a bus ride away in Exeter, at an imposing building in Gandy Street, part of the university.

"You might go there to study one day," said Dotey. Jess doubted that she would ever be able to complete all the necessary exams. However, she preferred the peace and quiet of the university examination hall to the stressful surroundings of the dentist's waiting room, and passed the music theory exam without difficulty. The music teacher had put her straight in at Grade 3, by-passing the two lower levels, since it was obvious that Jess's talents lay more with academic study rather than anything practical. This was quite exasperating for Dotey when visitors were expected, since she liked Jess to entertain them with a tune on the piano. Often, Jess's nerves failed her, she made mistakes and become upset. The visitors were embarrassed and Dotey would declare that she simply could not understand it, since Jess had played that piece beautifully yesterday. Maybe Jess was getting a cold? Showing guests the Music Theory exam certificate was not really as satisfactory…

Dotey's only consolation, given that her daughter was turning out to be neither pretty nor accomplished, was that Jess was hard-working; she was always near the top of the class in the days when positions in the ranking order meant everything. The first question most parents asked their children, (and indeed, the pupils asked their classmates) on the final day of term, was 'Where did you come?' After changing schools, Jess moved up from 13th, to 10th, to 4th; however, the following term she had slipped back to 7th.

"Whatever can have happened?" cried a distraught Dotey. Jess was tempted to supply the obvious answer, which was that six people had done better than she had. Instead she kept silent. To be 7th out of a class of 42 did not seem to be such a bad thing to her, but it was simply not good enough for her mother. Dotey herself had not excelled at all at school, but she had not been required to, since she was pretty, musical, lively, a good dancer and from a well-off background. If Jess let her studies slip, Dotey feared that she would be left with nothing. Jess resolved to work even harder, and the following term her position improved to 2nd. This had to satisfy her mother, who knew that nobody could beat the brilliant Margaret Blackmore, the daughter of a non-conformist minister, not only the cleverest girl in the school, but also an outstanding pianist; she had played a complicated piece called "Rustle of Spring" at Speech Day, to great acclaim. Then (and who knows how long Dotey might have been praying for it?) Margaret's father was sent to work elsewhere, and Margaret naturally went with him, leaving the field clear for Jess finally to be top of the class.

Margaret may have had the better brains and musical expertise, but there was one area where Jess did not have to wait for her rival to leave town before triumphing. This rather unexpected accomplishment was flower arranging.

"Mum wants me to enter the flower show," she confided to her school classmates. They were of course highly amused.

"What – be you going as a rose?" laughed one. Flower arranging was not considered a fashionable activity among the young at the time, and the local horticultural show struggled to attract many entries in the children's class, the specification for which was generally something along the lines of "A seasonal arrangement for Mummy's dressing table," or "A miniature arrangement in an eggshell." For two consecutive years, Jess won the Junior competition. The local paper carried a picture of Jess being presented with the silver cup trophy by Lady Joyce Amory, a renowned gardener, and the president of the Tiverton Horticultural Society. The cup reposed on Dotey's sideboard for the two years, and Jess was informed that if she won it for a third time, she would be able to keep it.

This year the Junior competition was "An Autumnal arrangement of flowers, fruit, nuts, leaves, seeds and grasses", and Jess scoured the local hedgerows for suitable items. She placed her collection in a small wicker basket on a wooden tray, with a few tastefully arranged sprays spilling from the basket, and a few berries scattered on the tray. She and Dotey agreed it was possibly the best entry she had ever submitted; even Jack was sufficiently impressed as to consent to drive her to the New Hall with the tray balanced on her knee, Jack carefully changing gear as the car climbed the hill so as not to jolt the arrangement. However, Jess was rather disappointed to discover the next day that she had received third prize out of only three entries. A small card had been placed beside her exhibit, on which was written: "This is quite outstanding – but ALAS – no flowers! Please refer to the specification for this class."

Jess had been so pre-occupied with collecting an interesting variety of nuts, seeds, fruit, leaves, twigs and grasses, that she had forgotten to include even a single sprig of heather. Dotey was even more disappointed than Jess, who would now be unable to retain the silver cup.

"At least we won't have to polish it again," said Jess, looking on the bright side. Dotey snorted in disgust.

"Those judges were very unfair, how extremely pedantic! Of course a child would only think the exhibit should include a selection of the items listed, not that it must contain every single one of them!"

Jack unhelpfully chimed in that the incident may have taught Jess a useful lesson, in that written instructions should be read carefully and followed to the letter, as he had learned in his army days.

"But Jess is ten years old! It's the Tiverton Flower Show, not the Devonshire Regiment!" said Dotey. She continued to maintain that Jess had been robbed.

Meanwhile, Margaret Blackmore had also visited the Flower Show and noticed the judges' comment, and she went out of her way to remark on it at school the next day. "Alas, no flowers!" Jess thought it sounded like an epitaph and never entered the Flower Show competition again.

Jess's piano teacher announced that she was organising the programme of entertainment to follow Holcombe Rogus village Harvest Festival Supper. Knowing that Jess played the recorder well, the teacher asked Dotey if she would be prepared to allow Jess to perform a piece, accompanied on the glockenspiel by the Squire of the village, who lived in the old Hall next to the church. Jess was not at all keen, but Dotey was, especially upon hearing mention of the Squire. Accordingly, the hem of Jess's best dress was let down as far as the material would allow, although it still did not quite cover her podgy knees. Jess had hoped that she might be permitted to have something new for the occasion, but her mother declared that the old turquoise wool would do perfectly well, and ordered Jess to stitch a double row of red ric-rac braid around the bottom, in order to disguise the faint but still visible mark of the previous hemline.

It being the weekend, Jack was on hand to drive the family out into the wilds of Holcombe Rogus. They had to arrive early, so that Jess could meet the Squire, and they could rehearse together. The Squire was very kind to Jess. He explained that their musical item was quite early in the programme, which meant that there would be less time for her to become nervous; however there was still the Harvest Festival Evensong and the supper to get through. In an effort to steady her nerves, Jess memorised the whole of the Apostles' Creed during the service, seeing it was inscribed in large black letters on the wall of All Saints church facing her. After the supper, the time for the entertainment arrived. Jess managed not to make a mistake, the Squire added the chiming glockenspiel accompaniment, and everybody clapped. Some people even shouted 'encore'; Jess did not know what that meant, and was trying to leave the stage, when the compère asked her if she would play something else. Jess shook her head, explaining that she had not prepared another piece, whereupon the compère asked her to play her original piece again. Jess was tempted to refuse, but seeing her mother in the front row of the audience, nodding insistently, she put her music back on the stand and played the piece once more. Again, she received warm applause. Finally, Jess was free to leave the stage and enjoy the rest of the evening, or so she hoped.

After the musical items came a barn dance, where Jack impressed a number of the ladies with his dancing prowess; the piano teacher commented to Jess that her father was extremely light on his feet for such a tall and well-built man. Meanwhile, Jess, who had never before been to a barn dance, had been hoping to sit quietly and let her supper go down. However, because of a shortage of women, she was obliged to partner an elderly man who had little more idea than she had of the correct moves. Being unfamiliar with the 'Gay Gordons' or 'Dashing White Sergeant', she was soon lumbering around like a turquoise baby elephant, obliged to rely on the more experienced men she encountered in the progressive dances to steer her in the right direction. The Daphne Brain School of Dance had not prepared her for this, but at least there was no barre, just a drinks bar, to which Jack was giving his assiduous custom, long before the introduction of the drink/drive laws. Jess realised in later years that these laws had been brought in with people just like her father in mind; men who insisted they could hold their drink, that it did not in any way impair their driving ability, men who had not even been required to pass a driving test because they had taken to the road before 1935; men who believed they possessed a God-given right to race around Devon's narrow winding lanes at top speed while inebriated, often almost ending up in the hedge because a fox suddenly appeared. Arrogant yet outwardly charming men, who, even when hung over in the mornings, inflicted their worse-for-wear singing on the neighbours:

There was ham, ham, mixed up with the jam, in the Stores, in the Stores! There was butter, butter, running down the gutter in the Quartermaster's Stores.

My eyes are dim I cannot see, I have not brought my specs with me; I have not brought my specs with me!"

"After the ball was over, after the break of morn,
After the dancers' leaving, after the stars are gone;
Many a heart is aching, if you could read them all;
Many the hopes that have vanished, after the ball!"
"Oh, oh Antonio, he's gone away. Left me on my own io, all on
my own io. I'd like to meet him with his new sweetheart; Then up
would go Antonio, and his ice-cream cart!"

Chapter 12

Soon after their arrival at Number 3 Dotey had decided to sub-let the self-contained basement as a separate flat. This comprised a living-room, a tiny kitchen, and a bedroom looking onto the back garden. There was a bathroom with a basin but no fixed bath; a galvanised tin vessel had to be filled up and emptied by hand. There was also a small separate lavatory. Over the years, a succession of tenants quickly came and went, since the lack of a proper bath meant that people could gain extra points on the waiting list for council housing. Several young married couples made the basement flat at No 3 their first home, but as soon as there was news of a baby on the way they qualified almost immediately for a house on the nearby Wilcombe estate.

Dotey's first tenants were the Hakes, a pair of newly qualified schoolteachers, who were to become her life-long friends. Then followed the Chidgeys, who greatly impressed Jess by arriving to view the flat one dark wet night on a motorbike. They eventually left to work in Nigeria, but returned to Tiverton many years later, when, by coincidence, they again became Dotey's neighbours. There followed a disastrous interlude when the Bagshaws rented the flat. Mr. Bagshaw used to shout and beat Mrs. Bagshaw, who could be heard by the family upstairs, sobbing and screaming. Jess especially was upset by this, and asked her mother to telephone the police, feeling that something should be done. Dotey said that there would be no point in calling the police, since the law permitted a man to chastise his wife, so long as he used a cane no thicker than his thumb, which explained the expression 'rule of thumb'.' This was widely, but falsely, believed to be enshrined in common law. Dotey also impressed upon Jess that one should never interfere between husband and wife, and that Mrs. Bagshaw probably would not thank anyone who did. Matters between spouses should always be kept completely private. So the upstairs family studiously ignored Mrs. Bagshaw's bruises and black eyes when they happened to meet her in the street. However, once it was Jess who was screaming, and Mr. Bagshaw who came to her rescue; Jess had accidentally trodden on a nest of ground-dwelling bees in the shrubbery and was stung all over her arms and head. Mr. Bagshaw promptly appeared with a kettle of boiling water and poured it over the nest to kill the bees and prevent a recurrence, while Dotey plucked the bee stings from Jess's flesh with a pair of tweezers. The Bagshaws eventually had a baby, and to the relief of those upstairs, the downstairs family moved to a council house.

Dotey then thought seriously about not re-letting the basement, in case more undesirables appeared, but there was still a severe housing shortage, and she wanted the rent revenue from the flat. The Kellys arrived, and stayed for several years. They were a pleasant couple, and Dotey could find no fault with them, except for the fact that they appeared to use an inordinate amount of hot water, so much so that there was often insufficient in the system for the upstairs family. The electric immersion heater had to be kept switched on full-time, and Dotey grumbled about the expense. She was making very little from subletting the basement flat at a rent of 30 shillings a week. Mrs. Kelly's sister visited at the weekends, and Dotey complained that she must be sitting beside the tap and drinking all the hot water, since there was none left for the children's baths. Jack, on one of his Sunday visits, said the sister appeared to have used the hot water to wash her smalls, judging by the array of garments fluttering on the washing line. And that was another thing – the sister's fondness for skimpy clothing upset Dotey, ("she's constantly running round in her nothings!") and as for the very idea of hanging washing out on a Sunday! Dotey tut-tutted. Sundays were special; the children were not allowed to play noisy games, nobody would dream of mowing their lawn, and washing should always be held back until Monday. Of course, the Kellys soon had a baby, which meant even more laundry. Dozens of terry nappies fluttered from the clothesline, leaving no space for Dotey to hang out her own family's washing. The Kellys seemed to be in no hurry to move to a council house, probably because they knew they were onto such a good thing staying at Number 3, with as much free hot water as they needed. Dotey acknowledged that Mrs. Kelly was 'scrupulously clean', the baby was always kept spick and span, but the electricity bills were now enormous. She vowed to leave the basement flat empty once the Kellys finally went. A second baby on the way meant that the flat was too small, and Mr. Kelly got a job as an agricultural worker, with a tied cottage. The basement at Number 3 remained unoccupied from that time on.

The residents of The Close generally kept themselves to themselves, with perhaps a brief nod when passing in the street. Dotey wryly observed that the lady at No. 5 had waited until precisely the tenth anniversary of her arrival in the Close before deigning to speak to her. This family, the Mosses, comprised an elderly couple with two unmarried middle-aged daughters, Betty and Bunty, the 'Misses Moss', as Dotey always referred to them. Bunty was shy, but Betty was more forthcoming, and the old gentleman, a keen amateur photographer, proved very friendly, showing Jess and Peter how to take pictures and giving Jess an old box Brownie camera. He enjoyed photographing the children and any visiting playmates in the Close, riding their bikes, playing 'tig', or blowing bubbles, and developed the black-and-white pictures himself, always presenting Dotey with copies. Jess enjoyed her photography lessons and was sorry when the Mosses moved away to a remote village.

The couple at No. 1 also left and were replaced by a family with a pack of Pekinese dogs which ran round their back garden yapping all the time, much to Dotey's annoyance. She thought the family at No. 1 were 'rather common', but as Jess was soon to discover, there were a great many people in Tiverton whom she chose to describe in this way.

No 2. was home to the Lowes. They were very keen on gardening, and Dotey always worried that insidious ground elder from her own garden would creep through the hedge to spoil Mrs. Lowe's perfectly maintained flower borders.

Mrs. Lowe had once paused from her weeding to chat with young Jess who was tending a small plot under the hedge on which she was growing a few pansies and marigolds.

"Who is that gentleman that comes to visit you in a black car on Sundays?" asked Mrs. Lowe

"That's our Daddy," answered Jess. "He lives in Exeter."

"Why does Daddy live in Exeter and not here with you?"

"Um, he has to live there because of his Store…"

"I see. What about the boys who visit from time to time?"

"Terry and Jeff? They're out brothers, they live in Exeter as well, with their father. They live next door to our Daddy."

"I always thought Mummy was a widow, but you say your brothers' father is still alive, so maybe that's not the case?"

Jess frowned. She could not remember the correct word, although she had heard it. "I think she's div- divorced?"

"Is she indeed?" said Mrs. Lowe, in a surprised tone. Jess was now starting to feel guilty, since it had been impressed upon her never to discuss family business with strangers, but somehow Mrs. Lowe had wormed it out of her. All Jess had wanted to do was to get on with her gardening, but of course, it had been drummed into her always to be polite to grown-ups, so Dotey's instructions appeared to conflict. Jess, fearing that she had given far too much away, knew better than to report this conversation to her mother.

The Lowe's grand-daughters often visited, three blonde little girls named Fleur, Freya and Francesca, who in summer were allowed to run about in the garden naked. The dining-table by the side window at No 3 overlooked the Lowe's back garden, and anyone sitting there could not but help witness the nude frolics, of which Dotey strongly disapproved. She put this unseemly behaviour down to the fact that the girls' father was from continental Europe, and was therefore 'a foreigner.' In Dotey's opinion, no truly British children would ever be permitted to openly disport themselves on back lawns in such an unseemly manner.

At No 6. lived two big boys who went to Blundell's, the local minor public school, and so were too old to play with Jess and Peter. No. 4. had a succession of occupants, beginning with Major and Mrs. Eyre; he was always known by his military title, and from time to time appeared on the dooR—step with a large bag of salt in order to extinguish a chimney fire he had detected. It seemed that Dotey did not get her chimney swept often enough. The Eyres left, and the Scott-Maxwells moved in; Mrs. S-M was an accomplished pianist who could be heard continually practising her pieces. She eventually had a baby, so the sound of the piano was augmented by little David's cries.

Later, the Scott-Maxwell family moved to a large house near the park, and a family with three little girls moved into No. 4. Jess played with them occasionally. One of the girls apparently had a degree of learning difficulties, "She's just not quite all there," was Dotey's considered opinion, something to do with the little girl's parents' incompatible blood-groups, it seemed, from snatches of conversation Jess overheard between her mother and Mrs. MacDougall. Disability was looked upon quite differently then. Jess remembered being annoyed at the pantomime when the child in the seat behind her was continually kicking the back of her chair, rather spoiling Jess's enjoyment of the performance. She kept turning round to give the child a meaningful stare, but this did not have any effect. Jess wondered why the parents of this child did not reprove their daughter, as her own mother most certainly would have reproved her, had she been annoying someone else. She whispered to Dotey, asking her to say something. Much to her surprise, her mother shook her head, giving Jess her sternest warning look. During the interval Dotey took Jess aside and explained that the child sitting behind her was a Mongol, and therefore could not be expected to behave according to generally accepted standards.

"She's come all the way from Mongolia?" asked Jess, intrigued, since it would be a long journey from central Asia to mid-Devon just for a pantomime. Noticing the child in question nearby, Dotey shushed Jess and told her to eat her choc-ice. The correct term for the little girl's condition, Down's Syndrome, was not then in common use.

Across the road from The Close was The Park, another six Victorian houses, where Dotey knew many of the residents. At No 1 lived a lady called Kathleen, who was originally from Ireland. When this lady learned that Jess's birthday was St. Patrick's Day, she brought Jess a sprig of shamrock from the bunch which her relatives always sent over for her from County Sligo. Jess therefore felt an affinity with Ireland, and hoped to be able to visit one day. Dotey still cherished her dream of revisiting Clifden, especially after a friend went on holiday and sent her a post-card; but it was to remain only a dream for Dotey, to be eventually realised years later by Jess's family, long after her mother's death.

Meanwhile, Jack had several Irish songs in his repertoire:

"If I was a blackbird, I'd whistle and sing, and I'd follow the ship that my true love sailed in; and on the top rigging, there I'd build my nest, and I'd pillow my head on his snowy white breast!"

"Down by the sally gardens, my love and I did meet. She passed the sally gardens with little snow-white feet. She bade me take love easy as the leaves grow on the tree; but I was young and foolish, and with love would not agree."

Chapter 13

The basement flat of No. 4 was home to a very elderly couple, Fern and Arthur. Arthur had poor health, and after he died, Dotey took Fern under her wing. Fern had no children, but was devoted to her hideous black and white cat, Bumble, whose main purpose in life appeared to be catching songbirds. This was especially grievous when Fern was away visiting her sister in Bournemouth, leaving Jess to feed the cat. An anguished cry would be heard "Come quickly, Bumble's got a thrush!" but by the time help had arrived and Bumble had been caught it was generally too late for the hapless bird.

One evening Jess noticed a strange car outside Fern's flat, and Fern at the door in floods of tears. "The vet's here – I'm having my dear Bumble put down!" Jess had not heard this expression, but sensed it must be bad news. Reporting back to her parents, Jack decided that Fern needed something easier to manage than a fierce feline, and declared he would buy her a budgerigar. So Bobby the blue budgie arrived, going some way to assuaging Fern's grief. When she went to Bournemouth, Bobby, cage and all, moved into No.3, where he entered into ear-piercing singing competitions with Noddy, the resident yellow budgie, until everyone had had enough and tea-towels were thrown over both birdcages, leading them to believe that it was nightfall and therefore time to roost.

Fern was becoming more and more absent-minded, and often sought help from No. 3. in retrieving parcels she had mislaid. Her slippered footsteps would be heard shuffling down the hall, her voice trilling, "Silly me! What do you think, Dotey, I've left my pork chops in the Post Office!"

Or "Oh dear, my sausages must still be in Mac Fisheries; I remember just resting my string bag on the slab when the young assistant was choosing me a nice piece of coley for Bumble's supper."

"Don't worry, Fern; one of the children will fetch them!"

A quick phone-call to the relevant shop to confirm that they still had the missing parcel, and whichever child was closest at hand was obliged to leave whatever he or she was doing at once and cycle down to the town as quickly as possible to collect Fern's dinner. The package was always exactly where Fern had left it, and Jess marvelled that no-one ever made off with anything Fern had left behind.

Fern enjoyed having the children round to watch television, and she even had ITV! Fern's favourite programme was 'The Saint', featuring lovely Roger Moore. She also had an old knitting pattern with a picture of dear Roger modelling a jumper, which she would take out of a drawer to show the children every week. The children could take or leave 'The Saint', but Thursday night was a regular fixture for 'Top Of The Pops.' Unluckily for them, it was about this time that Fern would decide to make toast. Many an evening's entertainment was spoiled for them by Fern jigging about in front of the fire, waggling her bottom not quite in time with the music, flapping the toasting-fork, with her eyes on the television rather than the bread, which often as not fell into the fire and burnt. "Fern, the toast!" Jess could not concentrate on the television while thus distracted, and the half-hour passed by anxiously, leaving her in no position to compare notes with her friends about the relative merits of the pop performers the next day. A game-show asking contestants if they wanted to take the money or open the box also distracted Fern. "Open the box!" Fern shrieked, her toast meanwhile incinerating itself on the coals.

The basement flat at No. 2 was rented by a rather refined lady called Norah O'Shaughnessy. Jess was allowed to visit her from time to time in order to watch television, and she noticed that Norah always had a glass of orange juice on the table beside her arm chair. Jess thought Norah must have led an interesting life, since once, while watching a travel programme about the Alps, she mentioned that she had stayed at a sanatorium in Switzerland; Jess did not know what a sanatorium was, and on asking her mother later, was told that it was a sort of hospital, where people who had diseases such as tuberculosis were sent to recover in the fresh air. Then, during the broadcast of a concert being given by the Halle Orchestra, Norah sighed, "Oh, there's dear John!" Norah had known celebrated conductor Sir John Barbirolli, a fact which greatly impressed Jess.

However, once when Jess knocked on the door, Norah took a long time to answer; she eventually appeared, leaning on her stick very unsteadily, and shouted at Jess to go away. Jess was perplexed, and for a while avoided visiting Norah, until Norah complained to Dotey that Jess never came to see her any more. Dotey told Jess that she should not hurt a lonely old widow's feelings by staying away, especially when Peter usually chose to watch television at Fern's, because of the availability of ITV, and Fern always boasted of this to Norah. Jess explained that Norah had shooed her away the last time she had visited, and noticed her parents exchange glances. Dotey said that Mrs. O'Shaughnessy had obviously been unwell that particular evening, but that Jess should now resume her visits, which Jess dutifully did. However, this time she found Norah weeping into her orange juice, and nothing Jess said could cheer her up. Val Doonican had been singing 'The Special Years', and Norah had become upset, telling Jess that she was about to enter the special years and should be sure to make the most of them, they passed so very quickly and could never come again... Jess did not think that there was anything very special about her life at the moment, it seemed to consist of school-work, homework and endless household chores. Unable to distract the weeping Norah with small-talk, Jess finally made her excuses, saying she had some homework to do, and left. There was clearly something wrong with Mrs. O'Shaughnessy, but Jess did not know what it could be. However, when she explained to her parents the reason for her early return, Jack seemed to know at once.

"Sounds like Norah's maudlin. Don't let Jess go again!"

But Dotey did not want to offend Norah, and told Jess that she should persevere. Meanwhile, if Mrs. O'Shaughnessy appeared weepy or unsteady on her feet, she must leave. So Jess tried again the following day, and found Norah in a good mood; they had an enjoyable evening chatting and watching 'Tonight'. All seemed to be fine, until Jess was returning home from the town the following Saturday afternoon, having been on an errand to retrieve Fern's green-groceries from the library, and noticed smoke billowing from Norah's window. She knocked on the door, but received no reply, so ran home.

"Mrs. O'Shaughnessy's flat is on fire and I can't get her to answer the door!" said Jess breathlessly to her parents.

Jack immediately ran to Norah's, while Dotey telephoned the Fire Brigade. By this time there was a large cloud of strange-smelling smoke coming from the living-room window, so Jack had to cover his face with a handkerchief.

"Norah – open up!" Jack hammered fruitlessly on the door, while Jess watched from a safe distance. Jack then leaned his shoulder into the door, which fortunately had only a Yale lock, and broke in He almost collided with an indignant Norah lurching across the hall in her dressing gown, seemingly unaware that her house was on fire, and complaining loudly at being disturbed. Jack led her outside as the Fire Brigade arrived. Norah had left her electric fire switched on at full blast in the living room, with a laden clothes horse pulled too close. The laundry had caught fire, igniting an armchair. Norah had meanwhile been asleep in the bedroom. Jess marvelled that anyone could sleep through all the commotion, the thick smoke and her father's shouting. Norah had to stay with her sister while her flat was renovated, and it was not until some years later that Jess discovered that Norah was an alcoholic, a fact of which her parents had of course been fully aware all along.

Chapter 14

At the end of The Close was a driveway leading to a bungalow, built on the site of an old coach house. There lived Thomas Ford, a former Mayor of Tiverton, proprietor of the Starkey, Knight and Ford Brewery, the source of the overwhelming smell of hops which frequently permeated the town. Tommy was one of the richest men in Tiverton, according to Dotey. He was a widower, living alone, with a housekeeper who came in every day to see to his meals. He possessed an old-fashioned car with running boards, and sometimes he would ask his chauffeur to stop at the top of the drive and allow the children to ride a short way on the running-boards. Tommy then requested that the children should call at the bungalow every evening to fill his coal-scuttle. So each day at five o'clock they duly arrived at his front door, to find the empty scuttle left out. As they filled it in the coal shed, the front door would slowly open and Tommy would appear on the doorstep. The children handed over the coal scuttle and in return each received a three penny bit, solemnly handed to them by Mr. Ford. Jess was not sure why the housekeeper could not fill the coal-scuttle before she left, but Jack reckoned that old Tommy enjoyed the ritual of dispensing alms to the neighbourhood poor.

Tommy also had a cat, which Jess was detailed to feed when he was on holiday. The cat was fed on offal; there was always a huge pan of 'lights' on the stove, which the housekeeper boiled up daily for Jess to put out for the cat's tea. Jess detested the smell emanating from the pan of greasy grey liquid with the revolting lumpy stuff floating in it, and always shuddered as she dished it up for the hungry cat. Dotey wondered why on earth a man as wealthy as Tommy could not buy tins of Kit-e-Kat like everyone else. In due course, Jess would receive a terse post-card from Bournemouth, ('Weather good, hope cat is well, Thos. Ford'), and upon his return, a florin or half-crown reward for her endeavours.

Tommy had a field containing a pony, Jenny; sometimes Jenny would appear at the fence separating the field from No.3's garden, and Jess would give her a carrot or an apple.

The children were allowed to play in the field, so long as they kept well away from the bungalow. They were able to cross it to reach the canal, where the boys had their rafts. Jack once decided to test a new fertiliser by sprinkling it in the field, then noting how much better the grass grew where he had applied the fertiliser. He wrote 'JESS' and 'PETER' with the fertiliser, and said that people passing overhead in aeroplanes would be able to read their names in the grass, although this was quite difficult on the ground.

Tommy's daughter and her family moved into The Close, becoming Jess's family's next-door neighbours. A long discussion arose between the landlord of Number 3 and Tommy about the state of the chimney shared by the two houses. Urgent repair work was needed, because the brickwork had deteriorated to such an extent that huge holes had appeared, and it was now possible to see daylight through the chimney stack. Tommy arranged for it to be mended, since a gust of wind could have brought the entire structure, complete with its series of giant chimney pots, crashing down through the roof onto his sleeping grandchildren, or indeed, onto the fillers of his coal scuttle, depending on which way it fell. The workmen had to erect enough scaffolding to reach up the four storeys from the back garden, and reported that it was a good job the work had not been delayed a moment longer, since they could actually put their arms right through the stack. Jack purloined the ornate discarded chimney pots and put them in the kitchen garden to force his rhubarb crop. Further difficulty arose when the residents of The Close were asked to club together to get the driveway resurfaced. No.3's landlord refused to pay, so new tarmac was laid in front of all the other houses, leaving the old rough track outside No.3. Jack was disgusted and Dotey embarrassed, until the landlord grudgingly relented and paid for new tarmac outside No.3, just before the workmen were about to leave.

No.3 had no central heating, but mysteriously, during the harsh winter of 1963 (which remains one of the severest on record) while the water supply to the other five houses in The Close froze, Jess's family was the only household with running water. Jack had lagged all the pipes with hessian sacking, and placed a few extra smelly paraffin heaters strategically throughout the house, which fortunately seemed to have done the trick. Of course, immediately news got round that there was still running water to be had at No.3, a procession of desperate neighbours formed, carrying buckets, jugs, watering cans and kettles; they trooped through the house to the kitchen, where the only working tap in The Close was situated. (This was quite extraordinary, since the conservatory kitchen faced north and was exposed to the elements, whereas the neighbour's kitchens were on the south side.) After filling the various receptacles, the neighbours trooped back through the house, only to return at teatime and do it all again. Jack took up the hall runner and put down yet more sacking – being an agricultural merchant, he had access to unlimited supplies of hessian, which came in especially useful when the soil pipe froze, and the family was unable to flush the toilet. Jack's solution was to light a huge bonfire of petrol-soaked sacking under the metal soil pipe, resulting in a dramatic and instantaneous thaw and a certain amount of consternation on the part of the people living next door.

The children were sent home from school because the boiler had broken down. Jack was also at home, the Exe Valley road being impassable. Hitherto, it was not the sort of neighbourhood where people were habitually in and out of each others houses, but now everyone quickly became like old friends. Jack said it reminded him of the war when everyone was united against the common enemy, only now of course it was the Big Freeze, rather than Hitler. Most of the neighbours were very considerate about the timing of their water collection, but Fern could be counted on to appear at the most inconvenient times, such as when Dotey was dishing up a meal; letting herself in through the seemingly ever-open front door, the family would hear her slow progression down the hall. "Coo-ee, it's only me!" After collecting her water, Fern hovered in the doorway, as an icy blast blew down the hall and into the living room, recounting in great detail something very unimportant and long-winded, while the family sat at the dinner table and froze. Engrossed in her story and distracted from the task in hand, Fern would allow her kettle to gradually tilt, thus letting water tip all over the floor. "Watch out, Fern!" Jack shouted. "Oh, silly me!" and Fern would blithely continue with the tale, while the children raced to fetch the mop.

In a desperate effort to keep the place warm, in a large house heated only by a coal fire in the living room and the meagre warmth of a few paraffin stoves, Dotey resorted to opening the electric oven door to heat the freezing kitchen. She was terrified that the quarterly electricity bill would be beyond enormous, possibly as much as a hundred pounds; however, when it arrived, to her surprise and relief, the bill was for only five pounds. Jack, who generally delayed paying bills until the last possible opportunity, rushed out to settle this one before any mistake could be discovered. His theory was that the meter had gone right the way round the clock, and then a little over, so that the electricity use appeared substantially less than was actually the case.

Jess's two pet goldfish had been frozen solid in the garden pond for weeks; Jess could dimly make out two orange blobs within the ice. Come the thaw, to Jess's surprise, the fish simply swam out of their icy tomb and carried on with their pond lives; she had expected them to float to the top, but they had apparently been in suspended animation. The water supply was eventually restored throughout the Close, so the neighbours ceased their twice-a-day visits. Everyone went back to their reserved former manners, bidding Dotey 'Good Morning', but little more. The hessian was taken up, the hall runner was replaced, the school boiler was declared fit for purpose, the Exe Valley road was again passable, and normal life finally resumed by the end of March.

Chapter 15

Jess's early childhood passed by to the accompaniment of the Light programme and the Home Service. Dotey was a devotee of the wireless, beginning every weekday with 'Housewives' Choice', followed by 'Music While You Work','Workers' Playtime', 'Women's Hour' and 'The Archers', interspersed with 'Listen with Mother' and 'Children's Hour'. One West Country regional programme, a particular favourite of Dotey's, was a serial entitled 'At the Luscombes', centring upon a couple called Harry and Flo and their daughter Dot, living in a village in Dorset. Dotey was upset when the actor playing Harry died, or maybe the character of Harry was killed off, or possibly both - Jess was unsure, she did not really follow the drama, although she liked the jaunty signature tune. Then there was a request programme, 'Very Much At Home', with a crooning West Country voice intoning the dedications, which seemed to be more or less the same every week. Jess thought that everyone in the South-West must be great fans of choral singing, what with perpetual requests for the Glasgow Orpheus Choir, the Vienna Boys Choir, and especially Manchester School Children's Choir singing 'Nymphs and Shepherds Come Away". Other favourites were Sir Harry Lauder's rendition of 'Keep Right On To The End Of The Road', 'The Old Rugged Cross', 'All In The April Evening', 'Abide With Me' and the twenty-third psalm to the tune 'Crimond', which, as the lugubrious tones of the announcer informed the listeners, brought such comfort to so many in times of distress...

The radio was in the living room, and rather surprisingly, programmes full of innuendo, such as 'Round the Horne', were permissible. Dotey, who actually had a raucous sense of humour, would chuckle away at the *double entendres*, satisfied that her innocent daughter had no idea as to what was so funny. More dubious hidden meanings filled many of the songs the children were required to sing on Monday mornings during the schools' radio programme 'Singing Together', when the Yorkshire tones of presenter William Appleby filled classrooms throughout the land: ("Sit up straight! No talking at the back! Now, everyone, turn to page 8.") There were songs about young women leading horses to stables to eat their fill of oats, and young women living in Amsterdam who were mistresses of their trade, although exactly which trade was unspecified and Jess of course did not have clue. There were also a number of stirring military songs such as 'Darby Kelly', 'The British Grenadiers' and 'Bonnie Dundee'. ('Singing Together' ran for many years and was still broadcast in 1976 when Jess was a teacher; but with a more carefully chosen repertoire.)

Dotey enjoyed Old Time Dancing, and when 'Those Were the Days' came on, she would sometimes grab Jess and try to teach her to waltz or foxtrot. Jess was clueless, so her mother carried on waltzing around the room alone. Dotey liked comedy programmes and once confessed, during an episode of 'The Men from The Ministry' that she had actually written a fan letter to Richard Murdoch, when he had been in 'Much Binding In The Marsh' during the war. Game shows such as 'Twenty Questions' and 'My Word!' were popular, especially the part of the show when Dennis Norden and Frank Muir were required to make up silly stories to account for the origin of common sayings, for example, "Marry in haste and repent at leisure" was supposed to have begun as "Marry in Hastings and repent at St. Leonards." It was generally believed that they had to make them up as they went along. Dotey also listened to 'The Petticoat Line', where a panel of well-spoken and very opinionated women discussed issues of the day, which for some reason Jess found extremely irritating, probably because if she herself ventured to give an opinion on anything at all she would be immediately silenced; so that she found herself envying these vociferous panellists, whom it appeared were actually paid to speak out…

On Saturdays there was 'Children's Favourites', with Derek McCullough – Uncle Mac; once Dotey sent in a successful request for 'The Dance of the Sugar-Plum Fairy' for Jess and Peter. Of course, it was more their mother's favourite than theirs, but it was nice to hear their names mentioned on the wireless. Some of the oft-requested comedy songs upset Jess as a young child: "I know an old lady who swallowed a fly" she disliked especially, with its final line of "She's dead – of course!" 'The Runaway Train' was also upsetting, Jess was terrified at the though of being a passenger on an out of control train. Even 'When Father Painted the Parlour' upset her, with its lines "Mother was stuck to the ceiling, the kids were stuck to the floor."

Literal little Jess wondered how they would ever mange if they got stuck to the floor, imagine trying to escape from a gooey morass, and what would happen if you needed the toilet?

The radio was always switched off at ten o'clock when 'Saturday Club' with Brian Matthew came on, since Dotey did not approve of jazz or pop music. Saturday lunchtime passed by to the strains of 'The Billy Cotton Band Show' with Kathy Kirby and Alan Breeze, while on Sundays there was 'Two Way Family Favourites', with Jean Metcalfe and Cliff Michelmore, whereby servicemen stationed overseas and their families could request pieces of music for each other. When Jack came to live at The Close the wireless was inevitably tuned to his favourite programmes, which included the football results, and Vic Oliver's 'Discord in Three Flats'. Jack also liked 'The Clitheroe Kid', featuring little Jimmy Clitheroe, who it turned out was actually a grown man. The children were permitted to listen to 'Pick of the Pops' with Alan Freeman, but when Jack wanted to switch over for the news they had to give way. Jeff, who had arrived to live with his Tiverton family at the age of twelve, solved the problem by buying a transistor radio, so he could enjoy 'I'm Sorry I'll Read That Again' and Radio Luxembourg to his heart's content. Jeff also bought a tape recorder, with which he recorded people unawares. Jess disliked this idea, and was accused of being a spoil-sport when she warned a visiting Norah that the machine was on.

"But I think people should be aware and give permission, what if they say something they later regret?" said Jess. Surprisingly, only Jack agreed with her. Norah returned later with a charming prepared speech for Jeff to record, hardly 'fly-on-the-wall' but at least with informed consent.

Sometimes Jess and Jeannie MacDougall were allowed to go to the local cinemas, the 'Tivoli' or the 'Electric', to see films which Dotey deemed suitable. Jess cried at the end of 'Last Holiday' when Alec Guinness fell under a bus in his delight at being told that his diagnosis of incurable illness was wrong, the test results having been mixed up with another man's. Cowboy films could also be upsetting, what with all the Indians slaughtered, not to mention the terrified horses. Musicals starring Doris Day, such as 'The Pyjama Game' or 'Calamity Jane' became standard cinema fare for Jess and Jeannie. The trick with children's shows was to try to get out at the end before the National Anthem was played. The usherettes would make a valiant attempt to block the exits, but they were no match for the crowd of impatient children who refused to stand respectfully still.

On a family outing to the 'Tivoli', ten year old Jess wept during a film about the Hungarian Uprising, so much so that her entire family had to leave halfway through, Dotey and Jack grumbling that they had wanted to stay and find out whether the hero managed to escape. They had hoped the children would learn something of recent European history, but the sight of tanks rolling into Budapest and the subsequent carnage had proved too much for sensitive Jess.

The films shown at school were usually no more cheerful. The pupils were once herded into the school hall to watch Eisenstein's 'Battleship Potemkin', with its unforgettable scene of an empty pram falling down the steps of Odessa after the massacre of a crowd of innocent civilians. Jess was also upset by a film about the building of the Berlin Wall, with its depiction of divided families, and people being shot escaping to the West. She also found herself having to look away during a road safety information film, involving a car accident in which a little boy was killed, and noticed that even some of the prefects had tears welling up. Adults appeared to have strange ideas as to the sort of films children should be allowed to see. Dotey's main criterion seemed to be that the film should contain no sex, or 'unpleasantness' as she termed it. The tragic Hungarian Uprising and any number of massacred Native Americans were all acceptable viewing; but when fifteen year old Jess was invited to the 'Tivoli' to see the film 'Peyton Place' by a well-meaning neighbour, Dotey immediately put her foot down. The bold neighbour said that it would be fine for Jess to go, it was classified 'Certificate A' and children could go if accompanied by an adult; whereupon Dotey sighed and said that she would have to come as well, presumably with the intention of shielding Jess's eyes if anything 'unpleasant' occurred on screen. It seemed that Jess, who owed her very existence to an extramarital affair, was always to be protected from any acknowledgement of human carnality, and constrained to live a censored and sheltered life so long as her mother had breath in her body.

Curiously, Dotey forbade the film of the musical 'Carousel' ("much too upsetting for you, Jess") while allowing her to go on a family excursion to Plymouth where members of the extended Annear family were performing in the same musical. Jess was enthralled by the dancing of her cousin Elisabeth as Louise. (Elisabeth went on to have a career on the stage, marrying the Irish actor Dermot Walsh.) Dotey carefully explained that although Billy the character had fallen on his knife and was dead, the actor playing him would reappear at the end of the show to take a bow. Jess had of course worked this out for herself. On another excursion to Plymouth, poor Judd Fry died in "Oklaholma" and then everyone sang and danced and had a picnic. This seemed a bit strange to Jess. Later, when one of Jack's nieces was in a production of 'Call Me Madam!' at Taunton, the family went to see it, and Jess really admired the character of Mrs. Sally Adams – a sassy woman Ambassador – but could not help wondering how many such female diplomats there actually might be in real life.

Predictably, Dotey was dead against sixteen year old Jess attending a controversial screening of 'The War Game' in Exeter. The trip had been arranged by Mr. Wood, 'the weirdy with the beardie' English teacher, who had a CND badge on his car. Dotey disapproved of both beards and the Campaign for Nuclear Disarmament, and found to her satisfaction that Exeter city fathers were with her, since the local Watch Committee banned all screenings of the film within the city limits, so the school trip had to be cancelled.

"Young Girl, get out of my mind!" sang Jess absent-mindedly as she dried the dishes in 1968. The song, by Gary Puckett and the Union Gap, was top of the charts, and was the sort of catchy tune which sticks in one's mind. Dotey immediately silenced her. She was certainly not going have any singing about child abuse under her roof.

Meanwhile Jack was as ever in good voice:
You are my heart's delight, and where you are, I long to be. You make my darkness bright, when like a star you shine on me!

Shine then, my whole life through, your light divine gives me hope anew, that dreams of mine may perchance come true, and I will hear you whisper, I love you!"

Chapter 16

Jess went every summer to stay a few days in Exeter with her godparents. Sometimes she went to Aunt Jane's in Pennsylvania, and sometimes to see Auntie Phyl and Uncle Cecil in Thornton Hill. Aunt Jane had never had any children, making do instead with a toy poodle called Midge. Jess did not care much for Midge, who had a bad habit of dancing on his hind legs and scratching visitors' calves, thereby clicking Jess's white knee socks. Jess never really wanted to go and stay with Aunt Jane but Dotey always insisted, since Aunt Jane was her well-off, childless godmother, and Jess must take good care not offend her. She must be on her best behaviour, pay attention to what Aunt Jane told her, and not be in a day-dream all the time.

Jess complained that Aunt Jane had a tendency to treat her like an infant, continually asking if she needed to visit 'The Aviary', her name for the lavatory, the walls of which were covered with bright yellow paper depicting various species of exotic bird. Jess was of course well able to take herself off to the toilet when she needed to, so always replied "No, thank you," but this never seemed to satisfy Aunt Jane, who always followed up with a stern "Are you quite sure?" Jess would firmly say "Yes"; however, her godmother inevitably countered with "It might be as well if you went anyway..."

Aunt Jane was the granddaughter of celebrated Victorian John Porter, who had trained racehorses for the nobility and even royalty, and went on to found Newbury Racecourse, in which Aunt Jane now held shares. (A race, the 'John Porter Stakes' is still run every Spring in his honour.) Aunt Jane had even once been presented to the Queen when the monarch was enjoying a day at the races. Jess knew that her godmother was generous and well-meaning, and tried to enjoy their trips into Exeter, shopping at Colson's Department Store, followed by three-course lunches at the Burlington Restaurant, when all she really wanted was to be back in Tiverton, out on her bicycle, or meeting up with her friends, or even helping her mother.

A visit to Auntie Phyl and Uncle Cecil was completely different. Since being appointed as Jess's godparents they had become followers of White Eagle, and had converted a small room in their house into a chapel for his worship. Jess admired the lovely portrait of White Eagle, with his beautiful feathered headdress. Phyl and Cecil went every week to Shaldon, to a fresh spring, where they filled copious containers of drinking water, not trusting what the authorities were adding to the tap water. This was well before general concerns were raised over the fluoridation of the public water supply. Auntie Phyl was very interested in alternative remedies, and seemed to drink a great deal of cider vinegar and honey and to use large quantities of comfrey, while Uncle Cecil kept a productive allotment. Jess always enjoyed helping him collect the produce for tea – tomatoes, lettuces, radishes, beans, carrots, cabbages and cucumbers. Every autumn Aunt Phyl made preserves – "There's jams in that cupboard dating back to 1066," said Uncle, when Jess asked for something to put on her toast.

Phyl and Cecil took Jess for rambles on Dartmoor, and once they came across a potter creating his pots in a remote hut. However, they had to return to Exeter promptly for one of Uncle Cecil's evening faith healing sessions. He had recently discovered he had the healing gift – Jess was not sure exactly how this discovery had been made, but judging by the demand for his unadvertised and unremunerated services it certainly seemed to work. He even succeeded with animals – who of course could not be expected to have faith – when conventional treatments had failed, and their distraught owners and all the vets had despaired of them.

"We must go home now dear; Uncle's giving healing to a horse!" Jess greatly admired her godfather and wished her father was like Uncle Cecil, who encouraged and praised her, instead of offering criticism, sarcasm and contempt.

Dotey shook her head in disbelief after Jess's return home.

"They were just plain C of E when I asked them to be your godparents! Goodness knows what's got into them! Spring water? Comfrey? Faith healing for animals? And just who is White Eagle when he's at home? Are you sure you want to stay there again? You don't have to if you'd rather not..."

But Jess said she loved going, she adored her eccentric godparents, whom she knew loved her in return; and she continued to visit them every year for the rest of their days.

Phyl and Cecil had two grown-up children, Anthony and Rosemary. Anthony returned from his spell in the Navy, married, and settled down, but Rosemary was unmarried; she had what Dotey approvingly referred to as 'a brilliant career', doing publicity work for Westward Television. This independent station, based in Plymouth, possessed a large rabbit puppet called Gus Honeybun, whose human side-kick read out children's birthday greetings over the air. Jess had no television at home, but managed to glimpse Gus occasionally at a friend's house. The usual request was for Gus to waggle his ears six times, or whatever number birthday was being celebrated. One of Rosemary's duties was to escort the celebrity puppet around the county, from village fêtes to city store openings. Once, when Rosemary and Gus Honeybun were appearing at Colson's, the volume of traffic generated by excited small children and their parents was such that the police were obliged to close Exeter High Street. Rosemary was also involved with the 'Miss Westward' beauty competition, and was required to travel on exotic holidays, as chaperone to the title winner.

"Just fancy, Rosemary's off to Jamaica this year! How marvellous! That's what a good career does for you, Jess!"

Dotey was full of admiration for Rosemary – the foreign trips, the cocktail dresses, the parties, and the glamour of working in television. Jess admired her too, although for very different reasons. Rosemary was always interested in what Jess was doing, and never poured scorn on her efforts. (When Jess's contributions began appearing in the national press in the 1980s, Rosemary was full of encouragement and praise, while Jess's partner was puzzled. "Why on earth would anyone want to read something you've written?")

Rosemary had a Chihuahua dog called Bambi, which she often left at Thornton Hill when she was working away. The resident dog, Muff, was told old to go for long walks, but Bambi needed exercise, and Jess was often detailed to walk her round the block. Sometimes Aunty Phil's brother, Uncle Spen, was there with his brown Labrador, so Jess had two dogs to take out, one large and one very small. The other household pet was a mynah bird, which issued a continual stream of commands and questions. "Fetch my slippers! Where's that dog's lead?" and "Go to bed, Muff!" at which the old dog always obediently went to its basket.

The atmosphere of her godparents' house was so happy and so different from the tensions back at home that Jess often wished she had the courage to run away to Exeter. Once, when her mother's depression became acute, Jess ran to the telephone box in despair and called her godparents, who immediately arranged for Dotey to spend some time at Thornton Hill. Afterwards, Uncle Cecil good-humouredly complained to Jess that Phyl and Dotey had talked non-stop throughout the entire visit, so that what with reminiscences about their salad days with the Post Office Telephones, the barking of the dogs, and the shrill dictates of the Mynah bird, he had been very glad to escape to the allotment…

When Dotey was feeling a little better, she posted Jess a card from Exeter, "Make my bed, light the light, I'll be home Thursday night!" Jack must have picked it up from the doormat, since Dotey arrived back home to the strains of 'Bye, Bye Blackbird', as her husband serenaded the neighbourhood from the open front bedroom window.

"Pack up all my care and woe, here I go singing low, bye, bye Blackbird:
Where somebody waits for me, sugar's sweet, so is she; bye, bye Blackbird.
No-one here can love or understand me, oh what hard luck stories they all hand me!
Make my bed and light the light, I'll be home late tonight, Blackbird, bye bye!"

Chapter 17

At eight, Jess had asked if she could join the Brownies. Dotey agreed to buy the uniform of brown tunic, woolly hat and yellow scarf, and Jess enrolled in the Heathcoat school pack. She was not very good at keeping her uniform tidy, and was often criticised during inspections for failing to tie her scarf with the required reef knot at the back of the neck; Jess found this so awkward that her knot frequently turned out to be a granny. The Brownie song was "We're the Brownies, here's our aim – lend a hand and play the game!" The pack was divided into four sixes, and Jess was at first assigned to Gnomes, whose song was "Here you see the laughing Gnomes, helping mother in our homes." Despite her uniform malfunctions, she was later promoted to be Seconder of Elves –"Here we are, the happy Elves, helping others, not ourselves." Eventually, she became the Sixer of Fairies, whose song was "We're the Fairies, glad and gay, helping others every day." She missed out on Pixies – "Look out, we're the jolly Pixies, helping others when in fixes!"

Jess enjoyed the games and activities, and managed to accumulate several badges, including those for cooking (stewed apple), laying and lighting a fire (in the examiner's back yard), needlework (sewing on a button and darning a sock) and learning to send and receive messages using semaphore. However, she hated the long solitary walk home afterwards. The friends she usually walked with did not stay for Brownies, so had left when school finished. The pack met for an hour after school on Tuesdays, which was also the day of Tiverton weekly cattle market. The pubs stayed open throughout the afternoon to accommodate the needs of the thirsty farmers and drovers, instead of keeping to the usual licensing hours, so Tiverton town centre on Tuesday teatimes was a scary place, and Jess had to run the gauntlet of all this mayhem on her own.

One summer afternoon Jess was walking along Fore Street as quickly as her short legs could take her when she felt a sharp thwack on the back of her head. She yelped in pain, and turned around to see a red-faced man leering at her. He wore the fawn-coloured overall and cloth cap typical of a cattle drover, and was armed with his cattle droving stick. He lurched past Jess, who had frozen in fright on the pavement, and then went on down the street, lashing out and hitting another young woman as he did so. She turned round and glared at the man, but continued on her way. Jess began to cry, but there was no-one around who seemed to want to help her, so she continued to Lowman Green, on the opposite side of the town, where Dotey usually met her. By this time, Jess had worked herself into a fine state of nerves, and on seeing her mother she burst into a flood of tears, sobbing incoherently about how a horrid man had beaten her with his stick. Dotey immediately marched her round to the Police Station and made a strong complaint. However, the desk sergeant was unimpressed, saying that there were no independent witnesses, so it would not be possible to corroborate Jess's allegation, unless the other girl came forward, lending credence to the story. Otherwise nothing could be done, since it would simply be Jess's word against that of the drunker drover. Children were not then regarded as reliable witnesses, their testimony was suspect.

As an indignant Dotey and tearful Jess were leaving, a young police constable took Dotey aside, and in a broad Devonshire accent said that he had a hunch as to just who the offender might be, there were several drunken drovers about, but one in particular was often very much the worse for wear after the market. However, "if 'ee do let a little maid wander through town of a Toosday then what do 'ee ecspec..." He made it sound like the Wild West Country. After this, Dotey arranged for Jess to go straight from Brownies to the office of the Pearl Assurance Company, where Jennifer Chidgey, then the downstairs tenant of No. 3, worked. Jess was to wait quietly in the lobby until the office closed at five o'clock, and then return home with Jennifer, who would be armed with an umbrella and a stern expression, to see off any potential malefactors.

An opportunity for Jess to redeem herself after her knot tying shortcomings arose at the annual Brownie Revels. These were generally held on the wettest Saturday in June, in a woodland hut in the grounds of Knightshayes Estate, by kind permission of Sir John and Lady Amory. The year Jess was nine the weather was for once fine. As a start to the festivities, the assembled Brownie packs from all over the district had been set the task of constructing a miniature garden. Jess, Tiverton's Junior Flower arranging champion, had an eye for colour schemes and proportions, and knew how to place the specimens for maximum effect rather than just sticking them in any old how as many of the girls were doing, in their haste to complete this boring task and get started with the more exciting games. Jess lingered over the miniature garden, perfecting the arrangement, unwilling to have to start chasing through nettles and brambles on the Treasure Hunt, which was the next item on the Revelling agenda. Her Brownie pack won first prize for the miniature garden, adding a few useful points to the day's overall tally.

Making her way home late in the afternoon, worn out with revelling and the heat, Jess suddenly found her way barred by a big boy brandishing a large stick, who growled at her, "Get down that path!" The track led between high hedges to some secluded allotments, and Jess desperately did not want to go. She turned round to try to escape, only to find the way blocked by two more armed boys, both grinning in a menacing fashion. The gang proceeded to beat Jess with their cudgels – sticks were evidently the weapon of choice in Tiverton in 1960. Jess screamed in pain and terror. The boys grabbed her by her Brownie tunic and began dragging her down the path, but fortunately for Jess, a woman appeared on the opposite footpath walking her dog, glaring at the boys, who were reluctantly obliged to let Jess go.

Back at the Close, Dotey was beginning to wonder why Jess was dawdling on her way home when she was under strict instructions to come straight back after the Revels had ended. Jess was actually hurrying home as quickly as she could, given that her knees felt like jelly, her heart was pounding fit to burst and the hot tears were pouring down her cheeks. Her tunic was all awry and her cookery badge was coming away from the sleeve of her tunic where she had been manhandled. It was in this dishevelled state that Jack found her, having been despatched in the car by Dotey to search for their missing daughter. Peter, in the back seat, had come along for the ride. Jess began to explain what had happened, as best as she could through her tears. They were quite close to the Police Station, but Jack knew from Jess's previous experience that reporting the assault would be of no use, so decided to take the law into his own hands.

"Get in the car!" ordered Jack, so Jess climbed into the back beside Peter. Jack drove to the spot where Jess had been waylaid, and sure enough, the three lads were still there, no doubt awaiting their next potential victim. "Those the boys?" asked Jack. Jess nodded. Jack slammed on the brakes, the car screeched to a halt, and before anyone knew what was happening, Jack had all three boys lying on the pavement, having felled them seemingly with one blow. Jess and Peter witnessed the scene open-mouthed, peering in stunned silence from the rear window of the car.

"Don't 'ee dare ever touch my daughter again!" shouted Jack, returning to the driving seat and turning the car towards home. The boys picked themselves up off the dusty pavement in stunned silence. There were very many occasions over the next decade when Jess had cause to resent Jack's attitude to women, but she never forgot the day when he had avenged her cowardly assailants. She bumped into two of the boys soon afterwards, walking home from school but this time she was with her friends and not wearing her Brownie uniform. Nevertheless, one of them recognised her. "That's 'er, Clive, now we got 'er!"

But Clive, the gang leader, shook his head, the force of Jack's blow still fresh in his memory, and Jess was not troubled by the boys again. Nowadays, Jack would have been on an assault charge and the boys would have claimed and no doubt received compensation for their bruises; but in 1960 it was still quite acceptable to chastise a miscreant.

Jess wondered why her parents allowed her to walk around unescorted, when it appeared that danger was continuously present for little girls, particularly those dressed in Brownie uniforms; but neither Jack nor Dotey was prepared to put themselves out for a 'great girl of nine' who should be able to make her own way home. Even when Jack discovered her in such distress following the terrifying assault by the gang of three big boys, he had not attempted to console her or dry her tears, there was no kissing or comforting; he had simply commanded her to get in the car. Jess attributed his surliness to the fact that the time must be approaching five o'clock on a Saturday afternoon, so he would be missing the football results. Her parents' attitude to girls was far from sentimental; it was always made clear that daughters were there to perform household tasks, so

Jess must be tractable and obedient and not expect to be indulged or 'spoiled'; and Jess was quite aware where she came in the family pecking order. Parents preferred sons who would carry on the family name and business, boys who were good at sports and were allowed to roam around outdoors, while girls made beds, cooked, cleaned, ran errands and carried home laden shopping bags. "It's a little girl's privilege to be able to help her mother," said Dotey.

"So did you regard it as a privilege to help your mother?"

"Of course," said Dotey, before eventually admitting that her family had kept domestic help... Jess wished she had a sister to share the burden of domestic duties, but when she dared to give voice to her wish, Dotey told her sharply not to be so silly and to finish peeling the potatoes. Dotey's life of privilege had given way to disappointment and drudgery, so she appeared to reason that if Jess's began in that way, then whatever followed could only be an improvement.

Chapter 18

When the children were young, Dotey often took them to the seaside for the day by train. The picturesque Exe Valley railway line, before it was closed by the Beeching reforms, provided Tivertonians with quick access to Exeter and onward to the nearest seaside resorts of Exmouth and Dawlish Warren, situated on opposite side of the beautiful Exe estuary. The children were content to spend all morning on the beach, paddling, digging, making sandcastles and looking into rock-pools, while Dotey sat in a deck-chair and read the Daily Mail, before serving up a picnic of hard-boiled eggs, Shippams paste sandwiches and tomatoes. Sometimes it would come on to rain, so they would rush to a draughty shelter on the promenade, or try to hide under some overhanging rocks; however, Dotey always declared that this was only a passing shower, it would soon blow over, and they should stick it out, and not return home until the tea-time train as planned.

When Jack joined the family, suddenly there was a car at their disposal, and when he was in a good mood the family could venture further afield, to Budleigh Salterton and Sidmouth, in the area now known as the Jurassic Coast. Budleigh was always Jess's favourite place. On Bank Holiday Mondays, at Whitsun and in August, while he still had his car and some money, Jack often took the family to Dorset, usually ending up at West Bay. Jess wondered why they did not go to the nearer seaside places, like Exmouth or Dawlish, or even Minehead, rather than trailing all the way across Dorset, but Jack seemed to like West Bay. (Jess later discovered from census records that he had actually been born at Weymouth, so was a originally a Dorset man.) The children had to be patient while their parents stopped for a lunch-time drink at the 'Blackbird Inn' en route. In those days, children were not permitted on licensed premises, and were simply confined to cars in pub car-parks, having to content themselves with a packet of crisps each brought out by Dotey, with the accompanying promise of 'we won't be long.' But Jack always broke Dotey's promise, so that it was often mid-afternoon before they eventually arrived at the seaside. Then they would have to find somewhere to park, since the earlier arrivals had taken the best spaces, and there would be a further delay before they finally made it onto the beach, which at West Bay consisted of shingle. Jess preferred sand, but still, it was the seaside. Jack, in his summer attire of white jacket, red braces and knotted hanky, always commented on the bracing nature of the air. The sea temperature was similarly bracing, but the children usually went in nonetheless. The sight of her daughter struggling to change into a bathing costume under a towel with some degree of modesty would prompt Dotey to sigh and utter her usual comments about Jess's size, while skinny Peter in his swimming trunks would be described as resembling a 'Belsen victim'. This was long before the concepts of 'political correctness' and 'self-esteem' were widely known, so Dotey spoke her mind.

The furthest the family ever ventured away from Tiverton was a short holiday to see Stonehenge. In those days, it was possible for visitors to walk right up to the stones, and even to sit or climb on them. By the time Jess took her own sons, thirty years later, there was a designated route to be followed, and the stones themselves were out of bounds except for solstice celebrations. Jess liked the New Forest, the Rufus Stone, the purple heather and the ponies. The family stayed at a Trust House hotel in Southampton, whereas on her return visit a generation later, Jess and her boys stayed at a Youth Hostel in the New Forest, with Jess wondering what on earth Dotey would have made of it.

Jack's line of business meant that he always attended large agricultural events, such as the Devon County Show and the Bath and West. He would usually leave his family to their own devices while he went to hobnob with his friends in the beer tent, strictly in the name of business... Then there were the Point-to-Point meetings at Eggesford, held on chilly Easter Mondays, where the cars were parked in a soggy field and often had to be pulled out by tractor at the end of an afternoon of unceasing rain. Jess detested Point to Point races, since she was always afraid that a horse would injure itself going over the jumps. She liked horses, but at a distance or with a fence in between; unlike many other girls of her age, she had no wish to ride the intimidating creatures.

Dotey's idea of an end-of-the-holidays treat was more congenial, she liked to take the children by train to Tiverton Junction, where the branch line met the main line to Paddington. They would sit on the platform for a while, watching the express trains rush through to Bristol and beyond to London, or to Plymouth and Penzance in the other direction, before boarding the next train back to Tiverton. Jess wondered if she would ever visit these far-flung destinations. Bristol was only 60 miles away, but was portrayed as being the ends of the earth. People who came from north of Bristol were said to be from 'somewhere up-country', which in Jess's imagination was an enormous wild and hazy region shrouded in mist and chilly dankness, definitely not the sort of place any sensible Devonian would ever want to visit, let alone live. However, she liked the sound of London and expressed a wish to go there. Dotey told her firmly that her time would come, and she would have the opportunity to travel further afield when she was older; meanwhile, however, she must be patient.

In fact, Dotey was able to take the children to London sooner than expected, after Jack had some sort of windfall. Jess thought he must have come up on the pools, or an accumulator at the bookies must have been successful, but the source of the holiday money was never explained to her. Jack himself did not go to London, since he said he still could not leave the Store, but he provided sufficient money for the family to stay at the Strand Palace Hotel. They travelled up by train, having lunch in the dining car as they sped across Berkshire – no paste sandwiches on this occasion – before arriving at Paddington. Then it was into a taxi and across to the hotel, Dotey sharing a room with Jess while Peter was with Jeff. They spent the next few days sight-seeing at all the usual landmarks. They went to Buckingham Palace to see the Changing of the Guard, queued at the Tower to see the Crown Jewels, fed the pigeons in Trafalgar Square, took a boat trip on the river, visited the National Gallery, St. James' Park and Piccadilly Circus, and looked at the flowers at Covent Garden. Dotey had arranged for them to spend the Sunday at Surbiton, visiting Cousin Barbara and her family, so they took the train out to the suburbs and spent a pleasant time with Barbara, her husband Dennis and their children, getting lost in the maze on an excursion to Hampton Court. However, Dotey was annoyed when Dennis said he would drive them to Berrylands station for the train after tea; she thought he really could have offered to take them back to the hotel, after all, the roads were quiet on a Sunday evening, it was by then raining, and the trains were not at all frequent at that time of night. Once Dennis had seen them safely aboard the train, Dotey continued to express her opinion of his supposed cousinly dereliction of duty; so much so that Jess and Jeff, discussing the London trip fifty years later, were amused to find that it was still their overriding memory of that day.

Halfway through the week, Dotey was obliged to phone Jack, asking him to send more money, since London was turning out to be more expensive than she had remembered. The money promptly arrived – Jess thought the horses must still be running in Jack's favour. It was a memorable week, and Jess often wondered to which noble steeple-chasers she owed the pleasure of that first trip to London. She thought she would have liked to visit their stables, pat their noses, and give them carrots or sugar lumps by way of thanks; but she never did discover their names.

Chapter 19

Jess never ceased to wonder at the amount of work it took to run the house, for as well as No.3 being large and inconvenient, all household chores took longer than they might have done had Dotey possessed any labour-saving devices. She had neither vacuum cleaner nor washing machine, making do with a manual carpet sweeper, and a galvanised tin vessel for boiling up laundry on the stove. Several times a week the kitchen was full of steam, as a stew of handkerchiefs, shirts and underwear gently seethed on the hob in a cauldron of Omo. Towels and tea-cloths were done separately, and of course, whites had their own wash. Dotey believed in boil-washing everything apart from the few delicate items she owned, which she washed by hand, and her laundry was always spotless; however, things wore out and became faded quickly because of the frequent boiling. Jess, as laundry assistant, was always being prevailed upon to fetch washing in from the garden or climb up to the attic to retrieve a forgotten pillow-case ("because your little legs are so much younger than mine.")

It seemed to Jess that she and Dotey spent the entire summer holidays washing blankets. If the forecast was good, her mother liked to start at crack of dawn. There were to be no teenage lie-ins for Jess; Dotey would wake her early "Rise and shine right away, there's *heaps* to do!" And so there was – a giant mound of blankets had formed on the landing, and it was Jess's job to deal with them.

In the days before duvets were heard of this side of the English Channel, and before houses had central heating, people slept under several blankets, three or four per bed in Jess's family, with paisley patterned eiderdowns and heavy bedspreads on top. That meant fifteen to twenty woollen blankets to be washed every summer. They were too cumbersome to go in the stove-top vessel and so had to be washed in the bath. Jess's task was to assist Dotey by preparing soapy water, immersing the blankets one by one, then climbing bare-foot into the tub to tread each blanket thoroughly in order to get the dust out, and again in two lots of clean water to rinse away the soap. Next she and her mother took an end each of the heavy sodden blanket, and twisted it tightly to remove as much water as possible. It took a whole morning to do just two blankets, after which came the task of lugging them down two flights of stairs to the garden and heaving them onto the clothes-line. This operation could take place only in fine weather, as there as nowhere indoors to dry large wet items. In winter there would be a clothes horse in prime position next to the living-room fire, preventing any heat from reaching whoever was sitting on the far side, and displaying the family's undergarments for all to see. At least the bed-sheets were sent to a commercial laundry, which collected and delivered every week; however, with the growing popularity of domestic washing machines, the laundry business eventually ceased operation, and Dotey was obliged to swallow her prejudice ("No machine can get things as clean as I can on the stove!") and take her bed-linen to the newly-opened 'Wurly-Wash', Tiverton's first launderette. This was not especially convenient, since the laundry bags full of clean washing had to be carried back up Canal Hill. Jack of course, saw no reason why his womenfolk should have the benefit of any labour-aving equipment, indeed Jess thought it likely that if they asked for anything, he might very well tell them to go down to the River Lowman and scrub the laundry on flat stones, as he had seen Indian women doing on the Coramandel Coast...

Jess was required to always be on hand when the beds were to be stripped and freshly made up, since it was so much easier with two people. She hated going into her father's bedroom, stinking as it did of cigarettes and other nefarious odours. She also found the dust made her sneeze violently, since Jack did not adhere to the house rule of everyone cleaning their own room. ("Why keep a dog and bark myself?") After his business went into liquidation and Dotey was obliged to dispense with the services of the cleaning lady, Jack had simply let the dust accumulate, so that changing the bed-linen was a real ordeal for anyone with a dust allergy. Eventually, after a year's accumulation of fluff and feathers, Jack engaged a local woman, Mrs. D, to come and clean his room every month. Of course, Dotey was embarrassed that the new charlady was to do only the one room, but her diminished housekeeping allowance would not stretch to having the whole house cleaned, and anyway she had an able-bodied teenage daughter whose services were free. Meanwhile, if Jess spotted one of the new fifty pence pieces – equivalent to ten shillings – in the fluff under Jack's bed when she was changing the sheets, she always braved the dust and gave it to her mother, since fifty pence was a significant amount in those days.

Jess's discomfiture knew no bounds when Dotey paused one day in mid-bed change in the attic in order to read Jeff's diary which she had spotted on his bedside table. Dotey had her suspicions that Jeff was becoming fond of a totally unsuitable girl, whose parents ran the chip-shop opposite the library. She and Jeff went horse-riding together, but Dotey wanted to find out just how far the relationship had gone. "Kisses!" she exclaimed grimly, while Jess, feeling guilty on her mother's behalf, got on with changing the pillowslips. "The little hussy!"

Jess wondered if her mother read her diary, which she had kept since the age of ten, and plucked up courage to ask.

"Of course I don't!" said Dotey reassuringly. "I always know exactly where you are and what you're up to, so there's no need. It's Jeff who worries me…"

Jess had been given a 'Girl' diary for 1961, which contained a varied cross-section of what the compilers thought modern girls were interested in, mainly film-stars, sports people and wildlife. Photographs of outstanding sportswomen were accompanied by patronising descriptions: "Beryl Burton – This 24-year-old Morley, Yorkshire, housewife is our leading cyclist and seems to make a habit of breaking records." "Betty Bird – This 26 year-old Chelmsford housewife just about hit her best form in 1959…" It was not of course thought necessary to state the marital status of the male sports personalities featured.

A singing star called Fabian was accorded this: "The president of a record company noticed Fabian Forte sitting forlornly on his doorstep after his father had been taken away in an ambulance." Fabian was apparently awarded a record contract on the spot because of his looks, without having to prove that he could actually sing. Readers were informed that his father recovered. Richard Harris, readers were told, "managed to continue his drama studies, but only by sleeping in the coal cellar of a coffee house."

The wildlife descriptions were similarly esoteric " Shag – if we approach the bird while she is sitting she does not fly away at once, but stretches her neck, raises the feathers on her head and hisses in a threatening manner." Jess wondered why on earth anyone would want to disturb a bird incubating eggs in a seaweed nest on a rocky ledge.

"The Jay may well be described as a handsome villain. He robs the nests of other birds, but he is beautiful to look at."

Other pages featured brief accounts of 'Ballet through the ages' 'The story of Tea', 'British breeds of Dog', 'Miniature Gardens' (a favourite with Jess); 'Animal Tracks', 'Fungi', and 'Footwear around the world', while no fewer than four pages were devoted to the different architectural styles of windows. Any girl receiving such a diary nowadays would be completely bemused, and Jess re-read hers with much hilarity. She noted that the editor of 'Girl' was a man named Clifford Makins, whose picture was featured at the front of the diary. Maybe wildlife and window styles, footwear and fungi were Mr. Makins' particularly favourite hobbies? And was there really no woman who could be trusted with the task of editing a publication aimed specifically at young girls in 1961?

Chapter 20

Shopping was a chore for which Jess must always be available. Twice a week, she and Dotey walked down to the town, and trudged back up the hill with their heavy bags. There was no bus service up Canal Hill at the time, but fewer shops were now delivering. Shopping with Dotey took a long time, since she always insisted on examining every purchase carefully, in order to ascertain its quality. This was before self-service supermarkets arrived in Devon, and the assistant fetched whatever the customer required; Dotey was certainly not going to be palmed off with soft tomatoes or squashy oranges from behind the main display. Certain shops stocked fresher eggs, but their bananas were often over-ripe, so that it was necessary to visit two shops and to carefully hide whatever had been purchased in the first one in the depths of a carrier bag before entering the second, in order not to give any offence. Jess forgot to do this one day, and the greengrocer, noting that her basket already contained oranges, asked Dotey why she had not bought them from her establishment. Dotey boldly replied that she had not always found Hill's citrus fruit to be of top quality, whereupon Mrs. Hill bridled and replied that there was nothing wrong with her Jaffas, no-one had ever said any different, and didn't the other customers present agree? Everyone else nodded fearfully, and Jess was embarrassed and afraid that her mother might be banned from Hills in future, but Dotey carried on blithely ordering cucumber and carrots; Mrs. Hill, although offended, was loathe to turn away a regular customer.

Sometimes, the expedition to town included a visit to the hairdressers, so that Dotey could have her hair cut, styled and dyed. Jess took a book with her on these occasions, since a hair appointment was always a major undertaking. The stylist would prepare a basin of the blood-red dye which Dotey fondly imagined would recreate her natural auburn. Jess privately thought it did not really suit her mother's complexion, the red colour was much too harsh, and she wondered at her mother choosing it, since Dotey tended to criticise those whose hair colour she considered looked 'brassy'. But maybe that only applied to blondes… Jess knew better than to comment, she kept her nose firmly in her book, resisting all attempts on the part of Dotey's stylist to engage her in conversation about school work or what she was doing over the holidays, or even worse, to enquire whether Jess had a boyfriend. This had actually happened once, and before Jess could shake her head and explain that a boyfriend would not in any case be allowed, Dotey emerged from under the noisy drier, and cut in firmly with a comment to the effect that Jess was far too sensible for any such nonsense, she was concentrating on her studies so she could have a good career. Jess wondered whether her mother could mind-read, but maybe she was able to lip-read and had been monitoring the conversation.

So far as Jess was concerned, the worst port of call on the shopping itinerary was Cook's butchers. It was always so cold there, the shop smelled of animal blood, and there were constant processions of men heaving beast carcasses out of vans and shouldering them through the shop into the nether regions of the establishment, from where the sounds of furious sawing and chopping could be heard. Jess knew that she and Dotey would invariably be spending longer in Cooks than in any of the other shops they visited. Dotey usually managed to choose the meat quite quickly, but she took an interminable time settling her bill at the kiosk, because Peggy, the woman who presided over Cook's accounts, was a member of the local Operatic club and Dotey was Secretary of the Amateur Dramatic Society. There was always a great deal of important information to be exchanged, taking at least twenty minutes; Peggy's head inclined confidentially, with her nose almost touching the glass front of the kiosk so as not to miss any juicy tit-bit, and Dotey likewise leaning forward in order to catch every last scrap of information. Jess would meanwhile be sitting forlornly on a wooden stool, guarding the shopping bags, and tracing patterns in the sawdust covering the floor with her toes, until Dotey, who seemingly had eyes in the back of her head, but who was actually watching Jess via a mirror at the back of Peggy's kiosk, turned around mid-tale to admonish her – ("Don't do that, Jess! You'll ruin those school shoes!") – before resuming her story in mid-sentence. Meanwhile, a lengthy queue of impatient would-be butcher's bill-payers would be forming behind Dotey. Hearing the sighs and groans of exasperation, Jess felt sorry for everyone having to wait until Peggy and Dotey had put Tiverton to rights in their own good time.

On these shopping expeditions, Dotey and Jess would often see Brian Probert and his mother riding around the town on their bicycles, string bags of shopping dangling from the handlebars. Brian was a few years older than Jess, and wanted to become a priest. Dotey always made an approving comment about how good Brian was to his widowed mother, but simultaneously shook her head, declaring that it was 'not natural' how much time the two seemed to spend together. Jess was astonished.

"But you always insist on me being with you, helping with the shopping and the housework! You always say you like me spending time with you, going for walks! Mrs. Probert is probably just the same, she enjoys her child's company."

Dotey sighed. "Of course it's not the same! It's one thing for a girl to be with her mother, that's only right and to be expected; but not a BOY! He should be with his pals, not cycling about with his mother! I tell you, it's just not natural."

Chapter 21

Every summer throughout the 1950s Terry and Jeff came for a fortnight's visit, in accordance with the terms of Albert and Dotey's divorce settlement. Dotey was naturally very pleased to have all four of her children under one roof, and always took a photograph of them together on the front steps. The children were usually lined up in age order, but on one occasion the boys were doing some Spring cleaning, Terry scrubbing the steps, Jeff sweeping, and little Peter waving a duster. For some reason, young Jess was not contributing to the cleaning effort, she was simply leaning against a wall in the shade, wearing a sunbonnet, holding a toy and watching her brothers. This was the picture which inspired one of Jess's contributions to the *Guardian* newspaper many years later.

Jeff was fulfilling his early promise as the liveliest member of the family, and was always full of ideas about what they could all do. The children, often accompanied by Jeannie MacDougall, packed picnic lunches and went for all-day hikes along the canal tow-path, they rode their bikes for miles around the lanes, sailed home-constructed rafts on the canal, or mounted dramatic productions in the shrubbery. These were roughly scripted and with considerable scope for improvisation, and usually featured Jeff in a leading role, with the others as his side-kicks. One memorable sketch had Dr. Jeff, in an old white shirt worn back to front, operating on unconscious patient Peter, who was stretched out on the ottoman, which had been dragged out from the living-room for the occasion. With a stream of dramatic flourishes and running commentary, Jeff produced all manner of unlikely items from Peter's stomach, including a string of plastic sausages, a saucepan lid and a bicycle pump; while Jess and Jeannie as nurses, handed him the essential tools of his trade such as the fish slice or a large screwdriver. When the young patient showed signs of waking up, Dr. Jeff unceremoniously hit him over the head with a plastic mallet. Meanwhile, Terry played the anxious parent, pacing up and down in the wings, wondering to what further indignity his 'son' might be subjected. These performances were given before an invited audience consisting of Dotey, Mrs. MacDougall, and any available neighbours, such as Mr. Moss, Fern, and possibly Norah (if sufficiently sober). Any passing tradesmen who had twenty minutes or so to spare were also welcomed, sometimes the paraffin deliveryman was in attendance and once the coal-man reckoned he was in need of a break. Jess and Jeannie served the audience cups of orange squash and biscuits, and Terry was on the door, collecting the entrance fee of threepence per head for the entertainment. A number of chairs would have been carried out to a small clearing in the shrubbery, so the audience could be comfortably seated, and an old curtain rigged up between two trees. On one occasion, the show took the form of a musical review, the highlight of which was Jeff and Terry's performance of 'We'll walk up the Avenue', dressed as 'a couple of swells' with the others as 'the horse we had was shot', using Peter's cap gun, (these were standard toys for little boys at the time.) A version of 'There's a Tavern in the Town' also featured in the programme, including the improvised line "and drinks his wine and eats his fill, and never, ever pays the bill." The dressing-up box furnished a useful array of costumes, including a cowboy outfit, a feathered Indian head-dress, and several versatile old blouses. Jeannie brought her own nurses' costume and she and Jess enjoyed rummaging about for different items to add variety to the proceedings. However, Dotey was very upset when Jess and Jeannie appeared in one sketch as society ladies in ankle-length needle-lace dresses, one white and one coffee-coloured, which they had discovered in a long-forgotten drawer. These turned out to be Dotey's 1934 wedding dress along with Grandma Olive's mother-of-the-bride outfit.

In 1960, Albert moved, for reasons of work, from Exeter to Cardiff. When Dotey and Jack, accompanied by Jess and Peter, drove to Wales to fetch Jeff for holidays in Devon they crossed the Severn using the old Aust Ferry, since the suspension bridge had yet to be built. The only other way to get to Wales by road was to drive up to Gloucester. The alternatives were rail, which went via a tunnel under the river, or the pleasure steamers which crossed the Bristol Channel from South Wales to West Country seaside towns. These were especially popular on Sundays, transporting the thirsty Welsh to resorts on the North Devon and Somerset coasts, since

Wales was then a resolutely 'dry' country on the Sabbath, making it necessary to leave the country in order to enjoy an alcoholic drink.

Once, Dotey took the younger children by train to Cardiff to deliver Jeff back to Llandaff. On their return journey, having changed at Bristol Temple Meads, they found the train very crowded, with no spare seats to be had in the third class compartments, so Dotey took them into First Class. When the ticket inspector came, another passenger with a third class ticket offered to pay the difference. Dotey was quietly furious as she ushered the children out into the corridor, reasoning that if the silly man had not offered to pay up, the inspector might very well have let them all stay in First Class. As it was, having accepted payment from one passenger, he could hardly turn a blind eye to their own third class tickets, and Dotey did not have the means to pay the difference. So Jess found herself perched precariously on a bag in the busy corridor, among a crowd of noisy sailors, likewise sitting on kit-bags, who were travelling to rejoin their ship in Plymouth. It was impossible for anyone to move along the corridor to the buffet car or the toilets without tripping over a child or a sailor, and Jess never forgot the look of pitying condescension from one of the gentleman in the First Class compartment, comfortably ensconced in his plush seat.

Jeff was unable to settle in Wales, so it was eventually decided that he should move back to Devon and live with his Tiverton family. Arrangements were made for Jeff to attend the Grammar School, since there was a place available in the year above Jess. The headmaster, Mr. Bradshaw, showed Jeff around the school one Saturday morning, accompanied by Jess, who was thrilled that her brother was joining her school. It had been such a lovely surprise, this business of Jeff coming to live with them, since as usual, Dotey had played her cards close to her chest, muttering about the family being hard up and the necessity of 'taking in a lodger' in order to make ends meet. Jess had been upset at the prospect of a stranger joining the family, and had not guessed the real reason for Dotey's disappearance for the day on another mysterious 'business trip', leaving the younger children with Mrs. MacDougall and Jeannie, before retuning late in the evening with Jeff. "Our new lodger!"

Of their half-brother, Nicholas, Jack's son by his first marriage, Jess and Peter saw never a sign. Nicholas would occasionally turn up in a car to visit his father, but always forewarned Jack of his impending visit and told Jack to be outside to meet him. "Ask Nicholas to come in!" Dotey said every time, but Nicholas would not enter the house.

Jess thought it very odd to have a brother whom she had never met. Of course, Jeff and Terry knew Nicholas well, as they had lived next door to him for years in Alphington. Nicholas was keen on cycling, and on his return from his outings with his elder son, Jack always praised him to the skies. Nicholas was always full of plans of which Jack heartily approved, he was by now approaching his thirtieth birthday and having tried a number of occupations was now considering teacher training. Jack was sure he would make a success of it, and he did. The one and only occasion when Jess was in the same room as Nicholas was twenty years later, when she was being interviewed for a teaching post in the school where her half-brother taught. By then, both Jack and Dotey were dead. Still Nicholas refused to meet her, and left the staff-room soon after she entered. Someone had taken it upon themselves to warn Nicholas that Jess was expected that day and would be invited into the staff-room for a coffee before her interview. Jess glanced across the crowded room and knew immediately which was Nicholas, he looked exactly like Jack. She wondered what her brother would do if she obtained a job at the same school, since he could not then avoid her indefinitely; however, the situation never arose, since Jess failed to get that particular post, and was never again in the same room as Nicholas, who went on to die of cancer at an early age.

Upon his removal to Tiverton, Jeff was installed in the attic bedroom above Jess's room, next to Jack's. Jess, lying in bed of an evening unable to get to sleep, began to wonder what the strange clattering emanating from upstairs could possibly be. It appeared that Jeff had sent for a 'Muscle-builders' course, which involved lifting full buckets of sand and other noisy exercises. Jeff possessed a transistor radio, and Jess would hear him laughing and singing "I'm Angus Prune, and this is my tune, I'm sorry, I'll read that again!'" This was far more entertaining than Jack's belches and slop bucket-clanging, which continued unabated, until Jack decided that he could no longer climb two flights of stairs, and demanded a room on the

105

first floor rather than in the attic. He proposed swapping rooms with Jess, which would give him the back bedroom, next to Dotey; but his wife was having none of this, for her own reasons. Instead, she gave Jack her bedroom at the front of the house, and moved into Peter's little room on the corner. Peter was sent up to the front attic, previously occupied by Jack, so that he and Jeff were now both on the top floor. Jess's room was located between those of her parents, and she was very soon to discover that it was not a good place to be. Meanwhile, she was unaware that Jack was beating her mother as she lay in bed, or trying to force his unwanted attentions on her, since Dotey always stifled her screams so as not to disturb her children. The night she was unable to contain her anguish and woke Jess in the next room with her sobbing was the night Jess's uneasy childhood ended, and at age fourteen she felt she had the cares of the world on her shoulders.

Chapter 22

One day in the summer of 1963 next-door neighbour Fern announced that she was going on a trip to visit the new Coventry Cathedral with the church Mothers' Union group; they needed more people to fill the coach, so would Dotey like to come? Dotey thought she would, and furthermore, she wanted to take Jess along as well. It would be a very educational day out, and Dotey had no difficulty in persuading the Headmaster that Jess should be released from school for this worthy excursion. Accordingly, twelve year old Jess found herself on a coach journeying to the Midlands, along with fifty mostly elderly ladies, all talking away excitedly, with the vicar and bus driver the only men in attendance. There was no motorway to the West Country in those days, and the route went via the A38, 'the longest country lane in England.' Despite the early start, it took all morning until they finally arrived in Coventry. Jess thought the new Cathedral was stunning, with the enormous Graham Sutherland tapestry and beautiful modern stained glass windows; so different from its medieval counterpart in Exeter, which of course was beautiful as well. However, Dotey, with memories of the terrible destruction of the war-time blitz, considered the new building to be more like an impressive concert hall rather than a church; for her, the real cathedral was still the adjacent bombed-out ruin.

The coach trundled back through Gloucestershire. Jess was tired and wanted just to sit back and admire the beautiful Cotswold scenery, but the Mothers' Union members were still chattering away and persisting in asking her questions about school and whether she had enjoyed the day. They stopped at Bristol for refreshments and the toilet, and Fern bought Jess a cup of hot chocolate. It was still a three hour journey back from Bristol to Tiverton, but by this time it was dark and past everyone's bedtimes, so they all slept.

Coventry was the furthest Jess had journeyed from Devon in her life, but she was shortly to revisit the Midlands, this time on a school trip to Stratford-on Avon by train. The English teacher, Miss Tilley, had arranged for them to see a matinée, and several classes were going. This was a lot more fun than travelling with the Mothers'

Union, since the train journey itself was an adventure, with everyone busily investigating their friends' packed lunches, and much comment on who was sitting next to whom. When asked by Dotey whether she had enjoyed the day, Jess nodded happily, giving all sorts of unnecessary detail about the journey and scarcely mentioning the play, Henry VI Part 1.

Miss Tilley arranged a residential trip to Stratford for the Sixth Form every year, so Jess again had the opportunity to see the Royal Shakespeare Company in 1967 and 1968. These visits involved the pupils being billeted in various guest houses along the Shipston Road; Jess had heard stories of wild midnight feasts and all-night dorm parties from those who had been on previous trips. Miss Tilley had issued the sternest of warnings about behaviour, saying that all the landladies spoke to one another, so that if Tiverton Grammar School pupils gained a reputation for unruliness, they would lose the goodwill of the entire Shipston Road, and the Stratford trips would be at an end.

The first play they saw was 'Macbeth' with Paul Schofield and Vivien Merchant. The following night was 'Romeo and Juliet' starring Ian Holm and Estelle Kohler. Daytimes were free for sightseeing, or boating on the river. The next season they saw 'King Lear' with Eric Porter, and 'As You Like It' with Janet Suzman. Miss Tilley had arranged a trip to a stately home on the second day, and Jess found herself on the coach sitting with her friend Mick. Their seats were behind those of Miss Tilley and Miss Gillen, who seemed to be asleep. Jess and Mick chattered happily about the trip, everyone seemed to have heeded the warnings about unruly behaviour, and there had been none of the all-too-probably exaggerated six in a dorm, three in a bed stuff they had heard of; at which, Miss Tilley unexpectedly turned round and solemnly declared that she was very relieved to hear it.

Chapter 23

A long-standing Tiverton tradition, observed throughout Jess's youth, was the annual 'Proclamation of the Fair', when the Mayor stood at Coggan's Well, the ancient source of the town's water supply, and threw coins. All the primary school pupils were let out early for the afternoon in order to scramble for pennies. It was a brutal affair, where children unashamedly stamped on the hands of others who were about to pick up a coin, in order to get them to relinquish the penny. The money was not safe, even in a child's hands, since the big boys would grab the clenched fists of smaller children, forcing back their fingers in order to release the clutched coins. The most Jess ever managed to bring home was eleven pennies (less than 5 pence in decimal money) and a sore head, where she had collided with a bullet-headed boy going after the same coin. After that, she decided it was not worth risking injury, and gave future Proclamation of the Fair ceremonies a miss.

However, it was not so easy to absent herself from the traditional parades which took place for the Mayoral ceremony every May and the Remembrance Service in November. All uniformed organisations were expected to attend; the weather in May was usually fine, but November was often a different matter. Jeff's Air Training Corps had warm grey coats, and Peter's Cubs at least had green jumpers, but the girls in Jess's Brownie Pack were always shivering in their skimpy brown cotton tunics. It was quite hard to concentrate on keeping in step with the military music, since the Brownies were generally placed a long way back from the band leading the parade; and Jess was always thoroughly miserable. Everyone was of course obliged to stand completely still for the Last Post and two minutes silence, and Jess thought she had never felt so cold in her life. It was even worse for those skinny little girls who had less natural padding then she had. Even in pouring rain, the girls were forbidden to wear a jacket or coat, since the Brownie uniform did not then include an outer garment.

Once, Jess became aware of the little girls opposite her laughing through their shivers, as they stood in facing lines for the two minutes silence; she could not understand why, until she suddenly realised that it no longer seemed to be raining on her side of the line, although heavy drops were still pouring down onto the girls opposite. Turning round, she found Dotey standing behind her, holding a large umbrella over her. It was really a miracle that none of the children fell victim to hypothermia; and mercifully, it was later decided that younger members of uniformed organisations need not take part in parades during bad weather, unless they had suitable apparel. The Brownies later modernised their uniform – out went the flimsy cotton tunics, awkward ties, and knee socks, to be replaced by sensible sweat-shirts and trousers, warmer and much more practical for parades and activities. Jess did not benefit from these changes. She had finished her time with the Brownies at age eleven, and decided not to 'fly up' to the Girl Guides, as the traditional ceremony was known. She was already worried about not having enough time for her homework and piano practice as well as all the household tasks she was expected to assist with, let alone additional activities. The prospect of Jess going camping with the Guides had not appealed to Dotey, who painted a bleak picture of outdoor living where Jess would certainly catch cold and be bitten or stung by venomous creepy-crawlies…

If the children were not taking part in the Remembrance Sunday parade, they were always called to the wireless just before 11am, in order that their parents could be certain they were observing the two minutes' silence. Everyone had to stand absolutely still and completely silent, with head bowed. Both Jack and Dotey were very strict about this, having lived through both world wars. The only sound was the usual whistling and wheezing of the ancient wireless, which was never completely cured, despite Jack's continual endeavours with the aerial, pointing it this way and that, in a vain attempt to improve the signal.

November 5th saw Bonfire Night. In the 1950s, most people had a few small fireworks in their back gardens, and organised displays were rare. Dotey usually bought Roman Candles, Traffic Lights, Silver Fountains, Catherine Wheels and of course sparklers. A single rocket would be placed in a milk bottle and pointed skywards. Dotey and Jess both disliked bangers, which in any case frightened the cat. Meanwhile, Jack would have prepared a bonfire, on which was placed an effigy of Guy Fawkes made out of Dotey's old laddered stockings and someone's worn-out jumper. Jess was always uneasy about burning effigies, but it was the custom for children to make a 'Guy' a week or so ahead and trundle it round in an old pram or wheelbarrow, asking passers-by for a 'penny for the Guy'. This was long before Halloween was widely celebrated in Britain. Dotey did once buy a turnip for the children to make a lantern, but it took so long to hollow out that they never again bothered. Pumpkins were not generally available locally at the time.

When the bonfire was dying down Dotey would sometimes serve sausages, with jacket potatoes cooked in the embers of the fire, washed down with hot cocoa. The following morning, the valley would still be full of smoke from the thousands of small bonfires. Fireworks were not on sale at any other time of the year, no-one had them for New Year.

October 1965 found Tiverton *en fête*, celebrating the 350th anniversary of the granting of the town's charter in 1615 by King James 1st. All manner of events and festivities were planned, including a royal visit by HRH Princess Marina of Kent, who was to plant a commemorative oak sapling in Peoples' Park. Tiverton had actually received a second charter during the Commonwealth, in 1655, but being a royalist sort of place, this was not celebrated to anything like the same extent, despite its effects continuing to be felt to the present day; it was actually by decree of the second charter that Oliver Cromwell had moved Tiverton market day from Monday to Tuesday, as is still the case. The reason for the alteration was in order 'to avoid profanity of the Sabbath by traders preparing their wares the day before the market, which had provoked God's wrath' as evidenced by the town's two Great Fires – the first in 1598, known as 'the Frying Pan fire', and the 'Dog Fight' fire of 1612.

Jack had unearthed several strings of bunting from the darkest recesses of the garage; these had last seen the light of day for the Coronation in 1953. Tiverton children were taken out of school to hear the reading of the original charter at the beginning of the week, and also visited the museum to view both charters. Everyone took the Friday afternoon off to attend People's Park and wave union flags for Princess Marina. The sapling duly planted, the royal visitor graciously went on her way. The following day it was discovered that the oak had been uprooted by vandals overnight, and a replacement had to be hastily obtained.

Saturday was the most eventful day of Charter week. The Tiverton Branch line had fallen victim to the recent cuts to rail services imposed by Dr. Beeching, but the old steam engine, the 'Tivvy Bumper' was due to make one last journey into town before being put on display. The town's former Member of Parliament and one-time Chancellor of the Exchequer in the MacMillan government, Derrick Amory, now ennobled as Viscount Amory, drove the engine into the goods yard, from where it was hoisted by crane to its permanent site on a plinth. (It was some years later removed to the town museum in St. Andrew Street.) This event attracted even larger crowds than Princess Marina. The programme of charter celebrations ended with an ox roast and firework display at Tiverton Showground – it was rumoured that there were £500 worth of fireworks in the display! The emphasis of the celebrations had been firmly on good King James, and Oliver Cromwell had scarcely received a mention all week.

Chapter 24

Throughout the summer and autumn, the family reaped the fruits of Jack's endeavours in the kitchen garden. Whatever his faults as a provider – stinginess with the housekeeping, a tendency to withhold it quite unjustifiably, resentment at having to keep the children while they were in full-time education – Jack was a diligent gardener, and every autumn harvested an abundance of home grown produce. Quantities of carrots were dug up and preserved in heaps of sand for the winter, runner beans were picked, sliced and put down in jars of salt, while Jack devised a cool dark potato store in one of the out-houses. Gluts of fruit were bottled in Kilner jars, or given away to the neighbours, until Jess learned at school how to make jam. At the onset of winter, with everything else harvested, only Brussels sprouts were left, bleakly sticking up above the frozen ground, watched over by the grey, Dalek-like chimney pots, which were silently guarding the dormant rhubarb crowns.

Of course, a fridge and freezer would have made life much easier, but Dotey never in her life possessed such items. Jess had always to remember to scald the milk when thunder threatened, otherwise it would be sure to 'turn'. Following a science lesson about evaporation, Jess devised a cooling device for the milk bottles, a foam rubber cover which stood in a saucer of water, so that the liquid rose by capillarity, and the subsequent evaporation was supposed to keep the milk cool. This was not entirely successful, so Jess returned to the scalding regime, whereby milk was brought almost to the boil and held at that temperature for a few minutes to improve its keeping qualities. She envied her friends whose families possessed fridges, and who could have exotic treats like yoghurt and honeycomb mould.

Coming in one day, Jess wondered what the commotion could be. Her father was leaning out of the kitchen window, waving his arms and shouting. "There's a pigeon sitting in that tulip tree, as big as a bucket, just waiting to have a go at my Spring cabbage! See him there, bold as brass, on that branch! If I had a shotgun, there'd be pigeon pie for tea!"

There eventually came the awful day, following Tommy Ford's

death, when his field was sold and turned into an estate of canal-side bungalows, removing the children's grassy playground and cutting off access to their rafts. The family who bought the property whose garden backed onto that of Number 3 asked the landlord if they could buy part of Jack's kitchen garden. Jack was not even consulted about the matter, merely informed that the sale had taken place, and one day he looked out of the window to find a newly-erected fence separating him from the tulip tree, the compost heap, the raspberry canes and the potato patch. Two little girls ran out of the bungalow to play in their new garden. Jack reached for the nearest object, which turned out to be the nozzle of an old cylinder vacuum cleaner he had recently picked up in a junk shop. He hastily aimed the menacing metal through the kitchen window, breaking the glass pane as he did so.

"Get off my land at once, or I'll shoot!" bellowed Jack.

The girls fled. Jack returned to the living room, sank into his favourite chair and picked up the 'Express and Echo'.

"Ha! That will show them!"

Dotey tried to remonstrate. "Jack, that was very foolish of you! They are just little girls! Their parents have bought the land, so they have every right to be there! I know it was very shoddy of the landlord not to ask you, but we don't own the property so we don't have any say in the matter!"

"Don't we? I'll see about that! An Englishman's home is his castle, even if he only pays rent for it, he's entitled to 'quiet enjoyment'; that's the legal phrase, one of my pals at the Club told me, and he's a solicitor, so he should know."

"But we don't rent that bit of garden any more, and they've reduced the rent by those few shillings to compensate."

Dotey broke off, as there was a loud knock at the front door. She opened it to find a young policeman, who said that there had been a report of a gunman at this address. Dotey immediately led him into the front room, where Jack was still ensconced in his chair with the evening paper.

"I take it you be the gunman, sir? May I see the weapon? And I take it 'ee 'ave a licence for 'un?"

"Yes, officer, you may certainly examine the weapon; and I think you'll find I don't require a licence for a Hoover!"

Whereupon, Jack smilingly reached behind the chair and produced the vacuum cleaner with a flourish. The constable was momentarily nonplussed, then began lecturing Jack, who did not appear in the least perturbed, replying loftily,

"You see, officer, I served in the Great War, fighting the Turks in Palestine. I was in the Home Guard in the last lot, striving to protect the freedom of the British people. You're too young to remember any of that of course. Now I've been betrayed by some fifth columnist who thinks he can take my land away. How Hitler would have laughed…"

"Be that as it may, you've no right to threaten folks with what appears to be a lethal weapon, especially when 'tis young children you be scaring, and they be lawfully playing in their own garden. 'Tis not a laughing matter, sir!"

Meanwhile Jess was sweeping up the broken glass. Jack would have to pay to have the window re-glazed; all in all, an expensive afternoon, especially if he was fined for threatening behaviour or breaching the peace. Luckily, the young policeman considered that his stern lecture would be sufficient reprimand for the war veteran, as no summons followed and nothing more was ever heard on the matter.

Jess mourned the loss of the tulip tree, recalling hours spent in her favourite sitting place, reading or simply surveying the world below, although as a teenager she was really too old nowadays to be climbing trees, as her mother often reminded her. She also missed the raspberries, having been recently taught at school how to make jam; raspberry was her favourite variety, tastier than strawberry, and it set more easily because of the higher pectin content. However, after the sale of the bottom half of the kitchen garden, Jack seemed to lose interest in the rest of the plot, although this scarcely seemed to matter, since his business soon failed and the family was obliged to leave The Close and find new accommodation. Luckily, the tulip tree remained, towering over the bungalow, and clearly visible from the canal tow-path, from where Jess anxiously observed it after her family moved to the council estate on the opposite bank. She was able to point it out to her own children, and it was still there, protected by a Tree Preservation Order. fifty years after Jess and her family lived at No. 3.

The canal tow-path was the easiest and safest place for the children to ride their bikes; everywhere else involved steep hills and narrow lanes. It was also a favourite place for a walk. One day in the summer of 1962 the children gathered a group of friends for a 'hike' as far as Manley Bridge. In all, seven of them set out from the Close, with sandwiches and pop packed for a picnic lunch. The weather was warm and the level of water in the canal was low. As the children approached Manley Bridge, they noticed pieces of metal partially submerged in the murky water. Jeff examined the metal and declared that it was from the fuselage of a Canberra bomber which had crashed the previous autumn. The two crew members had heroically not used their ejector seats, which would have meant the plane crashing over Tiverton, but had steered the aircraft away from the town, ditching it in the canal with no loss of civilian life. Both young airmen were killed. It was not until the canal was dredged in 2003 that further fragments of the plane were discovered and a memorial placed on the canal bank.

Chapter 25

Dotey had once confided in Jess that she had always wanted a little girl to dress. The problem was that now, married to Jack, she had no money, for dresses, or anything else. While her father was still alive, and able to subsidise his family, Dotey was able to buy school uniforms for Westfield, complete with Chilprufe vests and Liberty bodices for winter, a Panama hat and royal blue blazer for summer. After George's death much of Jess's clothing was sent by his widow, Gladys from North America. Aunt Gladys had emigrated to Canada, and following her third marriage, to German millionaire Otto, parcels of clothes regularly arrived for Jess. The skirts and dresses often had eye-catching patterns, and while some of Jess's classmates admired her summer outfits, others derided them as being too fancy, declaring that Jess was just showing off. Heathcoat School did not have a summer uniform, and girls could wear what they liked – or whatever their mothers liked. Jess hated being the centre of attention and longed for something plain. She was always relieved when the autumn term came and she could revert to her uniform box pleated navy-blue gym-slip, worn with a royal blue jumper.

Dotey had always been very well-dressed in her youth; as the only daughter of a comfortably-off family, she had been bought a new set of summer clothes every Whitsuntide, as was then the custom. Dotey's mother's favourite colour was mauve, so that every new item of apparel had to have a touch of this colour somewhere, perhaps a purple sash on a white dress, or lilac-coloured ribbons on a straw hat. Dotey's favourite colour was actually green, but this was for some reason considered unlucky. In contrast to Dotey's purple finery, Jess seemed to live her adolescent life in green, the colour of the Grammar School uniform. This comprised a bottle-green skirt with matching blazer, white blouse, green V-necked jumper, and green and yellow striped tie; the ensemble was topped off with a bottle-green beret, known as a 'tam' which was not only hideous, but also difficult to keep on when riding a bicycle. Girls would stuff their tams into their satchels, reluctantly putting them on only when approaching the school gates, where the prefects would be on headgear duty, ensuring that boys were wearing their caps and girls were sporting their tams in the correct manner. School uniform policy also decreed that girls should have bottle-green knickers, which were required for gym lessons, along with lemon yellow PE shirts. Most girls wore ordinary underwear and kept the school knickers solely for gym; however, Dotey insisted that Jess must routinely wear the horrid green pants since she did not wish to have to provide her daughter with two sets of underwear. Moreover, Jess was always required to wear each pair for two consecutive days, in order to cut down on the quantity of laundry her mother had to do, although she longed to be able change every day. She once asked Dotey for a more plentiful supply of underwear, but Dotey replied sharply that this was unnecessary, and Jess should know better than to ask for things; she, Dotey, knew exactly what was required and would provide Jess with appropriate clothing as and when the need arose. The surest way for Jess **not** to get anything was for her to ask for it.

The onset of the girls' periods at the age of about twelve meant that it was not considered seemly for them to do gym wearing the green knickers, so each girl was allowed to wear her grey divided skirt hockey shorts during gym lessons for one week in four. Menstruating girls were required to ask the gym mistress at the start of the lesson for permission to keep their shorts on. Sometimes the gym teacher would query the frequency of a girl's request; "Didn't you wear your shorts two weeks ago?" The girl would always say no, it was four weeks ago, and mercifully, the teacher never actually went so far as to check, so permission was always granted. Jess had hoped she might get some new underwear once her periods started. Instead she discovered to her dismay that her voluminous ancient navy-blue bloomers had been retrieved from the back of a cupboard, where they had languished since her primary school days, and were once more being pressed into service. The material had faded to a washed-out greyish mauve and the elasticated waist and legs were found to be too tight, but Dotey simply removed the old elastic and inserted fresh, deploying a true 'make do and mend' wartime spirit, although by this time, the war had been over for nearly twenty years.

One day after PE, a friend took Jess aside in the changing room and told her that she should be wearing a bra. Jess had only an old vest. "Ask your mother," said the friend. But of course, Jess did not feel she could, since she had been expressly warned never to ask for things, and new clothes would be provided only when Dotey saw fit. So Jess went bra-less, not because of any mid-1960s feminist ideology, but because Dotey did not consider it necessary for her to have new underwear. Summer came, with Jess risking possible overheating in her vest, which for the sake of decency she dared not discard. Then Dotey announced mysteriously that it was time to 'put a new layer' on Jess. She produced a skimpy white garment (at least it was not bottle green), the very smallest size of bra available, which was already much too tight for Jess's burgeoning figure. Jess had to make do by breathing in and fastening it at the outermost setting, then squeezing everything in as best she could. The lower seam cut deep dark red indentations into her flesh, which remained even when she undressed at bedtime. Jess was relieved when the cooler autumn weather meant she could revert to the comfort of her vest.

Jess's school skirt was voluminous, and flapped about when she cycled to school. Her friends protested at its unfashionable length, they wanted all the girls to support their ongoing protest about the rules on skirt lengths, with the bolder pupils wearing their skirts as short as possible while just retaining decency. Her classmates felt that Jess was letting the side down, and a plot was hatched among them whereby Anna, who frequently skipped games and hid in the cloakroom, was to bring scissors, needle and thread into the changing rooms, in order to shorten Jess's skirt while she was playing netball. Anna was eventually persuaded that this was not a good idea, since it would get Jess into a lot of trouble, and Dotey would undoubtedly have been furious. Jess was then prevailed upon to roll her skirt over at the waistband several times while in school, thus shortening it by several inches, and to unroll it again at home time. This was a useful tactic, since school rules decreed that girls should not wear their skirts any shorter than six inches above the knee. The boy prefects had the task of going about with six inch wooden rulers in their blazer pockets, which they could produce at any time, insisting that a girl suspected of wearing her skirt too short should immediately kneel on the floor while the distance from floor to hem was measured. This became a matter of great inconvenience for attractive girls, who were always being picked on by prefects to have their skirt lengths checked. However, the skirt–rolled–over–at–the–waist trick could be usefully deployed if a prefect appeared on the scene, since a quick unroll would prevent trouble, and a rapid re-roll would restore fashion once the danger had passed. Jess was never troubled by any of the boy prefects. (It seems unbelievable now that boys were able to sexually harass girls in this way on school premises, with impunity.)

The Grammar School summer uniform for girls was universally unpopular. It consisted of a straight up and down vertically striped shift dress in bottle green and white. A more unflattering outfit would have been hard to design. The girls protested that it had no shape, and made them look like sticks of peppermint rock. Many attempted to customise their dresses with belts made from school ties wrapped around the waist, but when Jess tried this she was forced to agree with Dotey that she looked like a sack of potatoes tied round the middle. Several girls refused to wear the dresses, staying in winter uniform all year long. Like everyone else, Jess loathed her summer dress, since it had a tendency to ride up her legs when she was cycling to school, and she was obliged to keep dismounting in order to adjust her clothing. Jess was also castigated for continuing to wear knee socks, when everyone else had gone into nylon stockings. Jess found stockings quite impracticable on a bike, because of the chilly gap at the top of the thigh, not to mention the discomfort of suspenders; and stockings seemed to ladder as soon as she looked at them, whereas school socks were practically indestructible.

Upon the collapse of Jack's business, and the necessity for him to apply for Social Security, Dotey discovered that she was eligible for a school uniform grant. She claimed it under conditions of great secrecy, since if Jack had found out that there was extra money available, he would undoubtedly have pocketed it to fund his alcohol habit. Jess was accordingly furnished with a new blazer and school jumper; there was a small amount of money left over, so Dotey bought Jess a bottle green school regulation swimming costume, which Jess hated almost as much as the green knickers.

Out of school uniform, Jess appeared a rather strange sight. Dotey's friend Winifred kindly passed on clothes for Dotey, she and Dotey were of a similar size and build, so Dotey always managed to appear well-dressed. Winifred had a daughter who liked to keep up with the fashions, and who also passed on last season's discarded clothes to Jess. However, Sue was several inches shorter than Jess, and was also a completely different shape, so nothing looked right on Jess; the skirts sat on her hips rather than fitting around the waist, and despite this, everything was still too short. Luckily, mini-skirts were coming into fashion around this time, but of course, Jess's parents disapproved of them, so she was obliged to let the hems of the donated outfits down to their furthest extent. Dotey tutted that Jess was wearing her skirts much too short, and Jess should realise she really did not have the legs for mini-skirts; until Jess showed her mother that there really was no more material to let down.

Jess's friends sometimes commented on her odd attire, but there was nothing Jess could do except grin and bear it (one of Dotey's favourite sayings). Jess often wondered whether she would have been permitted to have new clothes had she been pretty. Surely no-one, not even Dotey, would have made a pretty child wear such dreadful ill-fitting unflattering garments. But with Jess being 'hefty' and plain, she believed she had the clothes she deserved.

When the time came for Jess to be confirmed, she worried about what on earth she could possibly wear. It was the regulation in those days for female confirmation candidates to be attired in white, with white head-dresses; but these last items were the only ones supplied by the church. Jess's only white clothes were her summer PE shirt and unlovely tennis shorts, scarcely a fitting ensemble in which to be presented to the Bishop of Crediton. Again, she did not feel that she could approach her mother for help, since she was expressly forbidden to ask for clothes. She thought about going to a jumble sale, in the hope of finding a cheap white skirt to wear with her tennis shirt, funding the purchase from the meagre earnings from her Saturday job.

However, Janet Turner, a neighbour whose son was also being confirmed, had foreseen Jess's sartorial difficulty. She approached Dotey with the kind offer of buying a suitable outfit for Jess. This was to be a surprise, and was purchased without Jess's knowledge. In order to gauge the correct size, Dotey and Janet had taken a tape measure to some of Jess's things while she was out of the house.

These clothes were of course originally Winifred's daughter Sue's cast-offs, which did not fit Jess properly, so the newly-purchased confirmation clothes did not fit either, being much too large around the waist and rather roomy in the bust. However, the pleated white skirt was of a decent length, which pleased Dotey. Jess was very relieved to have the proper attire, indeed, to have anything new at all, and bought especially for her! The outfit proved a useful addition to her summer wardrobe after the confirmation service – with the skirt rolled over a few times at the waist.

The biggest battle Jess ever had with Dotey was over the wearing of trousers. Jess knew she had worn dungarees when a toddler, she had been shown photographs of herself playing in the garden as a two-year-old; however, once she started school, she was never again allowed to wear trousers. In vain did Jess point out that trousers were eminently more suitable than skirts when riding a bike, which she did every day on her paper round; she even suggested buying a pair for herself out of the paper-round earnings. Dotey expressly forbade this, which puzzled Jess. Dotey would not give any reason for her refusal, merely insisting that trousers were not suitable attire for women; in answer to Jess's questions as to whether she had ever worn trousers, Dotey confessed to having done so only when she was absolutely obliged to, on Fire-watching duties during the war. This deep-rooted opposition to women wearing trousers mystified Jess for many years until the thought struck her that in Dotey's young days, women wearing trousers had sometimes been suspected of being lesbians. Maybe her mother had thought that Jess would be sending out the wrong signals if she wore trousers? Then there was that obscure Biblical passage, "A woman shall not wear that which pertaineth unto a man, neither shall a man put on a woman's garments: for all that do are an abomination unto the Lord thy God." Dotey had a habit of trotting out Biblical references at odd times but did she really and truly believe this? By the 1960s everyone in Jess's circle of friends was wearing jeans, and her friend Alison even had a denim trouser suit, the very first to be seen in Tiverton, bought while on holiday in Bournemouth. This exotic ensemble featured a zip fly, at the sight of which Dotey curled her lip and commented to Jess that she really did not know what Alison's mother could be thinking of.

At the age of sixteen, Jess joined a school drama club, where improvisation was all the rage. After spending a session on the floor, as if struck down in the aftermath of a nuclear holocaust, all the while anxiously tugging at her skirt to avoid embarrassment, Jess announced that she was going to buy herself a pair of jeans, for the sake of decency, funding the purchase from her Saturday job wages. Dotey insisted that she would accompany Jess on her shopping trip, and would have a veto as to what Jess chose in case this proved to be something entirely unsuitable. Dotey decreed that the trousers must be bought from the Ladies' department at the back of Soundy and Sons Gents Outfitters, possibly the town's least stylish ladies' clothes shop, and insisted that the garment purchased should have a side opening, not the dreaded brazen front fly. She also made Jess buy a size larger than necessary, in order to avoid any possibility of her daughter being seen in anything remotely flattering; Jess wondered whether she would ever have clothes that fitted her properly. Still, it was a victory of sorts, her first trousers, a pair of side-fastening jeans in black, not indigo, a shade Dotey considered 'common'.

A further victory came when Jess refused to have her hair cut at Grattan's Barbers. Dotey had for years made monthly appointments for all the children; Mr. Grattan would give the boys a good 'short-back-and-sides' while Jess received similar treatment from Mrs. Grattan. Once, Jess prevailed upon the good lady not to cut her hair so short, but Dotey had telephoned to complain immediately Jess arrived home inadequately shorn. So the next month Mrs. Grattan had made sure to use the clippers halfway up the back of Jess's head, which Jess hated, and her fringe had been cut extra short, since no-one wanted to be on the receiving end of a second complaint from Dotey. Flushed with success over the trousers, Jess announced that she was growing her hair, and would never again cross the threshold of Grattan's. Dotey pursed her lips. "You know I don't approve of long hair!" This was becoming her mantra; she did not approve of girls in trousers, girls with make-up, or the films that Jess and her friends saw at the 'Tivoli'. But there was little Dotey could do now that Jess was sixteen and had recently and spectacularly passed her O level exams, finally giving her the confidence to demand freedom of choice in matters relating to dress, appearance and leisure pursuits.

Chapter 26

Dotey had always seen it as one of her chief parental duties to protect Jess from any undesirable outside influences, and went to what might today be considered extreme lengths to achieve this. She steadfastly refused to get a television, declaring it to be a source of unpleasant information, and frequently withheld access to the newspaper. The Daily Mail was hidden away in her room all through the Profumo scandal and the Moors Murders case, and at other times it appeared heavily edited, where items deemed inappropriate for young eyes had been removed. Jess was once looking for the Fred Basset cartoon, only to find a large hole.

"Why have you cut Fred Basset out of the paper, Mum?"

"There's something on the page behind which I don't wish you to see." The 'Lady Chatterley's Lover' obscenity trial was in full swing, the judge famously enquiring whether this was the sort of book anyone would want their wives or servants to read. Dotey certainly did not want her daughter to know about the trial; although Jess was surprised to discover a copy of the original Penguin edition of *Lady Chatterley's Lover* in a drawer after her mother's death.

To Dotey's disgust, Jack insisted on getting the 'News of the World' on Sundays, "for the half-time scores", but of course, the children were forbidden to touch it. Sometimes Jess would meet the Sunday paper-boy at the front door as she was leaving for Sunday School (because she had rather a crush on him and would plan her exit to coincide with his usual delivery time.) She would bring the 'News of the World' into the house for Jack, holding it at arm's length and resisting the temptation to look at anything more than the sensational headline. The paper was put in the coal-scuttle and used to light the fire on Mondays. Jack also kept a stash of cheap paper-backs under his bed, mostly Western stories with lurid covers, contemptuously described by Dotey as "blood and thunder", and of course strictly out of bounds to Jess.

Library books were no problem, since young people issued with a Junior ticket could borrow only from the Children's shelves, and the librarian would always notice if young borrowers tried to sneak out something from the Adult section. Dotey always perused the books Jess had chosen, just in case. A well-meaning relative bought Jess a copy of *Jane Eyre* one Christmas, but her mother immediately whisked it away, saying that it would be 'far too upsetting' for Jess. The same applied to a complete set of Dickens, the property of Aunt Gladys, who had left an assortment of her worldly goods with Jess's family on her way to Canada, where to her step-daughter Dotey's disgust she was shortly to fall into the arms of her German émigré millionaire. The Dickens was at once removed. "Such dreary stuff and really much too upsetting for you!" Dotey clearly had little regard for nineteenth century classics. Years later, Aunt Gladys asked Jess what had become of the books, which she and Grandi George had read together in the evenings in their Bournemouth days. Jess said that she did not know, but she feared that the volumes had been consigned to the dustbin. Dotey was eventually reluctantly obliged to permit Jess to read *David Copperfield* and *Jane Eyre* since they were set texts at school, along with Churchill's *My Early Life*, Emily Bronte's *Wuthering Heights*, Erskine Childers' *The Riddle Of The Sands*, Flora Thompson's *Lark Rise* and Blackmore's *Lorna Doone*. Jess enjoyed reading, and the only set book she ever gave up on was T.E. Lawrence's *The Seven Pillars of Wisdom*; she felt guilty about this, since Jack had of course met Lawrence in Palestine during the Great War, but she found the book quite unreadable. The Brontë novels simply confirmed in Jess Dotey's strongly-held opinion of 'the North' as being extremely bleak and peopled by mean characters, such as the wife-bullying Heathcliffe and Mrs. Reed, Jane Eyre's dreadful aunt. Jess was not too sure about the would-be bigamous Mr. Rochester either. At the same time, in a remote village in the hills not far from Tiverton, a reclusive woman named Jean Rhys was writing the story of the Rochesters' early life, the classic *Wide Sargasso Sea*.

Dotey's censorship policy caused some problems when the English teacher set Jess's class a piece of homework which involved selecting an item of good news and another of bad news from a newspaper and then discussing them. Jess was surreptitiously rummaging in the coal-scuttle for bad news, when Dotey came in. She was annoyed to hear about the homework task, declaring that she had never liked that English master, what with his beard and the CND badge on his car. This ridiculous homework assignment confirmed her suspicions, that he really was quite unsuited to be a teacher at the Grammar School. Jess was obliged to retreat to the town library to search out a bad news story from their uncensored newspapers. She sometimes tried to read the papers on the bookstall at WH Smith on Saturdays, when the regular assistant, Linda, was on her lunch-break. However, the manager would not permit the reading of newspapers or books, even when the shop was quiet, ordering Jess to do yet more dusting. Jess found that it was often impossible for her to dust the news stand effectively, because of the Blundells boys crowding around the top shelf. The boys, distinguishable by their grey flannels, white shirts, tweed sports jackets and boater hats, were let loose in the town on Saturday afternoons; and for many, the top shelf in Smith's, with its selection of 'girly' magazines, was their first port of call. Dotey, who admired the smartly turned out Blundells boys, was astonished to hear of Jess's dusting difficulties. "Imagine, public school boys from good backgrounds wanting to look at that sort of thing!"

Soon, a debating competition was announced; the motion being "This house defends media censorship," with Blundells proposing and the Grammar School opposing. The debate was to be held at Blundells School, and Dotey said that Jess could attend so long as she came straight home immediately after the debate and didn't dawdle. Jeff was also going. Halfway through the evening the debate was thrown open to the floor. Jess had been listening with great surprise to the Blundells boys, (several of whom she recognised as Smith's top-shelf customers) sanctimoniously defending censorship 'in order to protect innocent young minds'. She wondered indignantly just how they could be so hypocritical; then, with the debate thrown open to contributions from the floor, Jess unexpectedly found herself on her feet, much to the astonishment of her brother.

"Madam Chairman, I work on Saturdays in WH Smiths, and often have great difficulty getting near the bookshelves in order to dust, because of the crowds of Blundells boys reading 'Mayfair' and similar material from the top shelf."

She sat down to a huge burst of laughter and applause, whereupon one member of the debating team said sheepishly that he would like to remind the young lady that Blundells was after all a single sex school… The debate ended, with Blundells judged to have been the winners. Jess was making her way down the school drive, mindful of Dotey's instructions to come straight home afterwards, when she heard the sound of running feet coming along the path behind her and voices calling. "Wait, Miss, wait!" Jess turned around, mystified as to what they could possibly want. Two Blundells boys breathlessly approached.

"What's the name of the gorgeous blonde who's usually on Smith's bookstall?" Of course, they were not in the least interested in Jess except as a source of information about her pretty colleague Linda. Jess turned and walked away.

However, it was impossible to completely insulate children from the outside world, despite Dotey's best endeavours. The 'swinging 60s' passed almost unacknowledged in the house, but the children were permitted to watch some television programmes at the neighbours. They could see 'Top of the Pops', and nature programmes, but sometimes they contrived to stay after the permitted programmes had ended, and once even managed to glimpse part of 'The Likely Lads'. However, the neighbour had her suspicions.

"Are you quite sure your mother doesn't mind you watching this?" she asked. The children replied that it would be OK, but Mrs. O'Shaughnessy was no fool, and speedily sent them home when there was a reference to "couples copulating the length of the Doncaster by-pass."

One day after church Jess was delivering parish magazines, and since she had one for her friend Andrew's parents, she called at his house. Jess found Andrew with Gilbert, another school friend, their heads deep in a paper-back book entitled, *In Praise of Older Women*, from which they were reading aloud some of the more racy extracts. Andrew's parents were out, so Jess put their parish magazine on the hall table and left the boys to their reading. Just as she was about to leave, Andrew's parents were heard returning, and Jess was aware of a sudden agitated commotion in the room behind. "It's your book, Andrew!" "No it's not – you were reading it!" There was a thud, as the book was thrown to the floor, neither boy wanting to be discovered in possession of it. Jess turned back and picked it up, stuffing it into the pile of yet-to-be delivered parish magazines, smiling pleasantly to Andrew's parents as she passed them at the front door. When Jess reached home, her deliveries complete, she was carrying only her mother's magazine and the copy of *In Praise Of Older Women*, with nowhere to hide it. Dotey at once confiscated the book, astonished to hear that it actually belonged to a bank manager's son! Jess never knew what became of it; possibly it ended up in the same obscure drawer as *Lady Chatterley's Lover*.

Once she turned sixteen and started sixth form, Jess began cautiously to assert herself more. She and her friends, a group of half a dozen boys and a few girls who met at the town library in the evenings, sometimes went to the cinema after the library closed at 7.30, to see films which Dotey considered 'unsuitable', such as 'The Knack', 'Here We Go Round the Mulberry Bush' and 'Bonnie and Clyde'.

"I'm surprised at you, Jess; that sort of thing is quite unsuitable for a sensitive girl like you! Yet you persist in going to see these films, even though you know I don't approve! I'm disappointed in you, Jess, I really am!"

Dotey's determined efforts to protect Jess from any hint of 'unpleasantness' continued even after she had left home for university. During the first Christmas vacation, Jess's friend Alison visited. "I see Mr. G— is all over the Sunday papers!" said Alison, over one of Jess's home-made mince pies.

Dotey almost dropped her teacup, while a mystified Jess asked what Mr. G—, the middle-aged married curate who had prepared her for confirmation and run the church youth club for many years, could possibly have done in order to feature in the Sundays. Alison said he was supposed to have had an affair with one of the Sunday school teachers, a girl just a year older than Jess. Luckily for Dotey, news of the scandal had not emerged until after Jess had left home.

"Mrs. G— is quoted at some length, she appealed to the Bishop to try to help her save the marriage, it's really been quite a drama, Mr. G— said he was meeting the Rural Dean every Thursday but he was actually going to visit Sue, and his minibus was seen parked in lay-bys all over Somerset!

It all apparently come to light when Mrs. G— bumped into the Rural Dean and he asked after Mr. G—, saying he had not seen him for a while, so giving the game away…"

"Why didn't you tell me about this, Mum?" asked Jess. Her mother had the familiar pursed lipped expression, and was glaring meaningfully at the oblivious Alison.

"I didn't want to upset you; I know how much you thought of Mr. G—, ever since he prepared you for confirmation."

Dotey added "Of course, I never really trusted him – I always thought those teeth of his were much too crooked."

Dotey was wrong, Jess did not think very much of Mr. G— at all, she had actually been wary of him for a couple of years, ever since he had summoned her, as Youth Club secretary, to his study, in order to tell her off for being in dereliction of duty. It was summer, so the club was not meeting, and Jess's most recent duty had been to send a card to one of the members who was in hospital having her tonsils out. This she had done, but now a stony-faced Mr. G— was recalling some imaginary task which Jess had allegedly overlooked. He proceeded to verbally lay into Jess in the harshest possible manner, castigating her about neglected duties and how he knew what she was up to, engaging in frivolous pursuits such as bird-watching with Gilbert – oh yes, Mr. G— had seen them setting off on their bikes together. Jess was so upset at the unfounded nature of his criticism that she had burst into tears. She was quite unprepared for what happened next. Mr. G— folded her in his arms, kissed her forehead and stroked her cheek. Jess was trying to escape from Mr. G—'s creepy embrace when Mrs. G— entered the room, alarmed at the sound of Jess's sobbing. Mr.G— explained to his wife that he was only comforting Jess because she was upset… It dawned on Jess that Mr. G— had engineered the entire scenario, making up a spurious excuse to lure her to his study in order to find an opportunity to touch her. It seemed that even those in positions of authority, such as curates, could not be trusted to behave properly. Jess felt that maternal guidance as to the odd ways of men would have been helpful. However, she did not dare mention the incident to Dotey, or anyone else, for she felt somehow ashamed that it had happened, and anyway, who would believe her? After all, Mr. G— was a family man with a respected position in the community. And now, a few years later, he was all over the Sunday papers, those dreadful publications she had always been forbidden to read – and her mother had never said a word of it to her. The whole thing was really quite extraordinary.

Chapter 27

By the age of almost nine, Jess was aware that the downstairs tenants, the Bagshaws, had acquired a baby, then promptly left to live in a council house, but had never really wondered where babies came from. Mrs. Bagshaw ("Her Christian name is Jasmine! Really, how inappropriate for such a slattern!") – had always been enormous, so had not appeared to be any larger than usual throughout her pregnancy, giving Jess no clue. She vaguely supposed married people ordered babies from somewhere, possibly the hospital. However, partial enlightenment was at hand. One February day the redoubtable Mrs. MacDougall paused from her cleaning endeavours to take elevenses with Dotey and Jess, who was at home for half-term.

"I see the Queen has yet to produce her baby," remarked Mrs. MacDougall, in her decorous Morningside accent, as she sugared her tea. Dotey pointedly said nothing, so Jess took it upon herself to respond.

"Well, maybe the workmen haven't got it ready yet," she said, munching a digestive biscuit.

Mrs. MacDougall threw back her head, letting forth peals of Scots laughter, blithely ignoring Dotey's furious frown. "Och, Jess, you must know there are no workmen involved in making babies! They grow inside their mothers."

"Do they?" Jess was astonished.

"And just where did you think they came from?" Mrs. MacDougall was interested to know, concentrating her attention on Jess and pointedly taking no notice at all of Dotey, whose face by now resembled a thundercloud.

"I thought the workmen at the hospital must make them. When I go past the hospital, I often see people bringing babies out, but I've never seen one being taken in."

More Scottish merriment; then Jess's inevitable question.

"If they grow inside their mothers, how do they get out?"

Mrs. MacDougall was more than prepared, after all, she had successfully brought up three daughters and a son.

"They come out of their mother's bottom."

This sounded extremely alarming to Jess. "So – do the mothers go to the toilet and do a baby, instead of the, um, the usual thing?" she asked, delicately.

Mrs. MacDougall was highly amused. "Ha-ha! I always said they should have put our Sandy down the toilet! No, the mother knows when the baby is coming, and she has it in a bed, often in hospital, as you have correctly noticed."

Dotey could stand no more of this, and stiffly reminded Mrs. MacDougall that there was a great deal of cleaning to be got through before lunchtime. Mrs. MacDougall finished her tea leisurely and replaced her cup on the tray.

"I'm away to the stairs, then," she said, picking up her dustpan and brush.

Thankfully, Jess did not ask how the babies got into their mothers' tummies; she still imagined that it was necessary to place some sort of order, rather like requesting items from a seed catalogue perhaps; and of course, Dotey took care never to pursue the subject.

Soon after this, a stray dog turned up, and Jess was detailed to return it to the address given on the dog's collar, which was not far from the park in the town centre, over a mile away from the Close. Jack attached a piece of string to the dog's collar, to act as an impromptu lead, although it seemed rather reluctant to return home. Jess handed the dog over to its owner, who received it without comment. To Jess's surprise, the dog reappeared the following day, seemingly determined to become lost. Jack remarked carelessly that there must be a bitch on heat in the neighbourhood. Jess asked him what he meant, and her father looked as though he was about to tell her when Dotey intervened, glaring meaningfully at Jack and quickly instructing Jess to take the dog back yet again.

"My dad says there must be a bitch on heat near us", remarked Jess as she handed the dog back, wondering if the owner would care to explain. The woman looked startled, clearly this was not a subject she was any more keen to discuss with a nine year old than was Dotey. She took the dog from Jess without thanks, slamming her garden gate behind her. The matter was never again alluded to at home.

Next, Jess was mystified when Susan, the girl with whom she shared a changing cabin at the swimming baths, said that she would not be able to go swimming that week.

"Why not, are you ill? If so, you shouldn't be at school."

Susan looked miserable. "I'm not ill, but I can't tell you what's wrong with me, you'll have to ask your mother."

A puzzled Jess did indeed ask Dotey, not really anticipating an answer, for how could her mother possibly be expected to know what was wrong with Susan? But Dotey knew at once -Jess could tell by the way she sighed and groaned.

"I did hope not to have to tell you just yet! Goodness me, Susan's only ten, that's very early to start."

"Start what?"

Dotey then went on to explain about menstrual periods, how they were a curse from God affecting every girl and woman, from about thirteen until the age of about fifty. Girls would bleed from the place where they went to the toilet for a week every month. (The truth is very often a casualty of embarrassment, and Dotey did not feel there was any need to mention the uterus, or the female body preparing itself for the possibility of a baby.) As soon as Jess noticed any blood she should immediately tell Dotey, who would provide the wherewithal for her to cope, which would of course be towels; Dotey shared with certain religious denominations the decided view that tampons were suitable only for married women. Flushable towels had yet to be invented, and it was necessary to hide used towels in a special bag which would be collected by Dotey and taken discreetly to the bottom of the garden for burning. Jess wondered how people who did not have a garden managed. Sanitary towels were sold in plain brown paper packets, kept under the counter at the chemist's, never on display, and always sold by a female assistant.

Jess was also warned that she might experience a cramping pain. Dotey's own mother had not told her anything about periods, and young Dotey had believed she was bleeding to death when hers started. Luckily, she had been at school at the time, and another girl had noticed her distress, and explained that it was to be expected.

"But why didn't your mum tell you?"

"Because it's not a nice thing to talk about it! You must be very

133

discreet, tell only me when it happens, and wash out your panties in cold water without anyone else seeing."

"But why does it happen to women? Whatever good does it do, to have to bleed every month for years?"

Dotey's exasperated expression indicated that she was not prepared to answer any more questions. "I've already said – it's the curse, God punished Eve in the Garden of Eden, you can read it for yourself in the Bible! Now, no more of these questions, Jess. You have all the information you need."

Of course, Jess knew the Genesis story, how Eve was beguiled by the serpent to disobey God's instructions, and how she then encouraged Adam to partake of the forbidden fruit of the Tree of Knowledge. However, Adam could have easily refused, but he hadn't, he had also disobeyed God, so why didn't men have this curse as well? Why didn't they also bleed from the place where their wee came from? It seemed so unfair... Jess felt that there was something that her mother was keeping from her, but she knew that further questioning would be quite useless. A barrier had come down, and the discussion was now at an end. Dotey of course had not thought fit to take the opportunity to give Jess any information about female bodies preparing themselves for motherhood. She was not yet ready for the 'facts of life' chat with her daughter; nor indeed, as it turned out, would she ever be. Although not especially devout, she had found the Garden of Eden story a very convenient explanation with which to fob Jess off.

Jess still had no idea about how babies reached their mother's tummies, her knowledge of human reproduction having stalled since Mrs. MacDougall's elevenses chat just before the birth of Prince Andrew. She still imagined that the hospital was somehow involved; maybe a woman got a prescription for a baby to grow inside her from the clinic, when she felt she had enough time to look after a child.

Today it would be impossible and completely undesirable for girls to be kept in such ignorance, but fifty years ago, in her sheltered, censored life, Jess had no means of obtaining information about sex, until the day she found herself obediently turning to page 145 in the Biology textbook, and copying the diagrams of the human reproductive system into her exercise book, as the teacher instructed.

There was not time to finish before the end of the lesson, so the pupils were told to complete their drawings for homework, not forgetting to label them properly. Jess was working at the living-room table when Dotey came up and glanced over Jess's shoulder. She snatched the book up and sternly enquired of her daughter who had set this homework.

"Miss Plunkett," replied Jess, naming the very respectable middle-aged spinster who was the Biology teacher.

"Well, what a pity she has taken it upon herself to teach you this! There's absolutely no need for anyone to know about this, unless and until they get married; and you're not going to get married, Jess, you're going to have a career! Marriage for you would be a waste of that good brain!"

"But it's part of the O level syllabus, so I have to do it."

Dotey returned the text-book to the table with a heavy sigh, and disappeared from the room. Shortly afterwards she returned with a little red booklet, which she handed to Jess. Entitled "The Facts of Life", Jess noted from the cover that it was written by a doctor and intended for eight-year-olds.

"But I'm fifteen! Why didn't you give this to me before?"

"Um, well, yes, I suppose I have had it by me for some time; but I didn't want to go putting ideas into your head!"

On reading the little book, which managed to describe sex in bulls, frogs, dogs, Bower birds and Adèlie penguins, without extending the technical discussion to actual human beings, Jess thought there was absolutely nothing for Dotey to worry about; she was sure she would never want to indulge in the activity portrayed in those school text-book diagrams with anyone, it all sounded so rude and unpleasant and messy, and anyway, she had been taught always to keep those parts of the body firmly covered up.

Jess may have been very naïve, but there was nowhere she could have discovered sex information for herself. Sex was not considered a 'nice' topic of conversation, and there had never been any sexual activity, or even marital affection in the household so far as Jess was aware. Dotey and Jack had kept to their separate bedrooms ever since Jack moved in. On visits to friends' houses, Jess realised that the parents shared a room, but she imagined this was probably because

135

of a shortage of bedrooms. After all, not everyone was lucky enough to live in a big house like theirs in the Close, where every family member could have his or her own room. On a visit to a large rectory, Jess's young hostess innocently revealed that her parents had twin beds in the same room, despite there being rooms to spare. Jess supposed that the Rector and his wife liked to read to one another at bedtime, possibly from the Bible; or perhaps one of them was scared of the dark... Her family did not possess a television, and all library books were vetted. Reading newspapers on Smith's bookstall was discouraged in favour of endless dusting, and her father's 'News of the World' was strictly forbidden. So far as Dotey was concerned, Jess's innocence /ignorance was bliss, and there were no other female relatives on hand to enlighten her. Jess remained wrapped up in cotton wool, shielded from all undesirable influences, completely protected from any 'unpleasantness'.

She did not dare to discuss biological matters with her friends, since she had taken her cue from Dotey, that it was somehow shameful to talk about such things. "Always be discreet!" was her mother's mantra, supported by society in general. Jess knew it was pointless to ask Dotey anything when there was no chance of receiving an honest reply; instead she would be either referred to the Old Testament, or admonished for raising unsuitable topics about which Dotey considered it unnecessary for her to know. However, despite her references to the Bible in response to Jess's inconvenient questions, Dotey scarcely ever attended church, declaring that she was 'not good enough to go,' and that anyway, she did not have a suitable hat. This puzzled Jess, who had been taught that God forgave your sins if you truly repented. After all, everyone was a sinner, and Church was for the whole congregation, not just rare paragons of virtue. It was of course better to try not to sin in the first place, but the Gospel clearly said, "Let he who is without sin cast the first stone." As for the lack of a hat, Jess was sure that God did not mind. But Dotey minded a great deal.

Chapter 28

The National Health Service, still in its first decade, provided a variety of inspections and tests for children in council schools, and once Jess had left Westfield she became used to lining up for medical checks. The most frequent was the Nit Nurse, who peered closely at every child's head, parting the hair this way and that in order to detect the presence of head-lice. Dotey considered it to be a shameful thing for a child to be discovered to have nits, and so Jess was always very relieved when her head passed muster. Dotey told Jess how her own hair had been checked as a child, then patted and praised by the nurse as being 'a lovely clean little head.' The heads of the three young sons of a teacher, all of whom played with Peter, were found to be 'crawling with lice', and a shocked Dotey was quick to comment that this must be because their mother went out to work and therefore did not look after her children properly.

Dotey had expressed a dread of Jess having to wear glasses, although she herself was short-sighted and wore them, while Jack was long-sighted. Consequently, Jess always worked herself up into an anxious state before eye inspections. Once she made such a mess of reading the test card that she was given a letter, stating that her eyesight required further investigation at the clinic. On reading this, Dotey promptly burst into tears.

"I really hoped that you would never need to have glasses, Jess! Oh dear, how exceedingly vexing!"

Jess did not know why her mother dreaded the possibility of her having to wear glasses, it was common enough, and would probably result in some teasing along the lines of 'speccy four-eyes', but nothing like as bad as that which she had been obliged to endure at Westfield from Jake. After all, nobody was likely to 'get up a gang' against her simply for wearing glasses. Dotey accompanied Jess to the clinic, and after various lights had been shone in her eyes, it was decided that there was nothing wrong with Jess's sight, and her poor showing in the test had been due to excessive nerves. A relieved Dotey scolded Jess for being so silly.

Dental inspections posed no concern for Dotey's children, who of course always had their intake of sweet stuff strictly rationed, who always brushed their teeth, and never failed to eat their greens. No fillings for them! However, Jess was advised at the age of nine that she should wear braces on her teeth in order to straighten them. Jess refused. She knew some of her classmates wore wire braces, they were ugly and it seemed that food was always getting stuck in them. Jess thought she would prefer to keep her crooked teeth. The dentist, annoyed that she could not be persuaded to submit to his professional advice, issued his direst threat.

"If you don't wear braces now, your teeth won't straighten, they'll stay crooked and you'll never catch a husband!"

Jess was relieved to hear that this was the worst that could possibly happen, since it had been dinned into her from the cradle that she was never going to get married.

"Oh, that's all right then, I won't need to catch a husband, because I'm going to have a career instead," Jess politely informed the dentist, who of course thought she was being cheeky, and gave her a contemptuous look.

The most important test was the Heaf Test for tuberculosis. This was known as the Daisy Test, since the children were given tiny pinpricks on their arms in the shape of a small flower. These caused a reaction, so that the pin-pricks became raised and red, but most children found that these quickly subsided. Every day at school, the children would roll up their sleeves to compare their daisies, and Jess was surprised that hers was still exhibiting raised red lumps when everyone else's had faded. After a few days, the doctor who came to check the Heaf tests took one look at Jess's arm and sent a letter home, requiring that every family member promptly attend the mass radiography screening unit in the market place. Full of consternation, Dotey and Jack took Jess and Peter one evening for their chest X-rays, which were carried out in a special caravan. Jess did not like the bossy man who was operating the machine, telling her sharply that she must breathe in and hold her position quite still for what seemed to anxious Jess like an endless period. Fortunately, none of the family turned out to have TB, and it was a mystery just how Jess appeared to have gained some level of immunity to the disease. The only person that the family knew to have ever had TB was alcoholic Norah next door, but that had been several decades ago. However, Jess had the last laugh, since she was deemed not require the full BCG vaccination, which later left many of her classmates with sore arms. Jess's sore arm came when she was vaccinated against polio, which was still a common enough childhood disease, resulting in children having to wear callipers or even to be treated in an iron lung. (By the time Jess's children came to receive polio vaccine in the late 1970s and early 1980s, the dose was administered on a sugar lump rather than via an injection, and fortunately, polio was much less common.)

Dotey was obliged to have all her teeth extracted by Mr. Lewis, the dentist, because of recurrent gum infections. She was then required to wait until the gums had settled before a set of false teeth could be made. It was half term, so Jess was on hand to assist her poorly mother, who was keeping to her room and avoiding wider society in her toothless state. Jess spent the week carrying out Dotey's gummy instructions. Meanwhile, Jack had kept most of his teeth, and was having some fillings, under gas. Jack had a bad reaction to the anaesthetic, and when he came to, it was to find that he had a terrified Mr. Lewis pinned up against the surgery wall. Jack had no memory of leaving the dentist's chair, but Mr. Lewis did not forget the event in a hurry.

Meanwhile Jess was becoming worried about the health of Morag MacDougall, the middle daughter of the redoubtable cleaning lady. Morag was in the sixth form, a few years older than Jess, and she usually nodded to her in the school dinner queue, but there had been no sign of Morag for over a week. Jess had asked Jeannie MacDougall if her sister was ill, and noticed that Jeannie hesitated before nodding. When it got to two weeks with no sighting of Morag, Jess became concerned that Morag must be seriously ill. Soon it was half term, and Mrs. MacDougall was on the Spring cleaning war-path, attacking all the windows with her chamois leather cloth. At elevenses, Jess asked her whether Morag was feeling better. She noted with some surprise her mother's frown and sharp intake of breath, but it seemed that nothing phased Mrs. MacDougall, who replied in her customary calm manner, while carefully stirring her tea,

"I don't know how Morag is; she has not been in touch."

"But isn't she off school ill?" asked Jess, in surprise.

"No, indeed, to the best of our knowledge she is in Bristol."

"Oh, so she's away on holiday!" Jess was relieved, but still surprised that Morag should have been absent in term time.

"It appears that she has gone in company with a man."

At this point, Dotey intervened. "It's really not necessary for Jess to hear anything about this sort of unpleasantness!"

Unperturbed, Mrs. MacDougall carried on regardless. "Indeed, Morag has made her bed and she must lie in it! I'll away to the landing – now, where did I put my shammy?"

Mrs. MacDougall went to bring light to the landing, and Dotey rounded on Jess. "How dare you be so inquisitive? Morag's goings-on are nothing whatever to do with you! I've told you so many times, that little girls should never ask questions; when will you get this into your thick head?"

"But I thought she was ill; I was only trying to be polite! Has Morag been kidnapped? Can't the police find her?"

"Of course she's not been kidnapped! She's run away with a man, when she should be preparing for important exams. I'd hate to think that you could ever do anything to bring such shame on me, Jess; but if you did, I wouldn't have you back in this house again, do you understand? A well-brought-up girl from a good home should never put her family through this sort of disgraceful episode!"

"Is that what Mrs. MacDougall meant about Morag making her bed and lying on it – that she can't come home again?"

"It's up to Mrs. MacDougall and her husband whether they can ever consider taking her back. But if she was my daughter, she'd be horse-whipped! Now, that's all I intend to say on the subject. Haven't you got anything to do? Because if not, you can go and tidy your bedroom!"

Jess hated it when her mother was sharp with her, but realised that she would soon be forgiven since the following week was Speech Day and Jess was receiving a prize for Latin. Dotey never missed Speech Day, and always arrived attired in her best coat and the white cotton gloves without which no self-respecting woman considered herself properly dressed. Jack never attended, despite the fact that Jess won a prize most years. The prizes were always books; the winners were summoned to the hall the week before, and invited to choose from the selection of carefully chosen books on display. This year, with her GCE studies looming, Jess had picked out a copy of 'O level cookery' instead of the schoolgirl fiction she usually chose.

Jess hoped her clumsiness would not cause her to stumble off the platform. Those stairs could be tricky. The dignitary distributing the prizes last year had been Ted, later Lord, Willis, creator of the long-running 'Dixon of Dock Green' television series, which Jess had actually been permitted to watch at the neighbours. Mr. Willis had a word of encouragement for all the prize recipients, even the clumsy and self-conscious one. This year the celebrity prize-giver was to be Michael Croft, director the National Youth Theatre, to which Tiverton Grammar School had sent several pupils.

The afternoon began with opening remarks from the Chairman of Governors, a ginger-haired, florid faced local councillor, with the broadest Devonshire accent possible. Jess, sitting in the front rows near the stage with the other prize-winners, listened to his exhortation to the 'Poopuls' to work 'ardour and 'ardour this yeour, and imagined her mother squirming in her seat several rows back. Dotey commented without fail after every Speech Day as to how embarrassing it was for the Chairman of the Grammar School Governors to have such an undesirably broad accent, whatever did the visiting celebrities think; and surely it was more than time that the Governors found someone well-spoken to conduct the proceedings…

The teachers sat on the stage behind the Chairman, the celebrity guest and the Headmaster, in full academic dress. It was not uncommon for teachers in the 1960s to wear their black gowns when teaching, but their hoods only appeared at Speech Day. Dotey liked to while away the boring parts of the afternoon matching the colour of the hood linings with the universities they represented. She suggested that Jess should opt for one of the Cambridge colleges, with their lovely white-lined hoods, whereas it would be advisable to steer clear of any university whose hood was a drab colour. Jess eventually ended up at Leeds University, whose gowns had a green-lined hood, and green was of course her mother's favourite colour; however, this was to be of absolutely no significance as it turned out, since Dotey had not lived long enough to see her daughter graduate, and Jess could not face this ultimate prize-giving without her mother present, so arranged to have her degree conferred *'in absentia'*.

141

Chapter 29

Some time after his arrival in the town Jack became Secretary of Tiverton Constitutional Club. The post attracted a small honorarium, which caused Jack not a little trouble when he failed to declare it on his Income Tax return. Somehow the Inland Revenue had found out about it, and sent Jack a bill for several hundred pounds. Jack of course had no spare cash; but fortunately he managed to back an unlikely series of horses in a bold accumulator, and all the horses came in. Jack won £900, and settled his bill.

Jess knew that her parents were Conservatives, and that Tiverton was a safe Tory seat. The Member of Parliament and Chancellor of the Exchequer in the MacMillan government was Derrick Amory, one of the factory-owning Heathcoat Amorys. Jess had noticed her father chatting with Mr. Amory at the Boxing Day Meet of Tiverton Foxhounds, which Jack had dragged the children along to the previous year. The Conservatives supported the right of huntsmen and those awful yapping hounds to chase a poor fox all over the countryside and eventually tear it to pieces in the name of sport. Jack had put the children in the car and driven around the freezing lanes following the hunt. Every so often he would park precariously close to a ditch, jump up onto a gate and train his binoculars over the wintry fields. The baying of the hounds and the braying of the huntsmen's horns told them that the hunt was over. This became Jess's idea of what it meant to be a Conservative.

Jess saw Labour party posters on display in the windows of the houses in Westexe, which she walked past on her way to school. This area of the town was inhabited by the factory workers, and Jack and Dotey had expressed the view that supporting Labour on the part of Heathcoats employees was simply being ungrateful, 'biting the hand that feeds them'. Tiverton being in the depths of the West Country, there were also a number of Liberal Party members in the town. Dotey once bought a gold coloured lampshade for the hall, which caused the bulb to beam bright yellow through the fanlight, so that Jack declared everyone would mistake the house for the Liberal Club.

One evening in 1964 Jess awoke to the sound of her father shouting, "The buggers! Looks like they're going to do it!"

Jess was alarmed and went to the landing. "Mum, what's happening? Is Daddy all right? Who's going to do what?"

In the background she could hear the wireless whistling at top volume, and her father groaning and moaning and swearing, as the radio announcer intoned more bad news.

"Go back to bed at once Jess! Daddy's just listening to the General Election results; it seems that Labour might win."

Jess knew that this was bad news. The Conservatives had been in power for almost all of her life, and she had heard her parents talking in hushed tones about how dreadful it would be if Labour ever took over. She had once ventured to ask what would be so bad about a Labour win, and was told that the very first thing a Labour government would do would be to nationalise the Store. Jack would have his business confiscated, so goodness knows how they would manage. The next item on Labour's evil agenda was joining the Common Market, which would also be very bad news. Britain had fought two wars against the Germans, and now our country might have to allow those same Germans to come here to take over our jobs and houses. That was what being in the Common Market meant. Therefore a Labour election victory would clearly be an unmitigated disaster.

It always struck Jess as ironic that in later years it was actually a Conservative government which took Britain into the Common Market. Also, knowing her father's strongly held and frequently expressed views on a woman's place, Jess wondered how he would have dealt with the arrival of Conservative Mrs. Thatcher as the UK's first woman Prime Minister. In 1964, women were not even allowed into the Constitutional Club as full members, they could only attend special Ladies Nights. Jack actually died three years before Mrs. Thatcher's 1979 victory, which was maybe just as well; Jess wondered how many men of her father's opinion and generation had suffered an attack of apoplexy watching Mrs. Thatcher about to enter Number 10 Downing Street, sanctimoniously intoning the words of St. Francis of Assisi.

Jack frequently exhorted the teenage Jess to join the Young

Conservatives. In fact, several of her classmates were in the 'YCs', but Jess would not join on principle. Instead, in an act of rebellion, and to her father's great disgust, she enrolled in the Young Liberals. Some of her friends had told her that they gave the better parties. Dotey was pleased when she learned that the dentist's son was in the young Liberals, also the daughter of a solicitor who was the prospective Liberal parliamentary candidate. She even allowed Jess to hold a genteel Liberal Social Evening at The Close, watching all the while to check who had nice manners and to ensure no alcohol made its way in. On the strength of this ("They do seem to be quite nice people") Dotey was persuaded in 1966 to vote for the Liberal solicitor, ("On no account tell your Father!") although he did not manage to unseat the Tory incumbent, and neither has anyone since. One of Jess's more daring young Liberal friends, Marian, asked her to accompany a group which was planning to heckle the Tory candidate at a rally in the New Hall. Jess was relieved to hear that she need not actually do anything, apart from merely go along to make up the numbers. After some well-chosen heckles, Marian signalled that they were all to clatter out as noisily as possible, and make their way down to Heathcoat Hall, where the Labour party candidate was holding his – rather more sparsely attended – eve-of-poll rally. After a second stomp-out, everyone decided that they had done quite enough heckling for one night and went for a drink. This was apparently what being a Young Liberal was all about.

Chapter 30

Throughout the mid-1960s, Jess came increasingly to realise that there was never enough money for her family to live comfortably. She learned not to ask for anything, since she was always refused, and as often as not, she would be sharply told off simply for asking. The family possessed no fridge, record player or television, although these items were now becoming common in households throughout the land, in the 'never had it so good' era. Following a trip to London in 1964, financed by one of Jack's unexplained windfalls, probably connected with the football pools or racehorses, the family never again went on holiday together. School trips and pupil exchange visits were out of the question, although Jess did manage to go on geography club outings, which were inexpensive; she saved up and paid for these trips herself from her paper round earnings.

After her marriage to Jack, Dotey had no independent source of income apart from a few precious shillings of family allowance, which was then paid only for second and subsequent children. She was supposed to receive a certain amount of housekeeping money from her husband, but this was very often reduced according to Jack's whim. If he considered that the housework had not been satisfactorily completed that week, or if the meals had not been cooked to the standard he required, Dotey was punished by means of a reduction in the amount of her housekeeping. These deductions were often imposed quite arbitrarily, because Jack had spent the money in the pub or at the races. It was not unknown for him to treat everyone, strangers included, to a drink on the way home while Dotey was at her wits' end with money worries. She had a system of biscuit tins, kept under her bed, each one designated for a different fund – Bobby's Department Store account, the Wesleyan and General insurance, the wireless licence; however, each tin often contained simply an IOU made out to another tin.

Jess once came into the living room to hear her father telling her mother that the housekeeping was to be reduced by ten shillings that week. Her mother entreated that the amount should be reinstated, since there were a number of bills due, but Jack refused. Jess, aged eleven, tried to assist, by adding her pleas to Dotey's, but received no thanks. Jack rounded on her, saying that she should never, ever, interfere between husband and wife. ("That's a lesson you'd better learn right now, my girl!") while Dotey also told her to stay out of the argument. ("This has nothing to do with you!")

In desperation, Dotey took a job as a barmaid at a local pub, but the few shillings she earned were deducted, penny for penny, from the housekeeping allowance she received from Jack. She was obliged to tell him exactly what she was paid, since the law then regarded a wife's earnings as belonging to her husband, and he was responsible for declaring her wages on his tax return. At the time, it was not uncommon for wives to have not the least idea what their husbands earned, and certainly, Dotey never knew what amount of money Jack took from the agricultural merchants business. However, Jack did not care for his wife working in a public house, since this brought her into contact with other men, with whom she could share a joke as she pulled pints, so she had to leave the pub and work instead as a lowly-paid, part-time assistant in a dress shop. The only way in which a woman could achieve financial independence was by becoming widowed, living apart from her husband, or by embracing spinster-hood from the outset; and it was this latter course which Dotey continually urged upon her daughter as being the preferable option.

Dotey had just cause to resent the treatment of women's wages, since she had missed out on her post-war credits. The wartime government had imposed extra income tax, with the promise that this would be repaid after the emergency was over. The repayment programme dragged on for more than twenty years, and during the 1960s, Dotey began to hear of people receiving their post-war credits. She applied for hers, only to be told that the credits had in fact been repaid to Albert, her husband during the war, who had apparently pocketed the money without even informing her. Legally, the money was his, and there was no way he could have been obliged to hand it over, although morally of course it belonged to Dotey. Dotey was devastated; she was so desperately hard up, while Albert was comfortably off. The system was totally unjust, since she had worked like everyone else to help the war effort. Dotey began to lecture Jess at every opportunity regarding the iniquity and folly of marriage. She insisted that Jess should concentrate all her energies on having a career instead of ever getting married; marriage brought only servitude and heart-break.

"But won't you want grandchildren?" asked Jess.

"Of course I will, but the boys will provide them! There's absolutely no need for you to marry; you're bright – you could go far; to university even; become a teacher – then a headmistress! You can have your own life, your own money, your independence, long holidays, travel…"

Jess was not sure she liked the sound of this independent life, even with the prospect of nephews and nieces to comfort her. Becoming a headmistress was not something to which she aspired, she did not think she would be good at enforcing discipline, with all that scolding and caning…

Before Dotey and Jack married, Jess and Peter had received sixpence a week pocket money (2½ pence equivalent in decimal money) for which they were expected to do certain chores, such as wiping and putting away dishes and helping make the beds. They were sometimes allowed to call at neighbours' houses asking for 'any empties' – discarded pop bottles, on which there was a threepence deposit. Their weekly pocket-money was later increased to a shilling (five pence) until the collapse of Jack's business when it became necessary for the children to earn their own money. Jeff (who had come to live with the family in 1963) and Peter had morning paper-rounds for Smith's, while Jess was a Saturday girl there. She had originally been promised a job in a sweetshop run by one of Dotey's friends; however, a few weeks before Jess's fifteenth birthday Mamie engaged a new girl, telling a mightily offended Dotey that she had been unable to keep the job open for another month until Jess attained the legal minimum age for employment. Dotey then approached Miss Thomas, the Sunday School principal, who had worked at Smiths for many years, and secured the Saturday job for Jess. Jess also began babysitting for Dotey's Dramatic Society friends, where the going rate for an evening's babysitting was five shillings, increasing to six shillings if the parents returned after midnight. Demand for Jess's services increased sharply when the Dramatic Society was putting on a play.

Jess enjoyed the babysitting, since unlike her own family, Dotey's friends all had warm houses and often television sets, and the children were generally good. However, she did not really like working at Smith's. It was hard for her to be stuck in the shop every Saturday, while her friends were out in the town, enjoying themselves in the Tudor Rose café or Macari's coffee bar. They would wave at her as they passed the shop. Then there was the manager, a fussy little bespectacled man with a bristly moustache, who insisted that his staff should look busy at all times. This meant continually dusting the bookshelves during slack periods. Jess protested that she had dusted the shelves twice that morning already when she saw the manager approaching her, brandishing his feather duster. He had a horrid habit of tightly squeezing Jess's elbow while dragging her towards the shelves, hissing, "Miss; Miss; dust!" Nowadays, this would constitute work-place harassment, but nobody batted an eyelid at the time, although Jess, nursing a sore elbow, often thought there should be a law against it. Jess earned two shillings and two pence per hour, resulting, after a full day's work, in a gross wage of fourteen shillings and a penny; however, there was a compulsory deduction of three pence for National Insurance. Jess was outraged to discover that the manager's son, also aged fifteen, was paid two shillings and five pence per hour, qualifying for the extra three pence simply because he was a boy. Often he was given a light duty, such as sweeping the floor, while Jess was told to drag a delivery of heavy Christmas annuals up to the stock-room. Jess, straining at her task, had to endure the sight of the manager's son leaning on his brush and smirking at her as she went about her arduous work.

One Saturday in the summer of 1966 the shop was unusually quiet. The time dragged, and Jess was obliged to dust the bookshelves seven times. The manager kept nipping out of the shop for protracted spells; Jess wondered where he kept going, so watched him out of the door, duster in hand. He had not gone far, and could be seen a few doors down, watching the television screens in Curry's window. No need to ask where everyone was; England was playing West Germany in the World Cup Final. A mere twenty-one years after the end of World War Two, feelings still ran high against Germany, especially among the generation who had lived through the war, and Jack in particular often expressed the opinion that the 'only good German is a dead one.' Five-thirty finally came – time for Jess to leave work. To her surprise, her mother was there to meet her. As they walked past Curry's they were aware that the match was still in progress, having gone to extra time, so they lingered on the pavement, watching the bank of flickering black and white screens, until finally it was all over. England had defeated Germany, as everyone in Tiverton and the entire country thought only right and proper.

Jess was asked to go potato digging one October half term; she was paid two pounds for an afternoon's work, while men working on the same machine received two pounds ten shillings. The machine did the actual digging, while the workers were required to discard the rotten potatoes and any stones that were churned up. The main qualifications were the possession of sharp eyes and nimble fingers, and Jess considered that the women worked equally as well as the men, if not better, for a lower wage. It would be another decade before Equal Pay legislation was finally enacted.

Chapter 31

One of the girls who worked at W.H Smith, Pam, had her eye on Jeff. She often lay in wait for him to collect the papers for his morning round, and when she discovered that the new Saturday girl was Jeff's sister, she immediately resolved to cultivate a friendship with Jess. To this end, she discovered where the family lived, and announced that she would call for Jess one evening, to go for a walk. Jess felt rather sorry for plain Pam, although she did not especially care for her, and knew that the real object of her visit would be to see Jeff. She tried to make an excuse about having a lot of homework to do that week, but Pam waved this aside.

"Now the evenings is so light, 'twould be guid for 'ee to get some nice fresh air. I'll see 'ee Toosday, six o'clock."

Accordingly, Pam presented herself on the doorstep the following Tuesday, casually asking if Jeff was at home.

"I'm not sure," said Jess, her heart sinking, since she had just seen Jeff disappearing into the kitchen. Jess asked Pam to wait while she fetched her walking shoes. She reached behind the utility cupboard to retrieve them, only to find a cross-looking Jeff crouching among some cardboard boxes.

"Get rid of her!" mouthed Jeff in desperation. However, Pam was becoming rather fed up with waiting on the doorstep for Jess to be correctly shod, and had made her way uninvited into the living room.

"Wot a luvely voo! Why, 'ee can even see acrowss to the cemetery! We buried me poor Grandpa there last week…"

Jess was afraid Pam might wander into the kitchen, the better to admire the view. Jeff was still crouching in his sanctuary, so Jess quickly told Pam she was ready to go.

"It's so hot; can I 'ave a glass of water before we sets out?"

"Um, yes, I'll get you one, you just wait there for now!"

Jess was obliged to retreat to the kitchen and fetch a cold drink. Such was Jeff's agitation at the delay in the girls' departure for their walk that he knocked over one of the cardboard boxes, which clattered hollowly against the wall.

Pam looked alarmed as Jess handed her the glass of water.

"Wot were that? 'Ere, EE bain't be out there, be 'ee?"

"No, it's just the cat," said Jess, hoping she looked more convincing than she sounded. It was all she could do to stop herself having a fit of the giggles. Felix appeared in the hall, and nonchalantly rubbed against Pam's legs.

"But the cat's 'yere! You sure Jeff bain't be in the kitchen, cos I shouldn't like to think 'ee were 'iding!" said Pam, as Jess hurried her towards the front door.

"Different cat," lied Jess in desperation. "We're looking after the neighbour's as well, while she's away. It likes to hide among the boxes behind the kitchen cupboard."

Pam looked at Jess with contempt, and Jess realised that she did not believe a word of what Jess had said; of course, Jess was not very good at lying. The girls left for their walk without further ado, but Pam never called for Jess again.

Another girl with a crush on Jeff was Eve, a neighbour and trainee hairdresser. Jess was called upon to act as a model, which meant that Eve could practice various cuts and sets, not that there was much material to work with, since Dotey still insisted that, aged fifteen, Jess must keep her hair very short. Eve always wanted to know what Jeff was doing, and since she was brandishing sharp scissors, Jess felt obliged to tell. Jeff did not want anything to do with Eve, since he was going out with a girl from Cullompton. Eve's brother Kevin was supposed to like Jess, although Jess could not see anything in him, he appeared to her to be silent, spotty and charmless. After a summer evening trip to Sandy Bay for a beach-side sausage sizzle with the Church Youth Club, Jess was upset to find that none of her friends would let her sit with them on the coach home; instead they all shook their heads and indicated the bags and coats piled up next to them, leaving Jess obliged to sit on the back seat, the only one which appeared vacant. There to her dismay, she found Kevin in the corner; the whole thing had been planned to trick Jess into sitting with him. Jess perched on the edge of the back seat, right in the middle, so that she could dash forward and throw herself onto one of the piles of coats if Kevin was so foolish as to try anything. Her friends kept surreptitiously glancing back at her, and Jess returned their amused looks with a furious frown. She disliked practical jokes even more than she disliked Kevin, who soon got a job as a trainee manager at Woolworth's.

A friend of Jeff's, grandly named Torquil, but generally known as Twink, called one evening to ask Dotey if he could escort Jess to the fair; Dotey agreed, on condition that Jeff also went along as chaperone. Jeff groaned, saying that he did not want to play gooseberry, and quickly ran to fetch a delighted Eve to make up a foursome, there being no time to get his girlfriend over from Cullompton. Jess enjoyed the fair, but was not especially keen on Twink, so that when he asked her to go out one evening the following week, she gave him the time-honoured excuse that she was staying in to wash her hair. Soon, the O level results came out, and Jess's were the best in the school. She decided she had finally earned the right to grow her hair, declining to act henceforth as Eve's model, so no more unbecoming cuts and sets for Jess, just what Dotey disparagingly referred to as 'curtains' of hair to her shoulders – and no more fringe! Jess also decided that, at sixteen and a half, she could at last go out when she pleased. Dotey's mantra, "you won't pass your exams if you go gadding about!" was now meaningless; she had passed spectacularly. So Jess was allowed out, but with an appropriate curfew in place. The other penalty she was obliged to endure in exchange for this concession was that she had to report to Dotey every detail of the evening before she could be allowed to go to sleep. Dotey would come and sit uninvited on the end of Jess's bed and carefully question her in minute detail about her outing. What time had she got there? Who else was there? What did she have to drink? Who did she talk to? Had she danced with anyone – if so, who? What time had she left? Which route had she taken home? Who had accompanied her? It was no good a weary Jess saying she could not remember, that she simply wanted to be allowed to go to sleep, for Dotey would only exhort her to think harder and recollect all these details, which might be trifling to Jess but were seemingly important to Dotey. Jess was baffled as to why her mother required chapter and verse of her evening, but it later dawned on her that Dotey wanted to be certain that Jess had not had time to get up to any mischief, so every minute must therefore be accounted for. On the one occasion when Jess returned very late from a party, with her hair all over the place and her clothes awry, Dotey was unimpressed with the explanation that the car in which Jess had been getting a lift home had broken down and the passengers had been required to push it all the way to the top of the next hill in order to restart it.

"You must think I was born yesterday!" exclaimed Dotey, refusing to accept Jess's explanation for her untidy state. "You've been up to no good, you little liar – just admit it!"

Jess was astonished and upset that her mother would not accept that she was telling the truth. Jess had been brought up never to lie, since Dotey insisted that she would always find her out if she did not tell the truth. At this stage Jess knew nothing about her own origins in the back of Jack's Vauxhall in a secluded lay-by in Stoke Woods, so could have no inkling of the dread that old cars held for her mother, and the possibilities for illicit behaviour which they afforded. Dotey thought Jess's innocence an act; but Jess was far from being the accomplished actress Dotey was.

Chapter 32

An estate of new houses had been built on Canal Hill, and Jack suggested that the children should start an evening paper round. Neither of the established newsagents was interested in delivering the 'Express and Echo' so far out of the town. Accordingly, the children canvassed the new estate, and signed up a fair number of customers, enough for two manageable rounds. Arrangements were made with the 'E and E' to send up an extra packet of papers on the teatime bus from Exeter. The two regular newsagents also took delivery of their papers in this way, and the bus driver would have two large and one rather small package to throw off the bus in Newport Street. One of the children would meet the bus after school and collect the papers, which were then delivered around the new estate.

The 'E and E' wholesale price was two pence ha'penny, and the cover price was four pence. The profit on each copy was therefore a penny ha'penny. The paper was published every day except Sunday, so a full week's worth cost each customer two shillings. The children were advised to levy a delivery charge, which they set at the extremely low price of one penny per week. Some people paid exactly two and a penny on Saturdays, but others generously handed the children half a crown (two shillings and sixpence) and told them to keep the change. Any tips were pooled, and the assortment of coins was counted every Saturday teatime. The wholesale cost of the papers was handed to Dotey to keep in one of her biscuit tins under the bed, while the profit was split equally between the children. The amount each received was slightly more than the meagre set wage for doing a paper-round for an established newsagent, so the children were quite pleased with their venture.

The 'Express and Echo' sent their representative every month to collect the money. He was a cheery gentleman with a florid complexion, whom Dotey described as looking like a 'proper toper'. He did not seem to mind counting out the assortment of coins, so long as they totalled the correct amount, which miraculously they always did. Jess was continually fearful that the amount would be short, because she knew that Dotey would have rifled the paper money tin earlier in the month, in order to pay other bills. Her mother always informed her when she was about to do this, and showed her the IOU to be put in the tin. She then retrieved the money from one of the other tins just before the 'E and E' rep was due, and the whole monthly money-go-round business would begin all over again. The newspaper business lasted several years, until Peter, having proved that there was demand on Canal Hill, and about to go off to Polytechnic, finally sold it on to a local newsagent (including a modest 'goodwill' payment.)

Dotey prided herself on the fact that all her children worked part-time. One summer, Peter had a holiday job cleaning out the Leat, which was drained every year during 'factory fortnight' in order that all the debris such as old bikes and prams could be removed. Dotey also took it upon herself to find Jess summer holiday work as a mother's help for their former neighbour, Mrs. Scott-Maxwell. Jess really did not want to look after young David in the afternoons; after spending every morning helping Dotey with never-nding household chores, she would have welcomed some time to herself. Her mother insisted that she must take the job, since she had already promised Mrs. Scott-Maxwell.

"You could have asked me first!" grumbled Jess. She did not mind baby-sitting for the Scott-Maxwells when David was asleep and she could get on with her homework, although she had been rather disconcerted on arriving at the house on one occasion, only to be told that she would also be granny-sitting for the visiting Mrs. Scott-Maxwell Senior, (octogenarian American writer and philosopher, Florida Scott-Maxwell, petite, snowy haired and dressed in floor-length black.) Luckily for Jess, Granny had given no trouble and had retired to bed at the same time as her little grandson. In view of her additional responsibilities that evening, Jess had received an additional shilling in wages. Jess knew that amusing a lively toddler throughout the long, hot summer afternoons would be a challenging prospect, involving many boisterous games, not to mention being buried in the sandpit. Luckily, it turned out better than Jess had expected, although it was hard work being chased by David around the garden, pushing him on his swing, playing hide and seek, and making endless sandcastles for him to knock down, while Mrs. Scott-Maxwell relaxed in a deckchair with a magazine.

Every autumn, Jack bought the crop of cider apples from the owner of a near-by orchard. The apples were still on the trees, and it was up to Jack to arrange for them to be picked. All weekend leave for the children would be cancelled, and the whole family was obliged to set to and harvest the crop. Jeff and Peter climbed the trees to pick the fruit, while Dotey and Jess searched in the wet grass for the windfalls. Jack's contribution was to direct operations and to load the full sacks into the boot of his car. He delivered the precious crop to the gate, from where it was collected and taken to the cider factory. The late October weather would invariably be chilly and dank, and everyone quickly became dispirited, working in the soggy orchard often in the pouring rain for long days, until dusk fell and Jack finally allowed them all to go home. If the crop was good, the work might extend over the following weekend as well. However, no matter how many hours were worked, the children's final reward for their labours was always a ten shilling note each – fifty pence in decimal money. Dotey received one pound. None of the family ever had any idea of the price for which Jack sold the crop, but of course it was obvious where he spent the proceeds of their labours.

Jacks' agricultural merchants business was failing steadily throughout the 1960s. While it had originally provided employment for Jack and two of his brothers, the number of customers had declined to such an extent that Jack was obliged to let Raymond and Michael go, and to run the ailing business by himself. He blamed large companies which could afford to undercut his prices and which stocked a greater variety of goods. In truth, any business adviser would have flagged up the lack of investment, since Jack had a habit of pocketing all the takings to fund his extravagant lifestyle of drinking, smoking and gambling, instead of investing to improve and modernise the concern.

Each Sunday evening Jack brought out the ledger and tried to balance the books, while Dotey wrote out that week's invoices. Jess's task was to address the envelopes to the customers and stamp them. She was often amused at the lack of detail in addresses given, such as: "Farmer Jones, Tedburn St. Mary", or "E.J. Bye, Rewe." Apparently everyone in Rewe would know where Mr. Bye lived. This was long before post-codes had been dreamed up. Jack commented with increasing frequency that there were "Not too many invoices this week," and Jess was always pleased, because her task would be quickly completed, and she would then be free to go out and see her friends. However, when once she innocently said "Oh, good," Jack glared at her, and Dotey shot her a warning glance, followed by a sigh, since the paucity of invoices meant of course that there would be even less money coming into the household.

Despite being a poor provider, Jack was extremely heavy-handed in his use of groceries. Dotey stopped buying instant coffee since Jack insisted on using a dessert-spoon rather than simply a teaspoon to make a single cup, so that a tin of Nescafe lasted no time at all. The family generally drank tea, but visitors always seemed to expect coffee. Jess protested that she could no longer invite her friends if there was no coffee to serve them, so Dotey hit upon the solution of hiding the coffee tin in her stocking drawer, where Jack was unlikely to look, rather than keeping it in the kitchen cupboard. Jess could therefore make coffee for her friends, so long as Jack was out, and she later made sure to replace the Nescafe tin among the stockings. Jack also expected the best quality food, even though he gave his wife so little on which to manage. It was not uncommon for him to refuse what Dotey had prepared for him if he felt that she had economised in any way, perhaps by buying a cheaper cut of meat. He would rise from the table and announce that he simply could not eat it. "Dotey – remember, I'm an 'epicure', I possess an educated palate and can have only of the best." This often led to Dotey having to cook two meals, such as steak and new potatoes for her epicure husband, while the rest of the family ate stewed scrag end of lamb with old potatoes, such was Jack's position as family patriarch.

One of Jess's friends left school early and went to work in the National Provincial bank. This was where Dotey banked, and Jess was rather startled when Andrew remarked casually that her mother had very little in her current account, only fifteen shillings in fact. Privately, Jess was surprised to learn that Dotey had even as much as this, but she was worried that Andrew might be telling all and sundry about Dotey's financial circumstances. When she mentioned Andrew's comments to Dotey, her mother was understandably furious, and made an early appointment to see the manager, who happened to be Andrew's father. She received a fulsome apology, and Andrew quickly learned the importance of customer confidentiality.

Dotey finally left Jack in 1970, moving to a flat in the town centre and finding a part-time job in the Accounts Department of the brewery. She was able to claim a state benefit called Family Income Supplement, since Peter was still at school, and she also received some rent allowance. Dotey was at long last free and independent. However, even with her own income, she discovered that she was not able to rent a television set without a male guarantor. Her sons were students and so did not satisfy the criteria laid down by the rental company. Dotey named her cousin on Dartmoor as her only eligible male relative. The TV rental company said she could keep the set over the Christmas holidays while they wrote to him. However, in the New Year, they received a reply, stating that the cousin was not willing to act as guarantor for the rental, so they promptly arranged to repossess Dotey's television set, even though the payments were up to date. It was not until later in the decade that the law was changed so that women were entitled to be treated no less favourably than men with regard to the provision of goods and services, and sadly, Dotey did not live long enough to witness this. She would have rejoiced to see Jess, in her own home, financed by a mortgage on the same terms as those offered to men in similar circumstances, for Jess had indeed become a teacher and for a few short years was living Dotey's dream. Jess was among the first generation of women to benefit from sex equality legislation, so much taken for granted in the twenty-first century that Dotey's story now reads like a quaint episode from a long-ago era, almost a nineteenth century Dickensian tale, rather than being from a time well within living memory.

Chapter 33

As Jess progressed through her teenage years, her mother began to allow her to go out to certain approved events, provided that she had been told exactly where Jess was going, and had extracted a promise that Jess would be back no later than the time Dotey stipulated. Dotey's check-list included details of exactly what and where the event was, who else was going, the route Jess should take to get there and back, what time it would finish and when to expect Jess home. Once Jess was late home, because she had stopped to shelter from a heavy shower in a shop doorway. Her mother was cross, although Jess thought she had simply been sensible in avoiding a soaking. The next day Dotey presented Jess with a plastic folded rain-hood, decorated with tiny umbrellas, of the type favoured by elderly ladies to cover their perms; she decreed Jess must henceforth carry this bonnet in her bag at all times and wear if it came on to rain, rather than risk being late home. Jess's friends all declared that they would refuse to wear such an item, and would prefer to be wet through. But would they want to endure the sharp end of Dotey's tongue, Jess wondered, as she dutifully donned her rain-hood so as not be delayed on her way home during the next downpour.

Jess was permitted to help at the weekends with catering for the school rugby and cricket teams, providing pies after rugby matches and afternoon tea for the cricket matches. Rugby teas were so much easier, thought Jess, as she cut piles of sandwiches and buttered mountains of scones for the cricketers. The rugby matches were over after an hour and a half, and the boys ate up quickly, so that everything could be cleared away by lunchtime, leaving the whole afternoon free. With cricket, the match could go on all afternoon, and of course there were so many fiddly dishes of cakes to set out, plus gallons of tea to be made in enormous urns and poured into cups which would then require washing up. Disposable crockery would have been thought extravagant – why should the school spend extra money on plastic cups when there were willing girls to cater and clear away? Jess and her friend Judy could not help but notice that the boys who came and thanked them afterwards were usually from visiting public schools, whereas their own classmates from the Grammar school generally wolfed down the food and retuned their plates without comment. They seemed to think it was their right to be fed. The games master always thanked the girls, as well he might, since they were giving up their Saturdays to voluntarily prepare masses of food for mostly ungrateful lads. Jess gave up the catering when she started her job at WH Smiths and Judy found someone else to help.

Sunday school teaching was another activity which Jess was permitted to do, and she was assigned a class of unruly older boys. The idea was that everyone would meet in church for the first part of the service, and then the Sunday school would leave during the second hymn, crossing the road to the church hall where the lessons were held. Each pupil would be given a picture stamp relating to a Bible story, which they could stick in their books to copy and write a sentence about. Jess talked about the picture first, and tried to encourage the boys to contribute, but it was very hard maintaining their attention, since often they really wanted to do nothing more than kick each other under the table. None of them chose to come to Sunday School, but their parents insisted they must attend. Even after Jess had carefully explained the task in hand, the boys complained that they did not know what they were meant to be doing, or dropped crayons to provide a distraction, or were always rushing to the bin to unnecessarily sharpen pencils. It was all too much for their teenage teacher, and Jess seriously began to doubt the wisdom of teaching as her career choice. The Superintendent, Miss Thomas, came round at the end to collect the books, and often commented that Jess's pupils had not achieved very much. She herself presided over a class of tractable little girls, who wrote and drew without fuss, and generally did what they were told.

One Sunday, when Jess and her Sunday-school pupils arrived in church, it was announced that the service was to take the form of Holy Communion instead of the usual Morning Prayer. Some of the older children who were going to start confirmation classes quite soon asked Jess if they could remain in church instead of attending Sunday-school, so that they would know what to expect at a Communion service. They would sit quietly at the back and observe. Accordingly, when the rest of the children went across to the church hall during the second hymn, Jess held on to those children who had expressed an interest in staying in church. She had not been near enough to Miss Thomas to explain, but had whispered the proposed change in arrangements to her colleague Janet, who was sitting nearby. Janet agreed it was a good idea, and said she would take those of Jess's class who did not want to stay in church across to the church hall with her girls, leaving three of her own soon-to-be-confirmed pupils with Jess.

The half-dozen pupils who remained in church with Jess were very pleased to have witnessed Holy Communion, and thanked Jess for letting them stay. However, as soon as the service was over, Miss Thomas came storming back into church to find Jess. She was furious, even though Janet had explained to her what was happening. Since Jess and Janet taught the older pupils, including all of those who were shortly to begin confirmation class, Jess had not thought their arrangement would matter to Miss Thomas, as it did not affect her little girls. She had not expected to be torn off a strip so publicly – and in church too! She was scarlet with shame and did not know where to look. Her up-bringing at the hands of Dotey made it impossible for her to try to defend herself, since it was forbidden to argue with or question adults, who always knew best. However, it so happened that the Diocesan Sunday School Advisor was present, he was a fair-minded man and did not care to see Jess so humiliated. He approached Jess and warmly praised her, saying that in his opinion, she had shown laudable initiative and he was sure her actions had benefited the pupils who were about to prepare for confirmation. The Diocese really could do with more Sunday school teachers like Jess. Miss Thomas was silenced. Of course, all this being told off and subsequently praised had delayed Jess, so that she was late home for her Yorkshire pudding-making duties. She explained to Dotey why she was late, but her mother seemed unimpressed with her excuse.

"Really, Jess I've warned you before about not taking things upon yourself! It's not for you to decide what the Sunday school children should do, that's surely up to Miss Thomas and I can well understand why she was so cross."

"But I was using my initiative, to help the confirmation candidates. They wanted to stay in church."

"Humph, it really doesn't become young girls to use their initiative – so much better to do as you are told! You really are quite pig-headed sometimes! Now, quickly with mixing that batter, it's time the Yorkshires were in the oven!"

"But the Diocesan Adviser said…"

"Never mind what he said, it's Miss Thomas who runs that Sunday school, so it's her opinion that counts! Now, is that batter ready? More beating and less talking required from you, Jess! You know your father will be furious if there's no Yorkshire pudding to serve with the beef, so look sharp!"

Jess was very unhappy about this incident, since she had recently heard Jack praising Peter for using his initiative. This was apparently yet another aspect of behaviour which was deemed appropriate for boys but not girls, yet no-one seemed to be protesting about the unfairness of it. Dotey's small-town mentality, far from uncommon at the time, decreed that daughters must be kept under close control, their behaviour continually monitored, and any sign of a girl stepping out of line must immediately be stamped upon; otherwise any mother was simply asking for trouble.

Chapter 34

By far the most onerous household task was the cooking, which of course had to be done every day. Jack was so particular about his food that Dotey was generally in a state of high anxiety at tea-time. Would he accept the evening meal she had prepared, or would he take a mouthful and declare it inedible and retire to his arm-chair with a martyred expression and the 'Express and Echo'? Sunday lunch was the worst meal of all, because Jack himself would have chosen and paid for the joint, often at great expense, perhaps even as much as 24 shillings! He liked beef to be very rare in the centre, and refused point blank to eat overdone meat. The problem was that he was often late home from the pub on Sunday lunchtimes, so Dotey was faced with the difficult task of keeping the food hot without overcooking it. Jess was instructed to come straight home after Sunday school in order to make Yorkshire pudding, and of course, this was another dish that did not take kindly to being kept waiting. Therefore Sunday lunchtime became an ordeal for both mother and daughter, because the food was never as Jack liked it. He insisted on having vegetables served in separate tureens, rather than dished up straight from the pan onto the warm plates, so the sprouts and carrots inevitably cooled, and steam condensed on the lids of the dishes. ("These vegetables aren't properly drained!") Every Sunday, Dotey begged him to arrive back home at a specified time and attend to the veg himself, so that he would know it had been sufficiently strained, leaving her free to see to the meat. As for the Yorkshire pudding, Jess always knew that it would be somehow wrong – too heavy, insufficiently risen, or over-risen and collapsed; not brown enough, or over-cooked and burnt around the edges. Jack raged that she would have to hone her cooking skills if she was ever to find a husband, and that she should take much more care with food preparation. Jess wanted to say that any husband of hers would have the consideration to appear on time for Sunday lunch, but of course, she did not, she was too afraid of her father to answer back to him. Such was the tension around the Sunday lunch table that the meal usually passed in gloomy silence after Jack had issued his tirade of unhelpful comments. Dotey and Jess sat cowed and mute, stung by Jack's criticism of their best culinary endeavours, while Jeff and Peter maintained a sympathetic silence. The boys did however make sure to always thank and compliment their mother at the end of the meal, in defiance of whatever Jack had said.

Sometimes, much to Dotey's relief, Jack brought a joint of pork, which it would be practically impossible to overcook, although there was always the matter of scoring and salting the crackling correctly so that it crisped up. Jess would also be pleased, since an accompaniment of Yorkshire pudding was not required, only apple sauce, which was easy enough to make. A leg of lamb called for mint sauce, Jess chopping the leaves from the garden very finely and stirring them with vinegar; while chicken was easiest of all, since the stuffing Dotey served came out of a packet. However, chicken was a relatively rare and expensive treat in those days. Dotey never made a hot pudding; winter or summer, she simply opened a tin of fruit for dessert, a rotation of peaches, pears, apricots or fruit salad. All her efforts went into cooking the main course, and she resented having to spend her Sunday mornings 'slaving over a hot stove'. Afterwards, there was all the washing-up to be done, piles of greasy plates and pans, plus the hated vegetable dishes, so that it would be gone three o'clock before Dotey and Jess were released from the kitchen and could go out for a walk.

Jess dreaded visitors coming to tea, since Dotey would require her to bake. ("Just *knock up* a few scones, Jess," or "I'll need you to quickly *whip up* a sponge." Jess wondered why baking techniques always seemed to employ such aggressive language.) Dotey herself never baked except for pastry, she always bought in cakes and biscuits; but once Jess had been taught baking at school she was expected to produce something home-made and delicious. Jess's scones were usually light, but she did not find sponges at all easy. There were two methods, one involving creaming sugar and butter, while the more tricky fat-less version meant whipping the eggs and sugar until her arm ached, before lightly folding in the sifted flour. She did not have the use of an electric mixer, so everything had to be done by hand. For some reason, the cake usually failed when visitors were due, it would scarcely have risen, although it might taste all right. Dotey would hold an apologetic inquest; the eggs could not have been really fresh, or perhaps Jess had not beaten the mixture for long enough, or maybe the oven was slow – such a pity, since her last sponge cake had risen perfectly. The visitors were always embarrassed, Jess would be cringing, and the tea-party atmosphere blighted by the cake autopsy. If Jack happened to be present, he would feel duty-bound to offer his considered opinion as to why the cake had failed. Apparently, a chef friend at the Conservative Club knew all there was to know about cake baking, and after a previous failure, Jack had taken it upon himself to consult this gentleman on the matter of sponge cakes. The chef had decreed that the flour must always be dried thoroughly in the oven on a very low heat for several hours, preferably overnight, before attempting a sponge. Jess had never having heard of this technique, her cookery teacher had not mentioned it as being a pre-requisite for a Victoria sandwich, and anyway, it sounded quite dangerous – suppose the flour caught fire in the night and set the kitchen alight? Jack always insisted she make another cake, "If at first you don't succeed, try, try, try, again," was his motto so far as his daughter was concerned, although he did not seem to want to apply it to himself, thought Jess, recalling her father's business, sinking into its overdraft.

"I made the jam!" Jess would suddenly remember in the midst of the dreary tea-party, in an attempt to move the conversation on; jam was her strongest point, whether strawberry, raspberry, blackcurrant or gooseberry, all the fruit from Jack's kitchen garden was jammed in the days before domestic freezers became available. The visitors always praised the jam, which even Jack could not fault.

Jack was adamant that Jess's shortcomings must always be pointed out to her, or else she would never improve. He believed that praise made children complacent, causing them to rest lazily on their laurels, while criticism would spur them on to greater success. However, Jess found her father's endless critiquing simply disheartening. He seldom gave her credit for any achievement, never considering her scholastic accomplishments as being in any way worthy of note, choosing instead to focus on those areas where she was least able, such as cookery or sport.

It did not occur to Jess until many years later that in fact her father might have been jealous of the opportunities she now had; that he who had been obliged to leave elementary school at twelve might resent the fact that his daughter was receiving a free Grammar School education and could even go on to university if she chose, or indeed was permitted to. Parents were said always to want what is best for their children, but it seemed to Jess that Jack was the exception to this rule. As it was, Jack made it clear that he was allowing Jess to stay on at school until she was sixteen as a generous concession, so that she could sit her O levels, which would then increase her chances of obtaining a decent job. She was to put any nonsense about going to university right out of her head, since he was not prepared to keep her when she should be out earning money for the family. Besides, any higher education would inevitably be wasted on a girl; Jack simply could not see what benefit a university education could possibly bring Jess, when she would no doubt be getting married one day, despite her mother's protestations to the contrary. Jack recognised that Jess was plain and awkward and not much of a cook; but even so, some plain and awkward man who was prepared to put up with indifferent food and was not clever or rich or attractive enough to get anyone better might at some point be glad to make do with her. Just as Jess was amongst the last to be picked for school sports teams, so she would in all probability be lagging behind in the marriage stakes, in her father's opinion – unless her cooking quickly improved.

Chapter 35

Despite her success with jam, domestic science was actually Jess's weakest subject, along with PE. She won prizes for Latin, geography and history, and achieved good marks in English, French, music, art and RE. Even maths and science were more than satisfactory. A school science inspector had once visited Mr. Pike's class and commented approvingly on the level of the girls' involvement in the science experiments. On this particular occasion Jess had added the wrong chemical, or maybe the right chemical at the wrong time or in the wrong proportion, and created such a choking stink that she and several other female classmates had rushed out of the lab door onto the hockey pitch to escape the fumes. This apparently was fine, since at some other schools the girls did not even attempt science experiments, so Mr. Pike had received a commendation for the enthusiastic contribution of the girl pupils. Usually, it was Mr Clegg's class that could be seen retreating from the Chemistry lab onto the hockey pitch, since although Mr. Clegg taught Chemistry, his degree was unaccountably in history. Jess always found it a little disconcerting to see Jeff and his classmates spilling out onto the grass from the Chemistry lab next door, stopping only at a safe distance from the building, some covering their faces, some pinching their noses against a foul stink, and others with their hands over their ears as if to guard against an imminent explosion, quickly followed by Mr. Clegg in a state of some agitation. Meanwhile Mr. Pike simply sighed and told Jess's class to carry on with their work as normal.

In Maths, Jess had to concentrate hard; she laboured over algebra, calculus and trigonometry, but did surprisingly well with geometry. Arithmetic was taught by Mr. Timms, who one day threw a wooden board-rubber at Jess, asking her to repeat what he had just said. Fortunately, the object missed Jess, clattering onto the floor nearby. Mr. Timms looked abashed when Jess answered him word-perfectly. "You looked to me like you were day-dreaming, Frances!" he muttered, in an attempt to justify his violence. For some reason, he always confused her with a girl who did not resemble Jess in any way, since Frances had long fair hair and wore glasses. Jess thought it was Mr. Timms who was not paying attention, but did not dare to say anything. Answering back to a teacher, even one who unjustifiably threw the board-rubber, was punishable by after-school detention, and Jess did not want to risk making herself late for her paper-round.

It was just Jess's bad luck that the only one of her school subjects in which Jack took any interest was Domestic Science. Every week he would ask what she had made, and he was generally extremely critical of the choice of dish. ("Raspberry buns? Whatever good is that? You should be learning how to cook good roast dinners, my girl, I've a mind to come into school and tell them!") Jess explained that she had no control over the recipes selected by the teacher. However, she was quite sure that Jack would not complain at school, since he never attended any of the Parents' Evenings. Jess herself disliked many of the recipes, she was not particularly keen on rice pudding and she especially recoiled at the prospect of preparing soused herrings. Her friend Jackie had actually been sick when this dish was being demonstrated and the fish had been gutted in front of the girls in an overheated classroom. The worst lesson was when the pupils were shown how to draw a chicken. Jess was simply unable to watch, while around her, several other girls were fainting. It was always warm in the cookery room, and the chicken did not smell very fresh. The teacher, Mrs. Lamb, had delved in and retrieved some un-laid eggs from an interior cavity of the bird, which made Jess feel queasy. Surely a butcher would prepare a chicken for his customers, thought Jess. She always worked at a table near the door, opposite Jackie, the disadvantage being that the two girls had to act as door monitors for Mrs. Lamb's cocker spaniels. Unbelievably, the teacher was permitted to keep the two dogs, Polly and Pogo, in a basket next to her desk. They had the run of the cookery room, and it was not uncommon for someone to discover a dog hair in her saucepan during the moulting season. Concentrating on her short-crust pastry recipe, Jess, wearing ankle-socks, was distracted by Polly licking her legs, while the other dog stood nearby wildly barking at her.

"Door, Jess, quickly! Poor Pogo needs the hockey pitch!" Mrs. Lamb called imperiously across the room, so Jess had to hastily take her sticky hands from the mixing bowl, wipe them on a dishcloth, and open the door. Pogo's face later appeared at the glass panel of the outer door, barking to be let back in, so Jess had to stop work again. She was getting behind with her mixing, and this was made worse because she had been obliged to use self-raising flour instead of the recommended plain. Dotey did not keep plain flour in, and she refused to buy anything extra just for Jess's cookery lessons. The recipe stated only one teaspoon of water to each ounce of flour to mix the pastry, but try as she might, Jess could not get it to bind together. She surreptitiously added more water, realising that self-raising flour seemed to be more absorbent than plain. The mixture was then much too wet, so she had to tip in more flour. The girls had been instructed to bring margarine and lard, but Dotey would not buy margarine, declaring that the dreadful stuff reminded her of the war, so Jess had to use a mixture of half butter and half Cookeen. When it came to rolling out, everything stuck to the rolling pin or the table and had to be scraped off. The lesson was turning into a nightmare. The next problem was getting the pie-crust to fit the dish, since it was decreed that there should be no waste, the teacher even going to the lengths of inspecting the rubbish bins, the girls' bags and even their pockets during a previous pastry lesson, looking for signs of discarded trimmings, so that anyone who had not rolled out their pastry exactly was obliged to eat raw leftovers in order to avoid a telling-off.

At the end of the lesson the pies were placed on wire trays to cool. Mrs. Lamb tasted Jackie's pie, and pronounced it very good. Next, she turned her attention to Jess's effort.

"You've used *self-raising flour*! I can taste it! And the texture's not right either. Have you used *butter*? What did the recipe say? Yes, to use plain flour, lard and margarine! You've disobey my instructions!"

Mrs. Lamb interrupted her tirade to pause for breath, and Jackie took the opportunity to speak up.

"But Mrs. Lamb, I used self-raising flour." Her voice was steady, even though she knew she was deliberately putting herself in harm's way in order to support her friend.

Jess almost vaulted over the table to hug Jackie. How brave it was of her to own up to using the forbidden white stuff when her pastry had not only passed inspection, but had even been praised. Mrs. Lamb was looking incredulous.

"There was no taste of it, and I can always tell which type of flour has been used!"

"Mum didn't have any plain flour in, but she didn't think it would matter." Jackie continued. Everyone in the class was impressed with the stand she was taking in support of Jess, and waited to see what would happen next.

"But of course it matters! You have to be taught the correct method or there's no point! Jess, this pastry is a mess, you certainly wouldn't pass any exam with a pie like this."

Jess felt miserable, it was now time to clear up, and the pie was unlikely to elicit any praise from her father that evening. Her classmates, emboldened by Jackie's stance, all came to taste Jess's pie, and pronounced it delicious.

"I'm always going to use butter and self-raising flour in future," said Lyn. "This pastry tastes much nicer than mine. And there was a dog-hair in Anna's pie, but Mrs. Lamb didn't say anything because of her precious animals."

Back home, Dotey was not impressed with the dishevelled half-eaten pie, which she had been planning to serve for Jack's tea that evening. She grumbled about not being able to afford to waste good ingredients if the results were so indifferent, before quickly having to set to and make a fresh pie for Jack. Dotey's pastry was always light and tasty, she used self-raising flour and butter, and did not fiddle around with miserly teaspoons of water but took the mixing bowl straight to the cold tap, adding water in a casual manner such as would have given Mrs. Lamb an apoplectic fit. Trimmings were re-rolled and formed into a leaf decoration for the pie-crust. Dotey, in her turn, was horrified to hear that the teacher's dogs had been present during the lesson, since in her opinion, an animal's place was out of doors.

Jess began to realise that cookery was less an exact science, more a very individual art. She began to dread cookery days, it seemed that there was always some sort of disaster. Her ginger-cake erupted like a treacly volcano and stuck to the top of the oven, possibly because she had used rather too much bicarbonate of soda. Then her rock buns somehow escaped from their tin in her bicycle basket and rolled all the way down Barrington Street, ending up in the gutter close to the river, so that only the ducks would benefit from her culinary efforts that week. Potatoes for the shepherds pie burnt when she allowed the pan to boil dry while attending to the comings and goings of the cocker spaniels, and her cottage loaf had large holes. ("You can't have knocked the dough back sufficiently! Pay more attention!") Her chief success, apart from the jam, for which she had received full marks, was short-bread, the recipe including butter rather than the dreaded margarine. Even so, Jack begrudged his daughter praise: "Man cannot live by afternoon tea alone! Jam! Shortbread! Scones! You tell that teacher of yours, she should be getting you all to make a hearty stew next!" He persisted in trying to catch Jess out, quizzing her about cookery at inappropriate moments, with questions such as whether potatoes should be put in cold water and brought to the boil or placed directly in boiling water. Jess, trying to get to grips with a more than usually difficult Latin unseen, gave the incorrect answer, so Jack snorted contemptuously.

"She doesn't know! A simple thing like that, which any other sensible girl in the town would know at once, but she gets it wrong! Put that silly Latin away, my girl, and do something useful. Make me a cup of tea!"

So despite her many prizes for academic subjects and flower arranging, Jess felt a failure. Her father only wanted her to be good at domestic science, pouring scorn on her other achievements, while her mother demanded that she be outstanding at everything. Her parents were so very hard to please, they just did not seem to be able to accept her as she was, very good at some things and weaker at others. Jess felt under constant pressure; if she achieved high marks one week, Dotey would expect her to do equally well, if not better, the next, or she would face accusations of slacking. She envied her friends whose parents did not mind them coming comfortably in the middle of the class, and were not always fussing that they should have done better.

Dotey knew that Jess was not brilliant ("Of course we've always known she's a plodder in Maths…") However, her mother's theory was that if you worked diligently enough and tried sufficiently hard you would always achieve higher marks then those frivolous children who watched too much television and went gadding about at weekends. Dotey insisted that Jess must be single-minded and apply herself to her studies in a way Dotey had never done. Meanwhile, Jack was of the opinion that Jess's academic work was a complete waste of time and she should be preparing to leave school and get a paid job as soon as she attained the minimum leaving age, which at the time was fifteen. He repeatedly harangued Jess about how much he resented having to keep her 'until she was an old woman', how she should be contributing to the household income rather than being a constant drain on him, a leech-like child costing him money rather than earning a wage. Since all Jess's clothes and most of her shoes came from kind Mrs. Lee's daughter, she slept in an unheated bedroom and received free school lunches, her vests were in holes, and she had had no new underwear for years, Jess really resented being referred to as a leech. She once worked out that her main cost to the family budget was sanitary towels, about which surely even Jack would not dare to complain. However, she realised that it was better to keep quiet on this subject, in case her father ordered her to collect absorbent moss, like women in primitive societies, in order to save precious shillings which could then be diverted to his booze budget.

Of course, aged fifteen, Jack had already taken the King's shilling and was fighting for his country in the East, so it was not surprising that in his opinion modern children lived molly-coddled lives. Jack's ideas about the lack of necessity to educate women seemed to be firmly stuck in the Edwardian era, when some men seriously believed that over-taxing a woman's delicate brain with academic subjects would adversely affect her reproductive system, thereby rendering her unfit to fulfil her true purpose in life.

Dotey of course took the opposite view. It seemed to Jess that there was very little her parents agreed upon these days, except for subjects such as the need to control immigration and their admiration for the MP Enoch Powell. Jess sighed, realising that childhood was something to be endured, a stern test of character stretching ahead for years and years, a period filled with ever-increasing amounts of homework, housework and duty, until final release at age twenty-one (then the age of majority) or eighteen if the young person was lucky enough to get away to university. When people sighed sentimentally and said that childhood was the happiest days of your life, Jess simply refused to believe them. Life surely had to be better than this. This was the single hope that kept Jess going throughout the years of her parents' sulks and rages, nagging and criticism. Things would improve – eventually. She had to believe this.

Chapter 36

Jack had been very good at sport in his youth, and was pleased that Peter was taking after him. Peter enjoyed soccer and rugby and was in various school and house teams. He later went on to play for Tiverton Town football club. In contrast, Jess could not run fast enough to be of very much use in hockey, she was not agile enough to be very proficient at netball, and she lacked the necessary co-ordination for either sport. The only time Jess made it into a house hockey team was when there was a flu virus going round and half the regular team members, plus most of the reserves, were laid low. Whenever teams were picked, Jess expected to be always amongst the last chosen. However, when her father expressed his disappointment with her sporting prowess, she was able to point out to him that she did in fact contribute to the success of the school's sports teams in her own way, by providing the refreshments for the teams after every match and clearing up afterwards.

Every summer the girls had to do athletics, and Jess tried hard to achieve the standard for the Hundred Yards sprint. She even went into school one Saturday morning, because her house, Stuart, was lagging behind the other houses in the tally of standards, and a call had gone out for increased effort on the part of Stuart pupils. The Grammar School houses were named after four royal counterparts, Tudor, Stuart, York and Windsor, a great improvement on those of Heathcoat Juniors, which had honoured four so-called Great Men of Devon, Drake, Raleigh, Hawkins and Grenville. Why a quartet of privateers and slave-traders should be thought 'great' was anyone's guess. The houses at Westfield had been named after the Antarctic explorers, Scott and Shackleton, and Jess had been very relieved to be in Shackleton... Jess was not a runner and could never achieve the 100 yards standard, always missing out by half a second. Strangely enough, the only standard she attained every year was in High Jump. Jess's legs were short in relation to her body size, and she was one of the few girls who approached the bar from the left side rather than the right. The bar was set at 3'6", and somehow Jess managed to get herself over without dislodging it. At least she had contributed one precious point to the Stuart house total.

Summer also brought swimming, and the pupils had to walk in crocodile procession through the town to the open-air baths at the end of Leat Street. The summer term began after the Easter holidays, when the pool water was still extremely cold, and the girls were expected to swim in the chilly water. On arrival, those at the front of the crocodile would note the current water temperature chalked up on a blackboard. "Fifty-four, pass it back!" As the news was relayed down the line, the girls lingering at the back had the chance to disappear around the corner and absent themselves from the swimming lesson should they choose to do so. Water at fifty-four degrees Fahrenheit certainly took Jess's breath away, but this was one occasion when she was glad of her rolls of fat, which provided insulation along the lines of a seal's blubber, so that she quickly became acclimatised while the skinny girls were still shivering.

After the swimming lesson the girls had to quickly dry and dress in the chilly stone-floored, saloon-doored changing rooms. There were no hair-dryers, so those with long tresses became cold on the return trek back to school. Jess was glad for once that Dotey insisted on her always having short hair. If she changed quickly, she was able to buy, for the price of three pence, a cup of hot Bovril or Camp coffee from the grumpy old man who ran the baths; and if she had enough money, she could also get a packet of crisps. These would be plain, with a screw of blue paper containing the salt, since flavoured varieties and ready-salted had yet to be invented. It was the only 'junk-food' Jess ever had, since there was not the range of snacks available then as now.

The baths closed for the winter in September, so the swimming season was short. Unsurprisingly, Jess did not manage to learn to swim until she was twelve, finally achieving a length, with the PE mistress walking along the pool edge carrying a stick with a loop of rope, to which the novice swimmer could cling if she felt it was all too much.

Tennis was rather more fun. Again, the crocodile wound its way through the town centre to the courts behind the Town Hall, where the most enjoyment to be had was in trying to hit the balls over the wire netting into the river. It was not easy to get the ball into the correct space, and Jess's serves often ended up outside the tramlines, but as with everything she persevered. However, just as she was getting the hang of serving, the tennis term came to an abrupt end, and games lessons would be cancelled to make way for exams.

Jess had a problem with her games kit. This was kept in a cloth shoe-bag hanging from a peg in the cloakroom, but frequently when Jess went to put on her Aertex shirt and PE shorts, they were already sweaty and crumpled. Clearly, someone was borrowing her kit without permission. The same thing happened with her hockey boots, which were often wet and muddy when she went to fetch them. There were no school lockers at the time, so anyone could sneak into the cloakroom and take other people's kit. Jess had her suspicions, as a girl in the next class often forgot to bring her kit, and she was roughly the same size as Jess. Jess managed to apprehend Julie red-handed, stuffing Jess's once clean but now sweaty games kit back into her shoe-bag. "Oh, I didn't think you'd mind," said Julie lamely, when challenged. Jess made it clear she minded very much, and more to the point, her mother was furious; so in future Julie considerately rifled someone else's shoe-bag instead.

The boys were obliged to do a cross country, the Velvains run, every March. The girls were on hand to welcome them as they made it, puffed out, red-faced and mud-bespattered, back to the school grounds. However, Jess was becoming anxious about Jeff, who had so far failed to appear. She wondered if he had broken his ankle and was lying in pain under a hedge somewhere. The Headmaster was shooing the girls back indoors. "Boys who take this long to get round the course aren't trying, so don't deserve a welcome!" Jess thought this was hard on those who might genuinely be in difficulties, but the Head explained that Mr. Leaker was going round the course flushing out reluctant runners resting under hedge bottoms or in comfy ditches , so he and the marshals would find anyone who was hurt. Jeff and his pal Ron eventually appeared, as fresh as daisies, having enjoyed a pleasant stroll in the early Spring sunshine.

One activity in which Jess was happy to participate was the sponsored walk held to raise money for a school mini-bus. The walk was twenty-six miles long, up and down steep hills, taking in the villages of Silverton and Butterleigh. Jess borrowed someone's walking boots and obtained promises of a penny a mile from several of the neighbours and her paper-round clients. Jack promised threepence a mile, confident that she would never manage it, while one generous soul even pledged sixpence. It was essential for Jess to complete the walk in order to raise a significant sum of money, and she was determined to do it, but it was exhausting and took all day. Jess was amongst the last group to finally finish, grimly hanging onto the arm of the geography master, finding that her legs hurt more going downhill than up.

Dotey was far from pleased when Jess eventually limped home, her feet covered in red sores and enormous blisters. She roundly scolded her daughter for taking part in such a foolish venture, while applying witch-hazel and plasters to Jess's distressed feet; but Jess had a sense of achievement as she presented an astonished Jack with her authenticated sponsor-sheet and extracted his promised seventy-eight pence. She had actually succeeded in something physical, something other than the 'book-learning' her father so despised. Her sore feet soon healed, her blisters faded, but her sense of pride at her unexpected achievement remained.

Chapter 37

The school timetable allowed for three periods of Activities during the week, when pupils could engage in hobbies or attend clubs. Jess belonged to the Geography Club, which showed slides, invited local speakers, and also organised occasional field trips. Once Mr. Brian Elsworthy from Dotey's Dramatic Society came to show a film he had made about the recently axed Exe Valley Branch Line, and on another occasion an elderly man called Mr. Batt talked about his extensive world travels. He was about to set off on another lengthy tour, but sadly news later came that he had died on board ship and had been buried at sea. The field trips Jess went on took her to Lynton and Lynmouth, Coombe Martin and Ilfracombe, Montecute House, Nunney Castle and Ham Hill in Somerset, and Dartmouth and Slapton Sands. Returning to these locations in later years, Jess thought how lucky she had been to visit such beautiful places, all within fairly easy reach of Tiverton.

Jess was one of a number of school librarians who assisted Miss Gillen, and so was on library duty for one activity period each week, issuing and shelving books, covering new books with sticky-backed plastic, and telling people off if they were making too much noise or using the library inappropriately. It was among the library shelves that Jess experienced her first crush, on fellow librarian Robert, who seemed also to like her; however, he was soon distracted by Laila, another librarian. (This theme of 'love in the library' was to find echo much later in Jess's life and eventually formed the subject of her first novel, *Berringden Brow*.)

The third activity period was on Friday afternoon, and for Jess this always meant Country Dancing. Only girls participated in this activity, it was unknown for any male to be present except for the Deputy Head Mr. Leaker, who ran the club. Out of school, he was also a keen Morris Dancer and Football referee. Jess could not help thinking that his refereeing skills were too frequently put to the test by the galumphing maidens, such as herself, seemingly possessed of two left feet. It was common for Mr. Leaker to resort to climbing onto a chair and blowing his football whistle loudly in exasperation, in an attempt to bring the unruly young ladies to order, when a 'star' had run rampant, a 'basket' untidily disintegrated, or a 'strip the willow' ran amok. Girls were often to be found collapsed in gasping giggling giddy heaps on the floor, with Mr. Leaker shouting at them "Now you don't want to go like that!" while the pianist, a busy local woman named Ruby,who was also the Avon Lady and Akela for the Cubs, had a hard time keeping a straight face. Mr. Leaker would then choose a girl, and lead her round the floor in order to demonstrate the required movement; he was very light on his feet, while dancers such as Jess had a tendency to plod. Because only girls participated it was not always possible to discern who was dancing as a man. Jess's partner, her friend Alison, was considerably taller than her, so always took the man's part, but Jess often got muddled up in the progressive dances, grabbing the wrong girl in error, thinking she was a 'man'.

"What DO you girls get up to in Country Dancing?" asked Mr. Wood in amusement, as Jess and the others trooped back into class for the English lesson, rosy and perspiring, with their socks awry and ties undone. "I've been trying to put some work on the board and could hardly hear myself think with all the noise coming from the Hall. Such sedate, demure young ladies, such as yourselves, could hardly be credited with making such a racket – and look at you all, flushed cheeks, knee socks down around your ankles, hair all over the place… I shall have to have a word with Mr. Leaker about the state he allows you to get into. So very unbecoming for teenage girls! Now, please settle down!"

Despite the unfashionable nature of the activity, folk dancing was to feature in Jess's later life, when she found herself unexpectedly stewarding at Sidmouth Folk Week, chaperoning a visiting troupe of 46 Koreans; this not-to-be-wasted episode was duly written up in her fourth novel.

Dotey permitted Jess to attend any activity organised by the school, being confident that it would be properly organised, so Jess was a regular at poetry evenings and concerts. She also belonged to a church group run by the RE teacher, Mr. Gibson, which travelled to the surrounding villages on Sunday evenings conducting services in dissenting chapels. Often the group outnumbered the congregation, in oddly named places such as Black Dog, Holcombe Rogus or

Nomansland, deep among damp lanes or sodden moorland; Jess formed an impression of a hard core of Hardy-esque ancient country folk, often accompanied by a wheezing harmonium, played by a spinster of indeterminate age, keeping the faith in the depth of rural Wessex, with some incongruous assistance from the school group with their guitars, modern prayers and new-fangled up-beat hymns.

As a school prefect, Jess exhorted the lower-school to knit hundreds of six inch square woollen blankets for Oxfam, and she herself spent hours stitching them together. She was Vice Chairman of the school Charities Committee, and had the task of duplicating and circulating the agenda and minutes prior to each meeting. This was a messy task, as the pages were individually run off on an ancient Roneo cyclostyle, and Jess always managed to get ink everywhere. Jack had decreed that she should try to become a secretary when she left school, but Jess knew from her cyclostyling experience that she would hate it. The machine was forever breaking down, or running out of ink, or the stencil failed to cut properly. Who would choose to be a secretary, always fiddling with recalcitrant machinery? Not Jess.

English teacher Mr. Wood sometimes arranged trips to Exeter, to attend theatrical performances of productions such as 'Under Milk Wood' and 'The Beggars' Opera'. Once he took a small group to hear Lord Caradon, then Britain's representative at the United Nations. Dotey reluctantly allowed Jess to attend; she did not care for her to travel in Mr. Wood's estate car, complete with its CND badge. But at sixteen, Jess would have gone anyway.

Mostly, Jess spent the evenings with her friends in the library, studying until it closed and then going on the the cinema or to one of the friend's houses to listen to music. Andrew lived in the town centre, in the flat above the bank which his father managed, and he had a record player in his bedroom. Andrew and his friends regularly bought records by groups popular at the time: The Beatles, The Rolling Stones, Manfred Mann, The Searchers and Jess's particular favourites, The Kinks. One of the group, Mick, was very keen on The Moody Blues, and once invited Jess to his house to listen to "On The Threshold of a Dream" in order to demonstrate his new stereo. Jess was suitably impressed.

Mick was also keen on acting, and asked Jess to come with him to a young people's drama group. The class was short on numbers, and unless more people attended it would have to close. Jess went, only to be asked for a subscription. She had not realised that it was necessary to pay for evening classes. Jess had brought no money with her, and was embarrassed to have to admit this to the organiser. She reported back to Dotey that she would have to take the required amount the following week. Dotey of course had no spare money for fripperies such as evening classes, and said that Jess would be unable to continue. The fees would make a large hole in Jess's meagre paper-round wages, and she was reluctant to commit such a large sum for a whole term. However, the Drama education organiser for the county, who was also a member Tiverton Dramatic Society, got to hear of Jess's plight, and somehow arranged it so that Jess was excused payment. Dotey, never one to go into details, told her that everything was in order, and she should simply say 'I'm excused' if asked for a subscription the following week. So that is what Jess did, although some of her classmates were understandably puzzled. Jess wondered if people from families dependent on Social Security (as was hers, after the collapse of Jack's business) were allowed to attend for free; or maybe the Drama Advisor had quietly paid Jess' subscription for her in order to boost class numbers. She never did find out.

Chapter 38

Jess's stage debut had been as Grandma, in a production of 'Little Red Riding Hood' at Westfield School. This of course involved being eaten by the Big Bad Wolf; the swallowing scene was achieved by means of an enormous old fur coat which the Wolf, played by young James Brock, swirled around Jess in order to effect her disappearance. There was a song which everyone sang as Little Red Riding Hood tripped through the woods on her way to Grandma's cottage, which after more than 50 years Jess struggled to remember; but it went something like this:

There's a pat of butter, piece of cheese, slice of melon, tin of peas. Potted meat and gooseberries fine, jar of honey, damson wine; lemon jelly, blackberry pie: all packed inside my basket for my Granny.

Jess thought that it would have been a very heavy basket, with all those things in it, and that Little Red Riding Hood would have been better off with a tartan shopping trolley such as Fern next door used. After being eaten she remained in the wings until called upon to reappear, when the heroic woodsman sliced open the Wolf, and Jess emerged, blinking behind her granny spectacles and with her mob cap all askew, from behind the fur coat.

The Brownies were putting on a musical play, and Brown Owl had decided that Jess would have a small part. There had been no question of auditioning; girls were simply told what they would be doing. Jess was to play the mother of a little girl abandoned in a field. All sorts of woodland creatures come to life and sing to Christine, the little girl, while she is waiting for her mother to return; afterwards it is revealed that Christine has been asleep and dreaming.

Jess's opening line was "Christine, shall I leave you in this field while I walk on the farm by myself?" Jess could not imagine the circumstances in which her own mother or indeed any sane woman, would leave her little daughter alone in a field, and she felt that an eight year old would be unlikely to happily consent to this arrangement. Perhaps if the character of Christine was meant to have sprained her ankle and could not walk, so that the mother had to fetch help from the farm, and this was the only solution possible; but it still seemed unlikely. Jess was sure Dotey would have stayed with her until someone else came walking by and could be sent ahead to raise the alarm. But of course, Jess had not written the script. When she expressed her reservations, Dotey told her that plays often had unlikely scenarios, 'for dramatic effect'. Meanwhile, one of the songs from the current production went as follows: "We'll teach you to torture the fairies; we'll teach you that other can feel! We'll teach you to torture the fairies; we Brownies will teach you to squeal!" Most peculiar, thought Jess.

Next, Jess was told by her form teacher, Mr. Champion, that she was to play the part of the Sheriff of Nottingham's maid in a version of Robin Hood. Again, this was a small part, for which Jess was thankful. She was not sure she would have been able to remember all the lines had she been cast as Maid Marian. But of course, a pretty girl with long hair was playing that part. Jess had once more to wear a mob cap and a long apron and be sure not to miss her cue. Every form was contributing to the Heathcoat's drama evening, and Peter's infant class were doing some sort of meteorological play, with Peter cast as the king in a yellow jacket and golden crown, commanding the elements. At his order "Blow, little breezes, blow!" the half dozen breeze boys obligingly blew until they were red in the face, until eventually the sun-child came out with a beaming smile.

The following year it was announced that Jess's class was to put on the court-room scene from 'Toad of Toad Hall', and Jess was instructed to play the part of Badger. Her duties were to wring her paws and declaim, "Alas, alack, poor hapless Toad! Alas, alack, poor hapless animal! I knew his father, I knew his grandfather, I knew his uncle, the Archdeacon!" Jess had was no problem remembering the lines, but she hated the thick black and white stripes of make-up the teachers had plastered on her face in order to make her badger-like. Despite repeated applications of cold cream, this horrid substance refused to come off after the dress rehearsal, leaving Jess's face a ghostly grey. Various teachers were taking it in turns to vigorously scrub her face with a wet flannel, then retiring exhausted while another one stepped up to try their hand. Jess's face was becoming red and sore underneath the greasy grey film.

Dotey was horrified, and declared that the school must be using inferior make-up, how dare they send Jess home looking like death warmed up? Dotey tried again with warm water and a clean flannel, but to no avail. Jess still sported a ghastly sticky ashen complexion. Worse was to follow, since the next morning she found that her cheeks had erupted in large grey lumps. Jess was evidently allergic to the inferior make-up. And tonight she would have to go through the whole thing again. Dotey sent a note, saying that no more make-up must be applied to Jess's sensitive skin. The teachers then had the problem of how to turn Jess into a convincing badger. Eventually, the art teacher hit upon the idea of a black and white striped hood. One was quickly run up and popped over Jess's head. The effect was hot and extremely claustrophobic, Jess felt that she might faint at any moment and miss her cue. Maybe this was how the hangman felt, suffocating in his black hood, but at least his duties were over quickly, whereas Jess had to be on stage for an hour. The school hall, stuffy at the best of times, was packed with children and parents, and to make matters worse, Jess's badger costume consisted of an old moth-eaten black fur coat. She was in serious danger of over-heating, and asked Mr. Champion if the tiny nostril, mouth and eye holes of her hood could be enlarged to avoid suffocation. Jess had heard that dedicated actors were prepared to suffer all kinds of indignities for their art, but felt that this was a bit much to expect of a ten year old. It took more than a week for Dotey to finally manage to scrub all traces of grey goo from Jess's face; the lumps eventually subsided and Jess decided that her acting career was over. In future she would prompt or help with costumes or refreshments, indeed, undertake any role which did not require make-up or a fur coat. Any sort of performing, especially in animal guise, was so problematic.

There came an anxious moment when the Headmaster was considering her as a candidate to read the first lesson at the Grammar School Carol Service; the choice was between Jess and a girl named Katy, but fortunately for Jess, she developed what Dotey termed an 'absolute stinker of a cold...' in the days before the service, so the honour of reading went to Katy. Jess was relieved, since the service was to be held in the Parish Church and she had not wanted to have to climb up into the pulpit to read; those stone steps looked as though they would present an even greater hazard than the ones leading to the platform on Speech Day, imagine tripping in front of the entire congregation…

Dotey was of course disappointed, but Jess really had not wanted to read the first lesson. Out of all of the traditional nine, this was the one she liked least, since it was the Book of Genesis story of the serpent tempting Eve, which always made Jess think of menstrual periods. Her mother had told her that women had to endure their monthlies because of this very incident. Somehow it seemed to Jess to be quite indelicate to remind congregations of this every Christmas.

During the following years, Jess helped out behind the scenes with school plays, happy to maintain a low profile. She assisted with the costumes for a production of 'Our Town', which featured the Sunday paper-boy in the leading role of Stage Manager, providing a commentary on the lives of the inhabitants of the town as they unfolded throughout the play. The Sunday paper-boy was two years older than Jess, who admired him from afar. Her mother said he had nice teeth, and was always pleasant if she met him in the town. He was going out with Susan, another of the 'Our Town' cast. Jeff's girlfriend Jane was also playing a leading part, and Jeff had arranged for a bouquet of flowers to be delivered to her on the last night. Jess thought this very romantic, and told one of her friends about it; the news inevitably reached Jane on the backstage grapevine, and Jess was in trouble for spoiling the surprise, although she had not realised that it was meant to be a secret.

In the Christmas term of 1967 Mr. Wood was casting 'Love on the Dole'; Jeff had a small part as a bookie's runner and Jess was to be the prompter. Dotey had been horrified at the choice of play, especially when she saw Jeff's copy of the script. A drama about poverty-stricken unemployed people – set somewhere in the North? With a riot scene, a séance, and the singing of 'The Red Flag'? Where the disillusioned heroine eventually goes off to live with a rich book-maker, as a kept woman? How extremely unsuitable for the Grammar School! And it was all down to that odd Mr. Wood, still sporting his unsightly beard, with the CND badge still firmly in place on his car;

it really would be far more appropriate for him to be teaching at the Secondary Modern. Meanwhile, in Dotey's opinion, the Grammar School should be performing something like Shakespeare.

Then one of the girls playing a leading role learned that she was to be called for an interview at Cambridge University, and would be absent for the first two performances of the play. On hearing this, Mr. Wood immediately sought out Jess in the school library and told her that, as prompter, she was the person most familiar with the lines, so would be required to play the part of Mrs. Jike, the Cockney gin-swilling spiritualist. Jess's heart sank. Was there no-one else who could do it? Mr. Wood said it was far too short notice for anyone else to learn the lines, so it must be Jess.

Jess arrived at rehearsal that evening just as Mr. Wood was making his announcement to the rest of the cast, asking them to be helpful to Jess. There were audible groans from two of the girls with starring roles; they imagined that Jess's performance would be awful, since she was such a quiet lumpy thing. Jess had spent the hours since learning she was to play Mrs. Jike with her friend Mick, who was taking the part of O'Leary. They had gone over and over Jess's lines, and Mick had helped her with the Cockney accent; Mrs. Jike was the only character who did not speak with a Northern accent, the script specified Cockney, which Jess hoped would be easier for a Devonian to master than the Northern accent. Jess wished she possessed Dotey's ear for mimicry, since before the onset of her depression, her mother had the knack of imitating anyone, and used to have the children in stitches with her take-offs of people they knew or heard on the radio. According to the script, Mrs. Jike was supposed to be a 'tiny woman' with a man's cap, but of course, for two performances, the audience would have the rather more substantial figure of Jess.

Mr. Wood announced that they should rehearse the séance scene, where Mrs. Jike invites the spirits, "Are there any spirits present 'ere tonight, answer three for yes and two for no," and then pretends that they have indeed arrived by knocking surreptitiously under the table. She goes on to read the tea-leaves in heroine Sally Hardcastle's cup, with what turns out to be unerring accuracy, seeing two men, one fat, one handsome, followed by blood and darkness.

There had been a lot of lines for Jess to master in the space of a few hours, and she was relieved that, at the point when she dried up, the girl playing Sally (who had groaned when told that Jess was to be Mrs. Jike) quietly prompted her. Everyone seemed stunned that Jess had performed so well, except Mick, who told her he always knew she could do it.

There remained the problem of the make-up. Remembering the indelible badger stripes problem, Jess explained that she was allergic to stage make-up, but Mr. Wood was having none of this. How could an overweight, ruddy-cheeked girl such as Jess convincingly portray a wizened woman of the Hungry Thirties, even wearing her flat cloth cap and ragged shawl, without recourse to make-up? Her face would, of course have to be grey – again! – and streaked with lines of dirt. Jess recounted her previous problems with cosmetics to the teacher doing the make-up, who obligingly smeared only the minimum amount of grey greasepaint onto Jess's rosy cheeks, but Mr. Wood was not at all pleased. "You look like a cherub!" he shouted, before telling her to return and have yet another layer of grime applied.

On opening night, Dotey had a seat in the front row, as befitted the mother of not one but two cast members; next to her were Jess's friends Andrew and Gilbert. If the boys were surprised at Jess's performance, her mother was not, since of course, Jess had obviously inherited her dramatic ability from Dotey herself. Jess had an awkward moment during the riot scene when she was supposed to brandish a policeman's helmet, but the props girls had failed to put one out for her. This was going to be awful, since Mrs. Jike's possession of the helmet was gleefully alluded to in the dialogue. Jess had to grab one of the boys playing a policeman and beg him for his helmet just before she needed it. According to the script, Mrs. Jike quickly disposes of the incriminating headgear by tossing it into the oven in the Hardcastle's kitchen, and when Jess opened the oven door she found a helmet already there, left over from the dress rehearsal. She really would have to have a word with those props girls, so that they could ensure that the correct items were provided for Gillian, the original Mrs. Jike, who was returning to play the part later in the week.

When Mr. Wood was making his thank-you speech after the curtain had fallen on the final performance, he singled out Jess for taking over the role of Mrs. Jike at short notice. Jess was called forward from her place in the prompt corner to take a quick bow, with the audience and cast applause ringing in her ears. She was relieved when Mr. Wood went on to thank the lighting crew, a trio of gangling lads, who trooped onto the stage to an accompaniment of loud cheering and whistling. However, her brief stint as Mrs. Jike had given Jess the confidence to join Miss Tilley's after-school drama group, which often involved a great deal of improvisation, specifically, rolling about on the classroom floor; and it was because of this that Jess was able to finally persuade her mother that she should be permitted to wear trousers, for the sake of decency.

When it came to Dotey's Dramatic Society, Jess was always pressed into service to assist with all manner of things. She sent mail-outs to supporters, sold programmes, helped with refreshments, and once she even took a part. Following Jess's appearance as Mrs Jike, Dotey realised that she could indeed act, and got her the role of Doreen, the cheeky young waitress in a production of 'Separate Tables'. Jess tried her best, but felt somewhat miscast. She was not very comfortable playing the pert little thing the part called for, so that it was very hard to seem convincing. At rehearsals, it was difficult to know exactly from whom she should take directions; one of the other actors was peevishly complaining that Jess, with her laden tray, was standing right in front of him as per the director's instructions, which meant that he could not be seen, and it was hardly worth him appearing in the play at all. He actually got up at one point and flounced off the stage, so Jess quickly stood back, only for the director to tell her to go forward again. Meanwhile her mother was hissing at her to move further towards the centre. So much artistic temperament on display, even in an amateur troupe... The reviews in the local press described Jess as 'the daughter of the Dramatic Society's secretary', which she felt was unnecessary, since she would have preferred not to be so labelled, but to be judged simply as anyone else might be. However, the reviewers went on to say that Jess had given a good account of herself and had got several laughs, so she was pleased and relieved not to have let anyone down.

'Separate Tables' is a two-act play, dealing with life in a private hotel. The lead characters in the two acts are quite different, but the background cast, of staff, returning guests and residents, remains the same. Jess was struck by the storyline of the second act, where Sibyl, a dowdy and down-trodden daughter, meekly obeys her overbearing mother until encouraged to stand up for herself by a new arrival, a down-at-heel middle-aged man. Jess could see clearly herself in the meek daughter, always having to do as she was told and never being allowed to make her own decisions. However, Jess knew she should not rely on a man turning up to release her; university would provide her with a more realistic opportunity to escape. It was simply a case of getting through the next two years. Meanwhile, Jeff turned out to be a much more confident actor than Jess, taking several roles with the Dramatic Society over the years, including a French jockey and a dashing Lieutenant. He was the natural inheritor of Dotey's dramatic gifts, which re-emerged in the next generation in Jess's younger son, Alex, whose talent for mimicry had the family in stitches, exactly like the grandmother he never knew.

One summer, the entire family, even Jack, participated in a local dramatic event. A BBC producer called Leo Aylen arrived in the Exe Valley with a film crew, to shoot a television play entitled 'Dumnomia', the Roman name for Exeter. The story centred around a young woman, played by Polly James, later to find fame with 'The Liver Birds', who drops out of city life and travels to the West Country. Arriving at an idyllic village, she takes up with the Squire's son, to the consternation of his well-bred family and genteel fiancée. Tiverton Dramatic Society members were roped in as extras for various scenes, including a cricket match, in which Jeff took part, a sports day (where Peter won the Sack Race) and a village fête held in the grounds of Bickleigh Castle. Jess was given the job of looking after the Jumble Stall, which featured in a scene where Polly's hippy character squashes a cream bun into one of the jumble stall hats, as a gesture of contempt for the local bourgeoisie. For some reason the scene had to be re-shot several times, each take requiring a fresh cream bun and clean item of jumble. Jess thought she would be running out of suitable hats before they got it right, but fortunately it seemed that the supply of cream buns was limitless. Jess couldn't help thinking it was a waste of good food, but she was quickly realising the sacrifices often required for art...

The long-suffering extras were also required to watch an inordinate amount of Morris dancing, because the light or the sound kept being wrong. The Morris team was led by 'Sam-the-Dap' Leaker, the Grammar School Deputy Head, armed this time with a wooden cudgel and fluttering white hanky and with bells on his socks. So many takes were necessary that the audience became extremely bored and many vowed never to watch Morris dancing again so long as they lived. Some of the dramatic society ladies, Dotey included, had dressed up in flowery dresses and pretty hats; but it was turning out to be not at all a glamorous occasion, merely tedious; and after all that effort, disappointingly, the film was never shown, presumably ending up on the cutting room floor; and Leo Aylen gave up directing and went on to become a poet.

Chapter 39

Although they frequently disagreed about many matters, Jack and Dotey were of one opinion regarding people from ethnic minorities, whom they referred to as 'darkies', 'coons', or worse still, using the 'n' word, (heard with appalling frequency in those days.) Jess heard her parents discussing the recent appointment of an Indian man as deputy Borough Surveyor. Both her parents were strongly critical of the fact that he had been given a Local Authority job and a pleasant council house. How dare he come over here and take a good job and nice house, both of which rightfully belonged to a British person! When Jess plucked up courage to intervene mildly, suggesting that maybe the council considered the Indian gentleman the best candidate for the job, both her parents immediately rounded on her.

"Let me tell you, my girl, I was in India in the first war, and I know what I'm talking about! Before we went to these places, the natives were lying under the trees, waiting for the coconuts to fall, and we showed them how to climb the trees and PICK the coconuts... And in the last lot, we were defending the Empire for the next generation. Beats me why we bothered, you youngsters aren't a bit grateful, and now we're giving away our colonies to the darkies who can't govern them properly, so they're coming over here!"

"Jess, how dare you question your elders! How many times must I tell you, it is really quite unseemly for a young girl to be so opinionated! You have absolutely no experience of life on which to base these silly judgements of yours, and you really must get out of this tiresome habit of expressing yourself on subjects about which you know nothing!"

After this exchange, Jess realised her views would count for naught with her parents; she came to believe that she was not entitled to hold opinions, and felt guilty about doing so. She was unqualified to have anything valid to contribute to a discussion, and henceforth remained quiet. It was not surprising that Jess had no confidence whatsoever; to start with, her looks were constantly disparaged. Dotey admitted that Jess had 'fined down' a little following puberty, but she was still so ungainly and round-shouldered. Any opinions she dared voice of course did not count, her parents continually gainsaying them. Even her emotions were deemed invalid, with Dotey refusing to allow her hormonal teenage daughter to cry in their shared bed-room, assuring Jess that she had absolutely no reason for tears, she was simply being selfish, and that if she led a life as trying as Dotey's then perhaps she might have just cause.

Jess felt insecure, not only at home, but also at school. She marvelled at the confidence of other young people who boldly took issue with the teachers about some aspect of the lesson in subjects such as history; and was even more surprised when the teachers seemed to appreciate these opinionated pupils' interventions, and to give their views consideration. How did her classmates have the courage to speak out like this? Jess supposed they were so much better informed than she was because they had television, and took a different daily paper, or at least, one which they were actually allowed to read. Dotey continued steadfastly with her policy of hiding or editing the Daily Mail, wishing to preserve Jess' innocence; while Jess interpreted her mother's actions as a misguided attempt to keep her in a state of ignorance, and read what she wanted in the library.

The history teacher was explaining the Monmouth rebellion. The Duke of Monmouth could not inherit his father's crown because he was illegitimate, so the crown had to pass to Charles the Second's brother James instead.

"Now, do you all know what illegitimate means?" asked Miss Gillen. Everyone nodded or said that yes, they knew, although Jess had no idea what it meant, which was ironic, given the circumstances of her own birth. Jess would have liked to know what illegitimate meant and why it prevented a king's son from inheriting the crown, but she dared not ask, since it had been dinned into her from an early age that it was unseemly for little girls to ask questions or make comments. Dotey seemed to think that Jess's education should consist of her simply soaking up the information provided by the teachers, rather like a sponge absorbing water; but Jess was coming to realise that education was actually much more than this. Fact and figures about people and places and theorems were all very well, but Jess knew from the better teachers that this approach to education was incomplete, and that there were also questions and shades of opinion, and discussions to be had. Yet she lived in a household where any suggestion of debate was interpreted as insubordination and was anyway quite inappropriate for a girl. Jess had learned to keep her own counsel, since it increasingly appeared that her opinions were at complete variance with those expressed by her parents; and in any case, she was too lacking in confidence to even think of attempting to give voice them. It was not until she arrived at university, and the tutor, Dr. Leeming, misinterpreted her silence in the weekly seminars, asking Jess if there was any "furniture in her mind", that Jess realised that her mind was actually full of furniture; only it all seemed to be shrouded in dust sheets which needed somehow to be removed, and it would be the tutor's job to help her with this. In fact, Jess could not have had a more helpful tutor, who took time to encourage the less confident students, so that by the end of the first year, Jess was as opinionated as any twenty year-old had a right to be. However, this was some years into the future and in 1968 it was not just for her opinions that Jess was being criticised; seemingly, every aspect of her behaviour was found to be wanting.

"Jess, come here; I've got a bone to pick with you!" Jess approached nervously, as Dotey shut her bedroom door.

"How many times have I told you about being discreet! Your father's just torn me off a strip because he found a pair of your discarded panties on the bathroom floor! You know it offends his sensibilities to see female underwear lying about! Don't let it happen again, Jess; always pick up after yourself and don't expect me to have to do it for you!"

Jess was conscience-stricken. However, she could hear her father giving one of his occasional evening concerts from the front window, a selection from 'No, No Nanette!'

(Tea for two, and two for tea, me for you and you for me...)

"He doesn't sound too upset now! And anyway, why did he tell you off, when it's me who's in the wrong?"

(No, no Nanette, it's in my name...)

"Because he holds me responsible for you children's bad behaviour, it's yet another fault he can lay at my door, the fact that I'm not bringing you up properly! You must learn to have more consideration! Really, Jess, I had hoped by now you might have grown out of this thoughtlessness! Girls your age used to be out in service, they had to be very careful, living in someone else's house, they couldn't leave intimate garments lying around, or they would be sacked!"

(And it's no, no, no, no, no, no, no no, no, Nanette!

Evening, Fern, lovely day it's been. Forecast for tomorrow looks good, too. Aren't we doing well? I'll just round off now with an old favourite…*I want to be happy, but I can't be happy, 'til I make you happy too!)*

Chapter 40

One November evening found Jess busily preparing all the ingredients she needed for the following day's cookery lesson on baking Christmas cakes. Dotey had reluctantly been obliged to provide the required ingredients for Jess and was now fretting about the cost of dried fruit, glacé cherries, eggs and brown sugar, when it was quite possible that Jess's cake would be a failure and all the expensive ingredients would have been wasted. Dotey had never made a Christmas cake in her life; she always served up shop-bought Christmas cake from the grocers, which was invariably tasteless and dry. Dotey emphasised that she would not have the money to buy a replacement if Jess's cake failed, so Jess was fully aware that it would be her fault if the family had to go without Christmas cake that year. She felt the responsibility weighing heavily on her fourteen year old shoulders, although she secretly thought that any cake she brought home from cookery class could hardly fail to be an improvement on the dreadful shop-bought confections, which sat in the mouth like sawdust.

Jess had everything spread out on the table in the living-room, where she was carefully weighing and packing the precious ingredients into her basket. The table was opposite the door leading into the hall, so when the front door-bell rang, she went to answer it, since she was nearest. It was a chilly evening, and both Dotey and Jack were sitting close to the fire at the other end of the room, Jack reading the 'Express and Echo' while Dotey was darning one of Jeff's socks. Jess thought that Jeff was out. He was often at choir practice or doing something with the Air Training Corps.

Jess opened the front door to find that the callers were Sandra Jones and her father. Sandra was also in the church choir, and was going out with Jeff. Jess knew this, since not only had she been told that the pair were making sheep's eyes at each other across the chancel by another choir member, but she had come across Jeff and Sandra locked in an embrace outside the New Hall after a Dramatic Society performance. Sandra was five years older than Jeff, being twenty-one as against Jeff's sixteen. Sandra had been engaged, to a soldier in the Royal Engineers, the Sapper son of one of Dotey's friends; but sadly, this young man had been killed while working in the Far East. Dotey was absolutely furious about Sandra's relationship with Jeff – ever since a number of very well-intentioned people had reported to her that they had seen Sandra's car parked in secluded spots throughout the district, with the windows all steamed up – since Jeff was supposed to be studying for his O levels, not consorting with a floozy like Sandra Jones.

Dotey had actually gone so far as to visit the vicarage to appeal for help – after all, this unsuitable liaison had begun in church, right under the vicar's nose. The vicar had said sanctimoniously that his own nephew had recently sought his advice about marrying a woman five years older than himself, and after hearing his uncle's words of reassurance, had gone ahead with the marriage. He and his wife were very happy indeed, despite the disparity in their ages…

Dotey felt it incumbent to point out that Jeff was still a schoolboy, and that Sandra was an experienced woman; but the vicar had waved away all suggestions of impropriety within the ranks of his church choir, and Dotey had left feeling even more exasperated than when she had arrived.

Jess greeted the pair on the door-step, wondering what could possibly have brought them to the threshold of the lion's den. Sandra said that they wanted to speak to her parents, so Jess went to fetch Dotey. It was a cold evening, and she felt bad about leaving the pair on the doorstep, but her mother had repeatedly warned her never to let anyone into the house without her prior approval. This was after Jess had innocently asked a boy from the neighbouring street into the house to wash a cut sustained falling off his bike. Dotey had been furious to find Giles in the bathroom, saying that she did not want all and sundry snooping about.

"Who is it?" asked Dotey, looking up from her darning.

Jess replied that it was Sandra and Mr. Jones. Her mother almost stabbed herself, jabbing her needle into the sock.

"What on earth do they want? You haven't let them in!"

Jack looked up from the evening paper. "If I were you, I'd get rid of them as soon as possible, Dotey! We don't want any trouble!" with which he returned to the racing results.

Jess looked uncertainly towards the door. "What do you want me to do? I can't really leave them out in the cold…"

"Oh yes you can!" Dotey sighed and laid down her work. She made her way down the hall to the front door, where Sandra and Mr. Jones were shivering in the porch.

"Now then, Sandra, what is all this about?" Dotey's tone was as frosty as the weather. Jess returned to her table of Christmas cake ingredients, although she could not help but overhear the altercation taking place at the far end of the hall, especially since everyone was soon talking with raised voices. Even Jack could hear, from his place by the fire.

"Oi wants to tell 'ee that me and Jeff bain't be misbehavin', us be only going fer drives out together and having cawfee. Oi be a gud gurl, bain't Oi be, Dad… you tell 'er, Dad."

"Yus, yus; 'er be a guid maid, my Zandra…"

"Dotey – get rid of those people and come back in here at once!" This from Jack, comfortably ensconced by the fire.

"I find it hard to understand what possible interest you can have in my son, Sandra; he's only sixteen, and you are, after all, an experienced woman…"

"Us be only friends, we bain't be doin' nuthin' wrowng..."

"Dotey – tell those people to go away immediately!"

"Oi dunno what 'ee 'ave 'eard, but there be no 'arm in nuthin' what Jeff and me 'ave done, we be jus' friends and Oi be a guid gurl, bain't that be right, Dad?"

"Yus, yus, my Zandra, 'er 'ave allus been a guid maid..."

"Dotey – are those people still here? Get rid of them now!"

"Sandra, I repeat – you are AN EXPERIENCED WOMAN! Jeff should be studying for his exams, not spending his time with SOMEONE LIKE YOU."

Jess could hardly believe her ears. What on earth was all this experience her mother kept going on about? So far as Jess was aware, Sandra worked in an office and sang in the church choir. Dotey seemed to be implying that her life was so very much more interesting. Maybe Sandra was a spy? Did she perhaps speak Russian? Although Sandra did not look anything like the Bond girls Jess had seen on the posters outside the cinema, since she was really rather unprepossessing, being short and plump…but maybe it was not necessary to be glamorous to operate successfully as a spy, in fact, it could well be something of an advantage to be less than eye-catching… The thought then occurred to Jess, still weighing sultanas, although rather distractedly, that if Sandra was some sort of secret agent, and Dotey knew all about it, then she could not be a very good one.

"Dotey – I order you to shut that door and come back in!"

"Oi be prepared to swear to 'ee on the 'Oly Bible that me and Jeff bain't 'ave done nuthin' wrowng…!"

Jess was startled at this turn of events, and taking Sandra at her word, she went to the bookshelf to fetch a copy of the Bible. She placed it on the hall table, near where Sandra and her father were facing Dotey on the doorstep, but Sandra studiously ignored it, carrying on with her tirade.

"Tis a pity you 'ave bin listenin' to gawsip, cos me 'n Jeff 'ave dun nuthin' to be ashamed of, Oi gives you me wurd!"

"But Sandra, the fact remains that you are five years older than Jeff and have SO MUCH EXPERIENCE of the world. Jeff is just a young boy who needs to study hard if he is to make anything of himself, and you will be standing in his way if you persist with this inappropriate relationship."

"Tell 'er Dad, tell 'er what a guid gurl Oi 'ave allus been!"

"Dotey! Close the door and come back here in the warm!"

Jess thought both her parents were behaving really badly. Surely the best thing would be for everyone to go into the warm living room and talk it through over a cup of tea. She would have offered to put the kettle on, but Dotey had made it clear that Sandra and Mr. Jones were not to cross the threshold. Jess sensed that it was the class as much as the age disparity between Sandra and Jeff that her mother and father objected to. Despite being practically penniless and only renting, rather than owning, a large house, Jack and Dotey were both utter snobs. Sandra and her father spoke with broad Devonshire accents and lived in a less fashionable part of the town, which seemed to make Sandra 'unsuitable' in Dotey's opinion. Jess remembered Dotey examining Jeff's diary, and exclaiming over his relationship with the daughter of the chip-shop owner, and realised that she was likely to object to whoever Jeff went out with, for which girl could ever be good enough for her son? And as for Jack, Jess had heard him chatting with his farmer friends on many occasions, he could speak as broadly as they did, it was no doubt good for business to appear to be like one of them; but he would quickly switch to Received Pronunciation whenever the situation called for it.

Dotey finally closed the door, and Sandra and her father retreated to their car. Jess had finished packing her Christmas cake ingredients, her basket was full of goodies, covered with a gingham tea-towel. Dotey told her to quickly clear everything away and get herself off to bed. Jess hoped she had managed to weigh the quantities correctly, despite all the distractions. (She need not have worried, the cake turned out perfectly, being tasty and moist; and everyone, even Jack, pronounced it delicious.)

Jess was keen to try to find out what Sandra's intriguing 'experiences' might be, but when she asked Dotey, her mother gave an obscure and unsatisfactory reply, referring to the fact that everyone knew that of course Sandra had been engaged to be married to that poor young Sapper; so Jess was none the wiser. Jeff was often at the centre of any mischief, seemingly unconcerned about getting the cane, which he appeared to regard as an occupational hazard of schoolboy life. He once left his glasses in his back pocket, so that they were then broken during his receipt of six of the best, and was then unable to see the blackboard properly in lessons. Dotey was annoyed because Jeff now required new glasses; but Jack admired Jeff's independent spirit, which was in complete contrast to his timid sister.

The new headmaster had issued a decree banning home-knitted jumpers, insisting that everyone buy their school knitwear from the approved stockist. The pupils were attired in fifty shades of hand-knitted green, rather than the required uniformity of uniform. Tiverton's mothers were immediately up in arms, insisting that the quality of their knitting was every bit as good as that of the stockist's, and that their home-made jumpers could be produced for half the price. Jeff soon had a huge banner streaming from an upstairs classroom window, boldly proclaiming "Get your hand-knitted jumpers here!"

The story reached the press, the indignant knitters complaining about the high-handed jumper policy, with the result that a compromise was eventually agreed upon, so that the exact shade of bottle green was clearly specified for the home-knitted creations.

Chapter 41

Dotey's struggle to maintain the façade of a normal family life ended abruptly one night in 1966. Fifteen year old Jess had known for some time that something was very wrong. She was wakened late most nights by the sounds of her drunken father knocking on Dotey's closed bedroom door, trying to gain access, their conversations conducted in the loudest of stage whispers "Dotey – are you still awake?"

"No, Jack, it's late, go to bed, you'll wake the children…"

However, if Jess called out that she was already awake, she was sharply told to go back to sleep by her mother, while Jack retreated to his room. Jess wondered why he could not leave Dotey alone, what could he possibly want at that time of night? Whatever it was could surely keep until morning.

Then came the terrible night when Jack would not take no for an answer, and Jess awoke to the sounds of Dotey's screams. She jumped out of bed and rushed to her mother's room, almost colliding with Jack as he dashed across the landing. Jeff had also been awakened by the commotion and came running down from the attic. "What's going on?"

"Mum, are you all right?" Jess asked anxiously. Dotey's face was swollen and red. She had been injured attempting to resist Jack's drunken advances, believing him to be about to rape her. Jack was so much stronger than she was, and of course, she was lying down. Screaming had been her only possible defence, knowing that Jess would wake.

Jess offered to make her mother a cup of tea, which to her surprise, Dotey accepted. Her mother did not tell her to go back to bed and to sleep on this occasion. Meanwhile Jeff had jumped on his bike and gone to notify the police. The telephone had been recently cut off as a result of Jack's on-going financial difficulties, but the police station was only half a mile away. Jess brewed the tea, while Dotey went to bathe her face. Jess, in her innocence, could not understand why Jack should want to beat Dotey in the small hours. She had no idea why a man should be so cruel to his wife. Jeff soon returned. The police had refused to come, saying that they had no powers to interfere between husband and wife. Jeff had explained that his mother had been assaulted, but the police sergeant told him that it was a purely domestic matter, and that as such, no action could be taken.

"Why is he like this?" asked Jess, despairingly. Dotey explained that Jack's business was in financial trouble, and that since a family cost such a lot to keep, he now resented them all, they were nothing but a drain on his resources. This was of course only partly the explanation for Jack's behaviour; Dotey did not mention that Jack had been trying to obtain his conjugal rights by brute force, and in any case, Jess would have had no idea what conjugal rights could be.

"I wish you had never married him! We were so happy before he came!" exclaimed Jess through her tears. "Why did you marry him? We were managing fine, you, me and Peter, so there was no need for you to get married."

"I had to give you and Peter a name," whispered Dotey. Jess did not understand what she meant.

"But we had a name – Rapson was our name; and when you married Dad and told me I had to change it to Sanders, it caused trouble at school, with everyone teasing me."

Jess did not see why it mattered what surname anyone had, so far as she could see, it was used only to put everyone in the right place in the school register, and she had slipped still further down the list when she changed from initial R to initial S. Why should women have to change their names when they got married, or children change theirs when their mother re-married? It was as though they were someone's property, rather than people in their own right…

"You don't understand," said Dotey. "Rapson could never be the right name for you and Peter …you are not Rapson children; but when I found I was expecting you, Jack had to pay a sum of money in compensation to Mr. Rapson, for something called 'deprivation of conjugal rights' – don't ask me to explain what that is, Jess; and he resents the fact that you are so unlike him – not tall or fair, or good at games like Peter; he doesn't understand how he could possibly be the father of a plump, dark-haired child – although it does seem that you might be starting to fine down at last. I keep telling him that you must be a throw-back on my side."

More tears welled up in Jess's eyes. "So Mr. Rapson rejected me and now Dad resents me because he doesn't think I'm worth the money he had to pay Mr. Rapson!"

"You see what I mean, Jess, about the sins of the fathers being visited on the children. Jack resents having to support you, and now he's taking it out on me, because I had the choice of giving you up and putting you in the orphanage so everything would have carried on as before. But it's late, go back to bed and get some sleep. Don't cry – I can't bear to see you crying. Things will seem better in the morning."

"But we can't just forget it, and anyway, you're not safe!" Jess was still tearful. She could not help being a throw-back, but it did not sound like something anyone would really want to be. And as for Jack resenting the fact that she had seemingly been foisted on him, a dark-haired cuckoo when he was fair – that was something she could not help.

"We'll just have to be brave and do the best we can. You know, Jess, we are his possessions, a bit like slaves; we have to live with him, there's nowhere else we can go, and there's nothing else we can do. You heard what Jeff said – not even the police can interfere. We have no choice."

Jess went back to bed at her mother's command, but she could not sleep, since the whole episode had disturbed her greatly. She was in the middle of the two years' study which would culminate in her GCE O level examinations. After that, she hoped to stay at school for a further two years to take A levels, and then go on to university. Her father had commented recently that since she was now fifteen, the minimum school leaving age, she had better start looking for a job. Jess was top of the class and did not want to leave school. She knew Dotey wanted her to stay on. But if things were as bad as it now seemed, and Jack really meant what he said, all his talk of not wanting to keep her 'until she was an old woman' was no joke. He resented her, she was a drain on his resources, a burden. The Ten Commandments stated that children should honour their fathers and mothers, but Jess could not recall any reciprocal instruction for parents to love their children. Jess felt guilty, she had always struggled with her conscience because she could not keep that particular commandment; her father inspired fear rather than love, he drank too much and beat his wife as a result. And she had three more years of this to endure before she could think of leaving; whereas for Dotey, who had married Jack in order to give her two younger children a name, there was no prospect of escape. She was his wife and not even the police could protect her.

No wonder her mother was so insistent that Jess must never marry. Jess was aware that people usually married for love, but Dotey and Jack seemed to have married simply for the want of a name for her children on Dotey's part and a housekeeper on Jack's. Jess fell asleep wondering where all the love families were meant to have for one another had gone, if there had been much of it in the first place...

As for Dotey, this was the night that she began barricading her bedroom, pulling a small chest of drawers up to the door. Of course, it would not keep out a determined and powerful drunk, but if Jack tried again to gain entry and attack her when she was asleep, she would be certain to waken with at least a few seconds warning. And Jess would inevitably waken as well and come to her aid.

Chapter 42

Jess worked hard revising for her O levels. Driven out of the house by Jack's continual attempts to distract her, by turning the wireless up full blast or shouting for her to make him a cup of tea, she took her books out into the sunny fields on the hillside high above the Close, where she could sit under a tree and study in peace. Of course her mother wanted Jess to do well, but Dotey thought that Jess might be studying rather too hard, that she was possibly 'overtaxing that good brain', and that perhaps a spot of housework might come as light relief. The buzzing of passing insects, the mooing of cows in the next field, and the breeze blowing gently through the hawthorn bushes provided the perfect background accompaniment to Jess's studies, just as present-day scholars might listen to music on their i-pods when revising.

The first exam was the cookery practical. Jess's assignment, announced the previous week, was to prepare a packed lunch for two archaeological students going out all day on a dig, to include a home-made drink; and to also make a quick supper dish for their return. Jess could not believe that archaeologists would ever want to bother with anything more than sandwiches and ready-made squash, but of course, for the purposes of the exam that would not do at all, so Jess prepared meat-loaf sitting on a bed of salad, home-made lemonade and little shortbread biscuits. For the quick supper dish she found a recipe which involved eggs poached in tinned tomatoes within a nest of mashed potato. Jess was relieved to see that, for once, Mrs. Lamb's dogs were not in attendance, so that her services as canine door monitor were not required and she need not be distracted from the important task in hand. The morning went fairly well, despite the heat in the kitchen, with the sun streaming in on a dozen anxious girls, all frantically trying to get their various dishes cooked in the allotted time. Jess's meat loaf turned out well, so did the biscuits; but the supper dish did not work, the eggs had not poached, and now there were only five minutes remaining until it was time to down tools and have the work assessed. The examiner, who seemed to be a nice enough lady, had been coming round observing and asking questions about the recipes. Noticing Jess's look of dismay as she took her not-yet-poached eggs out of the oven, she suggested putting the dish under the grill. This worked a treat, the mashed potato nest browned nicely and the eggs set. Jess thought that real archaeologists coming home after a day in the field would have simply settled for beans on toast, but no matter, her dish was saved.

The day before the written exams were due to begin, Jess stopped suddenly in the lane on her way home from the revision field and there at her feet in a patch of grass was a four-leaf clover. This could be regarded as an indication of good luck by anyone even slightly superstitious, so she picked it and took it home to show her parents. Jack, the farmers' merchant, was amazed. He had heard of four-leaf clovers, but never believed that they actually existed; he had played out in the meadows all through his childhood and never found or even seen one. He examined Jess's cloverleaf closely, thinking that she had tricked him and somehow managed to stick an extra leaf onto an ordinary clover. He even got out his magnifying glass to see if he could spot the join, repeatedly asking how she had done it.

Jess protested that it was not a trick but absolutely genuine. Dotey, who had been brought up for four impressionable years in Ireland, and was the most superstitious member of the family, argued that Jess could have no interest in producing a forgery, since only a genuine four-leaf clover could bring her the luck she needed with her exams. Of course she had studied hard – possibly even too hard, Dotey thought - but she would still need a certain amount of luck in getting the questions she wanted. Jess said she had heard that four-leaf clovers were sometimes found where the ground had been disturbed, and often occurred in patches. She went back the next day after her first Maths exam, which had not been too bad, and found three more four-leaf clover specimens nearby. In all, that summer she found nine four-leaf clovers, corresponding to the exact number of subjects she was studying. She pressed them in tissue paper between the pages of a heavy book. Jack was forced to concede that four-leaf clovers really did exist; he even borrowed one to take to the Conservative Club to show his hitherto sceptical friends, which furnished them all with an interesting topic of conversation for the evening, and a change from the best method of baking sponge cakes.

After Jess had sat her O level exams there was a long and anxious wait of several weeks for the results, which were not due to be published until towards the end of August. The atmosphere in the house was toxic, with Jack daily reiterating that Jess should be out looking for a job, while Dotey maintained that Jess would do no such thing, as she was to stay on at school to study for her A levels. Jess was exhausted after the effort of the exams, coupled with anxiety about her future, and asked if she could go away for a short while. Dotey had friends living in New Malden, Surrey, and Jess asked if she could go and stay with Auntie Dorothy and Uncle Edgar. Dotey had her doubts about Jess going such a long way by herself, but Jess had found out from the travel agent that a coach from Exeter would get her to Staines, from where she could get a Green Line bus. Arrangements were made, and Jess found herself trundling up the A30 on the coach. At Staines she easily found the bus stop, and was met in New Malden by Uncle Edgar.

Dorothy and Edgar were childless, and lived in suburbia with an affectionate cat called Judy. They had arranged several outings for Jess, including a trip to Kew Gardens, which Jess loved, and shopping in Kingston-upon-Thames, where Jess saw colour television for the very first time in Bentalls department store. Of course, Jess's family were yet to acquire even a black and white set. Then came the day when Aunty Dorothy was rather tired and asked Jess if she could amuse herself for a few hours; a bus trip to Windsor was suggested, and Jess agreed with alacrity. A whole day to herself, unsupervised, would be a treat. Aunty Dorothy packed some sandwiches, made sure that Jess had enough money and her telephone number, and waved her off, telling her not to speak to strangers. In Windsor, Jess visited the Castle and walked by the river. She sat on a bench and ate her packed lunch, watching the boats pass by. It was a lovely summer's day, and the feeling of independence and freedom was delightful. The only person she spoke to was a passing dog-owner whose animal was showing rather too much interest in Jess's sandwiches.

Jess returned home after a delightful week away, and Dotey was glad to see her back. Jack had been more than usually difficult during Jess's absence, saying that she should be job-hunting in Tiverton, not gadding about Surrey. The O level exam results which would seal

Jess's fate were due out in a few days' time; they turned out to be everything she had worked so hard for, and that Dotey had dreamed of.

The four-leaved clovers had seemingly worked their magic. Jess was amongst a crowd of students peering at the list of exam results that had appeared in the school window a few days after her return home, and was shocked to discover that she had obtained the best O level results in the school, even passing Cookery at Grade Two! At the Conservative Club, Jack was warmly congratulated by Mr. Leighton, one of the Grammar School masters. He shook Jack's hand, saying that his clever daughter had achieved excellent grades. Jack had been unaware that Jess's results were due out that day, so asked exactly how well Jess had done. On hearing that she had achieved five Grade One and four Grade Two passes, he churlishly remarked that this did not seem to be much to write home about. Now, if she had got nine Grade Ones, that might have called for a celebration. Mr. Leighton told Jack that O levels were strictly marked, and very few scholars nationally managed to obtain grades as good as Jess's. It was a great achievement, Jess's family should be proud of her. Dotey was of course over the moon, and Jess was understandably thrilled, but she quailed at the sight of her father returning home with a face like thunder.

"Well my girl, I suppose now you'll be expecting me to keep you until you're drawing your pension!"

Jack would never praise Jess; instead, he insisted on her leaving school and getting a job, since his patience with this educational nonsense was exhausted. Dotey stressed that Jess was considered to be 'university material' and must be allowed to stay on at school for a further two years to do A levels. Jack refused, Dotey insisted, and neither would give in. Jack then offered what he considered to be a generous concession; Jess could go to Secretarial College, since 'the secretaries of today are the bosses' wives of tomorrow.' However, Dotey knew that Jess's talents lay with academic work, so she must be given the chance to study at advanced level. Jess knew that secretarial college was not for her, despite the prospect of marrying a boss. She admired Dotey's courage in standing up for her, realising that it would have been so easy for her mother to give in to Jack's bullying to keep the peace. It would be impossible for Jess to resist the pressure to leave school if both her parents insisted. As it was, she enrolled for A levels, and took care to stay as much as possible out of Jack's way. Unable to study at home, she stayed late at the library, or took her work to sympathetic neighbours' homes. Three spinster school-mistresses shared a house nearby, and generously put their attic at Jess's disposal in the run-up to the A level exams, so she had somewhere quiet to study, the only interruption being Miss Gillen bringing her a tray of milky coffee and chocolate digestive biscuits. So, with the support of her mother, the kind teachers and the neighbours, Jess was able to obtain the grades she needed. However, according to Jack, Jess had deliberately set out to disobey him, and he carried on his spiteful vendetta against her throughout the two years of the A level course. Jess had never heard the word 'misogynist', but on coming across it later, she knew that Jack had provided a text-book example.

Chapter 43

Several of Jess's school friends were going on exchange visits to France, Germany or Denmark which the school had organised. Jess knew there was no point in asking her mother if she could go because the answer would be negative. Dotey had no intention of letting Jess out of the country without a proper chaperone, even if such a trip could be afforded, which of course it could not. Parents had no idea what sort of people these foreign families might be, they were possibly very undisciplined, and their children might well be allowed to get up to all sorts of mischief. Dotey especially did not approve of the Danes, since some of the Tiverton girls had been paired with boy exchange pupils, and vice versa. There were shocking rumours of the Danish girl pupils being permitted to sleep with their boyfriends at home when they reached the age of sixteen, which was simply asking for trouble in Dotey's opinion.

Jeff was able to go to Germany when the school choir was invited to visit Hamlin. The trip cost only £5 for the week. Jess was not permitted to go, since she was at the time busy studying for her O levels. She could not help being rather envious of Jeff. Dotey applied her usual mantra – Jess's time would come, she must be patient, it was always good for a little girl to have to wait for things, which would then be appreciated all the more when they finally arrived... Jess felt that she had been waiting all her life, for clothes, for travel, for freedom; but she knew what was required of her. She had to get her head down and be disciplined and study hard for two more years, and then she would finally be free.

Then, unexpectedly, aged seventeen, Jess was allowed to go abroad. The church Youth Club was planning to take a party of a dozen young people to Belgium, Luxembourg and Germany. The curate, Mr. G— was to drive a minibus, with Mrs. G— accompanying the party as chaperone. It was this last detail which appealed to Dotey. She felt that Jess would surely be safe under the care of a curate's wife, whose young daughter was also to be of the party. There remained the question of the £20 total cost. Jess imagined that such a sum would be impossible to find, but to her surprise, Dotey was so determined that Jess should go, that she cashed in an insurance policy. She had been saving a few shillings a month with the Wesleyan and General for several years, and the policy was intended to mature on Jess's twenty-first birthday. However Dotey considered that this was such a good opportunity for Jess to travel abroad, that she withdrew the entire amount early. Jack was of course furious. He could see no good reason for wasting money on a European trip, including Germany of all places, a country against which Britain had fought a war scarcely more than twenty years since; in his oft-expressed opinion, the only good German was a dead one. When Dotey refused to take any notice of his objections, he took a different tack, and assured Jess that it was he who was the source of the largesse for her trip, since of course he was the family provider, the one who had earned the money for the insurance policy in the first place. Jess knew her mother had scrimped and saved to pay the premiums, so silently took a dim view of Jack's protestations. There could of course be no arguing with her father; his word was law.

A problem arose when Jess applied for a British Visitors passport. She needed her birth certificate, of which she had never had sight, so she asked her mother for it. Dotey was annoyed, saying she really did not see why this was necessary simply for a one year passport; but Jess said she would not be able to travel without it. Dotey rummaged about and eventually produced the short version of Jess's birth certificate, with no details of her parents. Jess hoped that it would do, but it was in the name of Rapson, and Jess had from the age of eight been firmly instructed to use the name Sanders. To Dotey's further annoyance, a solicitor's letter had to be provided to explain the name change. Short-term passports were obtainable at the Post Office in those days, and luckily Jess's supporting documents convinced the counter clerk, and the passport was issued.

After the Dover to Ostend sea-crossing, Jess's first impression of Abroad was surprise and shock that the Belgian police carried guns. The first night was spent in Liege, where the party was booked into a hostel which Mr G— could not find. Round and round the one-way road system they went, until Jess spotted a police station. She and her friend Marilyn had O level French, so went to ask for directions. However, their earnest questions fell on deaf ears, since the policemen all appeared to be drunk. There was much laughing, shouting and teasing, so the two girls retreated to the pavement to wait for the mini-bus to come round again, since it was still cruising the one-way system, unable to stop in a restricted zone. At this point, they were approached by two boys, who asked in English where they were going. Jess gave them the name of the hostel, and the boys said they knew where it was; they offered to escort them there, but Jess knew they must wait for the minibus. She could picture Dotey's horror, if she went off with two boys in a strange Belgian town on her first night abroad.

Luckily, at that moment, the mini-bus appeared. The boys gave Mr. G— directions to the hostel, which was apparently only just around the corner, and said they would meet the girls there. They were as good as their word, and offered to buy Jess and Marilyn a Coca-cola each. The girls sat with the boys, conversing in their O level French and as much English as the boys could muster, under the watchful gaze of Mrs G— across the room. Being abroad was turning out to be quite exciting, thought Jess. The following day, she sent her mother a postcard, assuring her that they had arrived safely, and had found the hostel with the help of two kind local boys. Peter later told her that Dotey had been alarmed to receive it, wondering why the G—s had not known exactly where the party was meant to be staying. However, it soon transpired that the G—s had only the haziest notion of the intended route. Jess found herself seated behind Mr. G—, giving directions to the next destination, since she had O level Geography and seemed to be the only one who could map-read. Finding the autobahns rather dreary, Jess decided they should take the scenic route through a forest; it was indeed extremely pretty, but the road was also very steep, with sharp bends, and at one point Mr. G— said they might all be required to get out and push. Thereafter, Jess stuck to the main roads.

This holiday was quite the most exciting thing in Jess's life to date. They visited Cologne, Koblenz, Luxembourg and Brussels, admiring cathedrals, castles, the River Rhine and grand squares. In the Black Forest, they saw two huntsmen carrying a dead deer through the woods, which upset them a great deal. It turned out that Marilyn talked in her sleep, since that night, in the room she shared with

Jess, Hilary and Julie, she was sobbing and crying out "don't kill the poor deer!" to the consternation of her room-mates. It was their first experience of 'Continental quilts' as duvets were then known; and no-one had the least idea what a bidet might be used for. One of the boys, David, began to take an interest in Jess. Some surreptitious kissing took place, but there was never any danger of anything else, since the room-mates and Mrs. G— were always on hand. David was shorter than Jess, and a few months younger, being in the school year below. Jess was not looking for a boyfriend, she still had a crush on the Sunday paper-boy, whom she continued to admire from afar, so declined to meet David after the trip, except at Youth Club, preferring a quiet life.

On their return, Mr. G— decided that the young travellers should give a slide-show presentation for the parents. Jess was required to speak about their time in Arensburg, the town at the most Southerly part of the journey. Nobody mentioned getting lost in Liège, or the upsetting sight of the dead deer. The parents were satisfied that their £20 had been well spent. Jack did not attend the presentation; he was still annoyed with Jess for visiting the land of his old enemy, appearing to take it as a personal insult, despite the fact that Jess had not lived through the war, and anyway, many German/English town twinning initiatives were now springing up across the land in an effort to heal old wounds.

Chapter 44

Dr. Foster's daughter, Alison, was about to marry her dashing fiancé. Alison was just a few years older than Jess, who had watched their glamorous neighbour being driven about in the fiancé's red sports car, with the top down, Alison wearing sunglasses and with her long hair tied under a flowing scarf. Fern from next door was to be a guest at the wedding, but Dotey had not been invited, despite the fact that Alison and Jess had had piano lessons together, and Jess occasionally minded the telephone and took messages for Dr. Foster when everyone else at High Meadow was out. Fern, in a state of high excitement about the event, seemingly oblivious to Dotey's hurt feelings, and dithered about what she should wear, asked Dotey's advice on the important matter of choosing a new outfit. This of course only rubbed salt into the wound, and Dotey declared herself too busy to go shopping with Fern. Accordingly, Fern took the bus to Exeter on her own, and appeared at the front door of No. 3 in a light green and pink floral silky dress and jacket, the ensemble topped with a pink straw hat, although the overall effect was somewhat spoiled by the fact that she was as usual wearing her fluffy slippers.

"What do you think, Dotey? Will it do?"

"It's very pretty, Fern," was Dotey's stiff reply. However, as soon as a smiling Fern had shuffled off back home, Dotey turned to Jess and clicked her disapproval.

"Tch, that outfit is really much too young a style for Fern! She looks like mutton dressed as lamb!"

"But you told her it was pretty!"

"I chose my words carefully, it IS pretty; but it's meant for a much younger person, that colour scheme does absolutely nothing for her complexion. Women of Fern's age really should stick to navy and white, which suits everyone."

Dotey was developing a puzzling habit of saying one thing and meaning another, Jess noticed. The greengrocer's daughter was also getting married, to a young bus driver. On meeting the couple in the town, Dotey congratulated them on their forthcoming marriage, agreeing that there was absolutely no point in long engagements.

However, as soon as they were out of earshot, she shook her head, gave her disapproving click and muttered to Jess, who was as usual struggling with several large shopping bags, that of course it was becoming quite obvious that Sally 'had to get married', and that the wedding dress had better be a smock.

The expression was new to Jess. "Doesn't she want to marry Reg, then?" Jess was surprised, since she had always thought that Reg seemed so nice, the sort of man that any young woman would be glad to marry.

Dotey sighed at Jess's naïvety. "They're only getting married so soon because she's expecting a baby."

Just why Dotey should find her daughter's innocence so exasperating puzzled Jess, since for so many years her mother had done everything possible to protect her from any knowledge of the facts of life, or anything deemed the slightest bit 'unpleasant'. Jess recalled the disappearing newspapers and censored library books, not to mention the lack of a television set. And had not Dotey herself been obliged to marry Jack, with whom she already had two young children, so was she really in any position to judge others? However, Jess knew better than to pass comment, or question her mother. She supposed that such things must have been excusable in the difficult days after the war, as compared with to the present 'never had it so good' era.

Similarly, Jess always felt very uncomfortable hearing the comments liberally dished out by her mother, referring to women who 'did not make the most of themselves' or who 'had really let themselves go'. Dotey's criticisms as to physical appearance soon extended to any boy who showed the slightest interest in Jess. At seventeen Gilbert had joined the Grammar School Sixth Form from an all-boys boarding school in the Home Counties, and Jess befriended the newcomer, telling him about the church youth club of which she was then secretary. (Discussing the onset of their friendship years later, Gilbert admitted that since he had no experience with girls, he thought at the time that Jess was inviting him to the Youth Club on a date, rather than simply doing her duty as club secretary.) Dotey rolled her eyes in an exasperated manner and pronounced Gilbert 'a real little shorty' when he walked Jess home afterwards.

Another boy, a young member of the Dramatic Society, was criticised because of his acne, while a third lad had uneven teeth. Dotey sighed despairingly, declaring that she must have a strong maternal instinct, it was obvious she felt sorry for these boys and wanted to mother them because they were so ugly or lacking in stature. But Jess did not feel at all maternal, she liked to have friends of both sexes. Andrew the bank manger's son was one, and she often went to tea or on days out to the sea with his family. She even assisted Andrew's father with sorting out honey jars when the bee-keeping bank manager was bottling the season's honey harvest. Andrew was yet another short lad, and of course, he had already greatly angered Dotey by disclosing to Jess the amount of money in her mother's bank account.

Then the dentist's son sent Jess an unexpected postcard from Copenhagen; at first Jess could not work out who it was from; it was signed 'love Aiden', but Jess could not think of anyone of that name. Then she remembered that she had met Aiden at a party given by the Young Liberals. He was the club secretary, so she must have given him her address for their records. For once, Dotey seemed quite pleased, since Aiden attended Blundells School and was several inches taller than Jess; but he had obviously failed to make that much of an impression on her daughter. In due course, Jess settled for a tall, clever engineer, whose hard-working parents had owned a small-holding, which they had been obliged to sell because of ill health. The whole family spoke with broad regional accents, dismissed by Dotey as being very 'common'. ("You know, Jess, you could do so very much better for yourself!") However, Jess realised that nobody she went out with would ever satisfy Dotey's exacting criteria, and even if, by some miracle, she should one day appear with the Prince of Wales in tow, her mother would still find a disparaging comment to make.

Jess never had a crush on Reggie, although it would have been easy to do so and many girls did. He was the good-looking lad, with curly brown hair, and a quiet manner who sat at the desk behind Jess in the Lower Sixth, in the sunny bay widow of Blagdon, the former Mayoral residence on the school campus, then used as the sixth form annexe. Reggie lived on a farm outside Cullompton, and helped his family with jobs such as hay-making and the harvest. One fine summer evening, Reggie was hurrying to get a tractor-load back to the farm. He wanted to go to a barbecue being held that night at his neighbour Stubby's place, to celebrate the end of the exams. Almost all the sixth form were going, including Jess, who had received Dotey' permission to attend, now the exams were finished. The tractor Reggie was driving overturned suddenly and he was killed. His friends noted that he was not at the party, but imagined that he was having to work late on the farm while the weather held. Most of his class-mates did not hear the awful news until the following Monday morning when they arrived at school. Jess was appalled to think that they had all been enjoying themselves while Reggie was lying dead only a few miles away. She had actually walked up the road to school with Stubby, whom she had met by chance coming off the Cullompton bus, and they had been discussing the barbecue. Stubby had not mentioned Reggie's death to Jess, so it was a dreadful shock when their classmate, Marilyn, came to the front door of Blagdon and told her. It was not then a requirement that tractors should have a safety cab, so Reggie had had no protection. He was seventeen years old.

The Lower Sixth form pupils were much too shocked to do anything in the way of work that day; they clubbed together to send a wreath of red roses for Reggie's funeral. For most, it was their first experience of the loss of a young life.

Sitting at the next desk to Reggie in the bay window had been Leigh Jackson. He did not study any of the same A level subjects as Jess, so she did not know him very well. He was often heard debating some point of literature or history with the teachers or fellow classmates. Many years later, Jess was watching the children's television programme 'Grange Hill', about a London comprehensive school, with her own sons, and noticed his name among the script-writing credits. Leigh Jackson became an award-winning screenwriter, and his old classmates got a surprise when his drama, 'Warriors', aired in 1999, since many of the main characters bore their surnames. Skeet, Hookway, Stone, James and Sprague were all in that same sixth form class, while Gurney and Feeley were the names of the English and History teachers. This was remarked on at a school reunion in 2004, attended by many of the pupils who had unwittingly given their names to characters in the hard-hitting drama; but sadly, by the time of the reunion, Leigh Jackson had died of cancer in his early fifties.

Another classmate, Penny, left suddenly because she was pregnant. Dotey was appalled, the more so when new mum Penny reappeared the following year to resume her studies. "How brave" said Jess. "Huh, how brazen, more like!" said Dotey. "I'm surprised that the school allowed her back. Not much of an example for the younger girls, is she? Had a baby, back at school, carrying on as if nothing happened.. That's not what's expected at the Grammar School, she should have been sent down to the Secondary Modern."

"But she passed the eleven plus, and she wouldn't be able to do her O levels at the Secondary Modern..."

"She doesn't deserve the opportunity to sit her O levels! Not after what she's done. If you ask me, it's disgraceful!"

Chapter 45

The failure of Jack's business was a tremendous blow, affecting every aspect of the family's lives. For a start, the car disappeared; it was listed as a business asset and so had to go towards paying the firm's creditors. The business was a limited liability company, so Jack was not made personally bankrupt, but the shame of insolvency affected him deeply. He was well past retirement age and so qualified for a state pension, enhanced because he had a wife and school aged children to support. However, he was obliged to apply for a top-up of Social Security, which he bitterly referred to by the old-fashioned term of 'National Assistance'. It was paid by means of a Giro, presented weekly at the Post Office, and Jack resented very much having to stand publicly in a queue, in order to receive a government hand-out. He tried to shield his Social Security papers behind an old car tax renewal form, in an attempt to conceal his true purpose at the Post Office counter.

Such was his shame and mental collapse that the previously dapper businessman, always neat in jacket and tie, took to wearing an old tweed overcoat, with several buttons missing, loosely tied around the waist with baler twin; the outfit was topped off with a hood from Jess's old gabardine raincoat draped over his head when it rained. Jess, coming home from school one wet day, was shocked to encounter a shambling apparition, which turned out to be her father in his ensemble of degradation. At first she had thought he was a tramp, but then Jack's head emerged from beneath the hood, and nodded to her. Jack dressed in the equivalent of sackcloth and ashes, he would never get over the failure of his business, blaming the 'Big Boys', large firms with the ability to buy in bulk and charge much lower retail prices, who were squeezing out smaller concerns, by means of what Jack considered to be unfair competition. The fact that he had failed to invest in his business and had squandered the proceeds on drink was never mentioned.

The telephone had already been cut off, which hit Dotey hard, since because of her father's job as a telephone engineer, she had always been used to being on the phone. She was still secretary of the Dramatic Society, and people often needed to contact her about meetings, rehearsals and publicity, so she asked if the Dramatic Society could pay for the telephone to be reinstalled, but her request was refused. This meant that anyone needing to contact her urgently had to walk or drive all the way up Canal Hill with a note. Still, no-one else appeared to be willing to take on the onerous task of being Secretary, so Dotey soldiered on.

In 1968, the lease at No. 3, The Close fell due for renewal, and of course, it was no longer possible for the family to afford the rent. There was no other option except to apply for a council house. A small estate of new social houses was being built on the edge of Wilcombe, on the opposite side of the canal, and Dotey applied for one of these. Jack happened to know the official in charge of council house allocations, he was a fellow member of the Conservative Club, so Dotey was permitted to attend the council offices and choose which house she would like. Jess accompanied her on this mission and picked out one next to the canal, but this turned out to have only two bedrooms, and a family of five required three; so Dotey chose a house at the end of the terrace, at the far end of the new estate, with the garden backing onto a field.

Under normal circumstances, the mother and father of a family would share a double bedroom, the two boys would have the other large room, and the only daughter would occupy the small room. However, as Dotey explained to Jess, there was no way in which she was going to be forced to share a room with Jack. Jess would have to forego her entitlement to the West-facing single room, which was to be allocated to Jack. Dotey and Jess were obliged to share a back bedroom, hardly ideal for either of them, since each had been used to having her own room at The Close, and both resented the loss of privacy. Coming from the large house to the much smaller council house, they all felt on top of one another. Also, there was nowhere private that Jess could escape to for a good weep in order to relieve the tension, since Dotey forbade her daughter to cry in their room, preferring the stiff upper lip approach and declaring that anyway, Jess had no absolutely no reason for tears, and if anyone was entitled to cry it was Dotey herself. In her mother's opinion, Jess was simply being self-indulgent. So Jess, a hormonal teenager, was obliged to jump on her bike and pedal some distance along the canal tow-path to a secluded bench under the trees, in order to sob her heart out whenever she felt it was all getting too much, which was quite often nowadays. Privately, Jess thought there should be a law forbidding mothers from sharing bedrooms with adolescent daughters; but she accepted that in her own family's straitened circumstances, there was no alternative.

In many respects, the council house was an improvement on The Close, having a new fitted kitchen and a downstairs cloakroom . There were electric storage heaters rather than coal fires, and the estate was served by an hourly bus service. Jess was pleased to discover that their former sub-tenants at The Close, the Chidgeys, newly returned from Nigeria, were living just along the road. These kind people welcomed Jess when Jack tried to stop her from doing her homework in peace. Dotey was upset that Jess had to leave the house in order to study, but there was no other solution. Jess accepted as many evening baby-sitting engagements as possible, being sure of coffee, biscuits, and – provided the baby behaved – peace and quiet.

Increasingly, Dotey disliked being left alone in the house with Jack, she was always fearful that he would attack her, either physically or more often verbally; but such was the terrible atmosphere at home that the boys always went out again after tea, and Jess was driven away by her need to study in peace. Luckily, Jack usually caught the quarter to eight bus back down to the town, and spent his evenings at the Club, relying on one of his pals with a car to drive him home about midnight. One evening, he was carousing until very late, after one of the Club steward's private back-room parties, and was observed kicking a tin can along the main street, in company with another reveller, in the small hours. Several people made sure to approach Dotey in the town the following day, with this important piece of information.

"I heard a noise and looked out of the window, and I seen your hubby and Mr. Rice in Gold Street, really merry they was, playing football with a beer can. What a commotion!"

Dotey later told Jess that she felt ashamed to show her face. What with the baler-twine belted coat and the raucous late-night goings-on, Jack no longer seemed to have any pride. His former ebullience and self-confidence gone, he turned all his rage and resentment upon his long-suffering family. Jess begged Dotey to consider leaving him, but she had no separate income with which to support herself and three children, and it would be well-nigh impossible to find a landlord who would agree to rent a property to a single mother with no male guarantor. Additionally, Dotey was too depressed, too subdued by the tranquillisers prescribed by the doctor, to have sufficient strength to contemplate a move, even had she been able to find somewhere to go. If she had plucked up courage to apply for a different council house, the news would be sure to get back to Jack at the Conservative Club, with his network of local official member spies reporting on everyone's doings – there was no such thing as confidentiality in a gossipy town like Tiverton – and the theoretical option of Dotey instigating legal proceedings against Jack, obtaining an injunction obliging him to leave the house on grounds of violence, she believed would have been to sign her own death warrant.

Dotey accepted that she was stuck with her violent spouse, regarding it as a deserved punishment for her previous sins. At least Jeff was able to quickly escape, since his father had retired and returned to Devon, buying a house at the coast. So Jeff went to live with his father and step-mother, while Jess hoped to go to university as soon as she had done her A levels, and only Peter would be left at home with Dotey. Jess worried about what might happen to Dotey then, going so far as to say that she was tempted to put her university plans on hold; but when she discussed it with Miss Tilley one day after drama class, her teacher told her firmly that she must go to university as planned, since no-one was indispensable, and her mother would manage somehow.

Jess was especially worried when Dotey became ill with flu and was laid up for three weeks. All the household chores, the cooking, cleaning, washing and daily food shopping fell to Jess. At least Jack ate out every day during this period, so as not to be subjected to Jess's indifferent cooking; however, he did not in any other way lift a finger to help Jess with the burden of domestic duties. Jess tried to discuss with her mother what would happen when she left home, but received by way of reply only a small sigh, "Don't you worry your head about what might happen next year, I may very likely be dead by then, so it won't matter." This of course worried Jess even more.

Dotey, in her depressed and tranquillised state of mind, had become fixated on the idea that she would soon die; and not only that, but the children would also all predecease Jack, so that he would be left gloating at how he had seen them all off. Her state of mind deteriorated even further when Jeff appeared one day and announced that his father Albert had died suddenly, having lived only a short while to enjoy his retirement. As for Dotey, Jess felt that if only she could be removed from the terrible domestic situation in which she was presently living, she would have a good chance of regaining her health and strength, but how to achieve this? Dotey continued with her old mantras about having made her bed and being obliged to lie on it, and the sins of the fathers being visited on the children. People who did not know what went on within dysfunctional families always said that childhood was the happiest days of your life, but Jess clung stoically to the belief that this could not be as good as it would get. Somehow, surely, life would improve. Yet, without money or helpful relatives, it was difficult to see how this could be achieved. If Jess went to university, and then trained as a teacher, as her mother wanted her to do, it would be four more years before she was in a position to assist financially, and Jess feared that Dotey might not last that long, becoming mentally and physically worn out with depression, high blood pressure and stress.

When her depression lifted to some extent, Dotey did try to free herself from Jack's domination. Divorce Law Reform was being introduced, and Dotey could receive Legal Aid. She made a preliminary visit to an Exeter solicitor – using a Tiverton lawyer would have aroused suspicion, since many belonged to Jack's club, and anyway, she might well be seen entering or leaving the premises of a local solicitor. The lawyer whom Dotey consulted suggested she draw up a list of evidence, dates on which Jack had beaten her (she had them all noted down in her diary;) a list of the weeks when Jack had refused her housekeeping money, and all instances of verbal and mental cruelty over recent months. He further suggested that Jess might like to give evidence, since the law now accepted eighteen-year-olds as adults. If Jess could provide an account of all the incidences of her father's unkindness, for example relating to Jack preventing her from studying, this would be useful. Jess attended the solicitor's office with her mother and the lawyer duly noted her remarks. He then asked if there had ever been a time when she could recall being happy. Jess thought back over ten long years to 1959, beyond her father's relentless criticism and her autumn landing vigils when Jack had refused to pay for a baby-sitter, and said that she could remember being happy before that fateful St. Swithin's Day; prior to that, she, Peter and Dotey lived an untroubled life. Nothing could have prepared any eight-year-old for the decade of sustained misery that was to follow. The lawyer duly made a note of her comments. However, Dotey was to remain married to Jack for the remainder of her life.

Chapter 46

"I hope you haven't arranged anything for tomorrow evening, Jess. I have a committee meeting and shall need you to stay here and get your father's tea. I'll leave a chop." Dotey announced briskly.

"But I've said I'd meet everyone at the library tomorrow. We're working on our 'Great Man' project."

"You'll just have to cancel it. I'm sure they can manage quite well without you for one evening." Dotey did not think very much of the 'Great Man' project, since Jess's group had chosen Latin American freedom fighter Ernesto 'Che' Guevara. She considered that they should have picked someone more entitled to the epithet of greatness, such as Churchill or President Kennedy. Jess explained that other groups had chosen these men, and more importantly, since Guevara had just died, there was plenty of information about him readily available in the Sunday supplements.

"But I don't want to have to cook Dad's tea; anyway, last time he complained I made a mess of it," said Jess.

"Nonsense, it's easy enough to grill a chop. You can heat up a tin of soup to begin with, and a tin of rice pudding if he wants any afters. I must get to my meeting, they can't do without the Secretary."

"Why can't he get his own tea?" wailed Jess.

"You know perfectly well that your father expects to find his meal ready and waiting for him when he gets home."

"Why can't Peter get it? Why does it have to be me?"

"Now you're simply talking nonsense! Look, the only way your father will allow me to go out is if I can promise him faithfully that you will be here to see to his meal, and you know that the Dramatic Society is the single bit of pleasure in my life. Surely you don't want me to have to give it up, just because you can't be bothered to stay in for once?"

"I know you love the Dramatic Society, but you get to the rehearsals OK, they aren't held so early, and you're always saying that you don't want to go on being Secretary! Every year you complain that no-one else will take it on, so why not tell the committee that Dad

225

won't let you go out to the meetings, then you'll have a good excuse to give up…"

"Of course I can't give up being Secretary in the middle of the year, these things have to be done properly, an officer should only resign at the AGM. It's just that they've altered the time of this particular committee meeting to suit the majority, and I was out-voted."

"So – you're not going to do it? You don't care about seeing me give up the one thing that I enjoy, my only opportunity to get out of the house and see my friends? How selfish you've become, Jess! There was a time when you would have gladly helped me."

"But if I stay here and miss my Che Guevara meeting, then I'll be letting my friends down, and that's just as bad as you not going to the committee… "

"What nonsense! Swanning off to see your friends in the library can't in any way be compared to my committee meeting. I'm very disappointed in you, Jess."

Jess thought that if Jack had to get his own tea for once then maybe that would be a good thing. But her mother would not let the subject rest.

"I'm really quite surprised at you, Jess; after all, you know you call yourself a Christian, and surely a true Christian should be more than willing to sacrifice her own pleasure in order to help her mother…after all, it says in the Bible that children should 'Honour thy father and thy mother' … as you know, it's one of the ten commandments."

"But the library meeting is about a school project, not pleasure; and maybe I'm not a very good Christian."

At bedtime, in their shared room, Dotey refused to respond when Jess wished her goodnight, she merely uttered a tiny sigh. Jess was almost asleep when she heard her mother speaking in a very small voice, as if on the verge of tears. "Funny, I never thought you'd side with him, against me…"

Jess roused herself. "What's that, Mum?"

"I said, I never thought that you would turn against me, to side with him…" Her mother was still speaking in the same flat small voice which Jess had to strain her ears to hear.

Jess sighed. "I'm not siding with him! I think you should go out whenever and wherever you please – you shouldn't have to get his permission."

"But you know quite well that's the way it is. I can't go out until he has had his tea, and he will only let me out early on condition that you promise to be here. One of us has to stay in, and I did hope that you would be co-operative… if we both go out you know he'll simply turn nasty."

"But Mum, I did get his tea once before, don't you remember, and he was nasty then, he said that the potatoes weren't mashed properly, and the fish was too bony... he wasn't a bit pleased or grateful."

"Well, a chop should be much easier, and the peas are straightforward...you just need to make sure you mash the potatoes thoroughly this time. You know, Jess, if you loved me, as you always say you do, you'd willingly do this for me. Of course, if you continue to refuse I can only draw the obvious conclusion… After all, actions speak louder than words," said the small voice occupying the opposite bed. Dotey settled down, satisfied that her work was done.

"OK, I'll do it," sighed Jess, knowing when she was beaten.

The following day Jess made her excuses to the others in the Che Guevara group, saying that she had to go home to cook her father's tea. "Tell the old man to get it himself!" said Mick. Jess explained why she could not do this. "He's very old-fashioned, he thinks a woman's place is in the home. He was born in 1899," she added vaguely. "So he's Victorian." Her friends' fathers were all much younger and had been born in the reign of George 5th.

"Jess, it's the 1960's now! What can he do if you don't stay in? Beat you? Lock you in the house? We really need to get on with the project, time's running out, old Bacon wants it finished by the end of next week!" However her friends stopped haranguing her when they noticed how miserable she looked. Either she had to let her friends down, or her father would be furious and her mother would believe she did not love her; an unenviable choice for a sixteen-year-old. Jess did not tell them that her father would get nasty if she did not cook his tea, she was very much afraid that he might indeed beat her mother or lock her in the house. Dotey always insisted that what went on at home behind closed doors had nothing to do with anyone else.

Dotey's mood had improved considerably. She showed Jess

exactly where everything was, and told her what time she should start preparing the various elements of the meal, before dashing off to her committee meeting. Jack had been forewarned as to his wife's absence and greeted Jess with "Now then, my girl, let's see just what you can do." Jess laid the table with a cloth and cutlery, put the chop under the grill and set the peeled potatoes to boil. She heated up the tinned soup, and poured it into a dish, which she carried carefully to the table where her father was sitting.

"What's this?" Jack, glared over the top of his bi-focals.

"Cream of tomato, I think."

"No, what's this bowl?"

"A soup dish?" asked Jess, wondering what the catch was.

"But that's not my bowl! The soup goes cold quickly in that, I always have my soup served in a nice glass basin."

Jess removed the soup and retuned to the kitchen where she found the glass basin in a cupboard; but when she poured the soup into it and returned to the table, Jack made a face.

"It's gone cold! Re-heat it!" So Jess had to put the soup back in the pan and return it to the hob. Meanwhile, the potatoes were boiling over and the chop was beginning to burn. While she turned her attention to this, the soup began boiling, so she hastily tipped the soup into the basin and served the steaming stuff to Jack for a third time. He gave her a look of utter contempt.

"Didn't you read the instructions on the tin? You should never boil soup, since this impairs the flavour! I can't have this. It's tasteless, been boiled to within an inch of its life!"

Jess, by now feeling very flustered, rushed back to the cooker, where the potatoes were about to boil dry and the chop needed to be turned over. Her father was calling from the living room, using a familiarly dangerous tone of voice.

"There's a hungry man here who's done a day's hard work, grafting to keep his family! So what's keeping you, girl?"

Jess managed to salvage most of the potatoes and mashed them with butter, using the largest fork she could find. They still smelled rather burnt though, and she doubted her father would find them acceptable. The chop was now browned thoroughly on both sides, although it did seem to have shrunk a lot during the cooking process.

She had forgotten about the peas, still in their packet on the draining board. She put the chop and a heap of mash on a dinner plate and took it in, quailing as she set it before her father. His expression told her that he did not think very much at all of her culinary efforts.

"Vegetables? Gravy? Warm plate? You know, the way to a man's heart is through his stomach, and you'll certainly never catch a husband at this rate," raged Jack, waving his cutlery at her in an alarming fashion. "Never mind all this history and Latin and geography that you're meant to be so good at – by far the most important lesson a girl needs to learn is how to serve men! Remember, the Bible says, 'Woman was created as a help-meet for Man.' You don't need to know Latin for that" He cut a piece of the chop.

"Inedible, it's dried up, I can't eat it! You should realise by now that I'm an epicure – know what that means, girl?"

"Not really, Dad."

"You're meant to be so intelligent yet you don't know what an epicure is! It means I have an educated palate and must always have the best of everything. This food is awful, take it all away! I'll have to go without – or do some eggs."

Jack's preferred way of doing eggs was to boil them in the electric kettle, which in those days did not have an automatic switch-off feature but carried on boiling until manually switched off. This cooking method relied on the eggs having thick shells and Jack remembering to turn the kettle off after three and a half minutes. Jess thought she may as well leave him to it. She despondently cleared everything away and decided to head for the library. She might just catch the last twenty minutes before it closed, and try to salvage something from her dreadful evening.

When she returned home, there was no sign of her father, but her mother was at the sink, washing the dishes. Jess asked how her meeting had gone, but Dotey simply nodded curtly without looking at her or replying.

"Well, I did my best," murmured Jess. "I warned you that he didn't like my cooking…"

"Yes, well done, Jess. The old man was furious, he forbade me to leave you in charge of his tea ever again; a clever little scheme, making such a mess of it that I can never ask you to do it in future!

You always were pig-headed, but I hoped I might have drilled some sense into you by now."

"But it wasn't deliberate!" cried Jess. "After I used the wrong soup dish everything else just went wrong, like a chain reaction, and he wouldn't make any allowances."

"Well, at least you've learned one important lesson tonight. When it comes to food, men DON'T make any allowances, they expect their meals to be on time, properly cooked, and nicely served. There is no margin for error. I thought it would be straightforward enough, after all, you're meant to be an intelligent girl, but oh no, you can't even manage to cook a simple meal, and so I get the blame! Luckily the Committee has agreed to put the time of the next meeting back to 7.30 so I won't have to go through all this again."

"But he treats us like servants!"

"Yes, because that's exactly what we are; Jess – better get it into your thick head, women are servants so far as men are concerned. In fact, we are worse off than servants, because they at least receive a wage and are entitled to a few days off every month. We have to be on duty all day every day, unpaid too, so really we are more like slaves! And the only way to avoid all this is not to get married. Just as well to put any silly romantic notions out of your mind right now; if you marry, you are at the disposal of your husband, morn, noon and night. The law of the land supports it. A wife has to make do with whatever money her husband chooses to give her, because the law does not stipulate how much house-keeping she is entitled to; and if a married woman does get a job, any money she earns – like those few shillings I get helping out at the dress shop – that money don't belong to me, but to him. My wage counts as his income so he has to puts it on his tax return."

"But that's so unfair!"

"Yes, it's iniquitous, but you can easily avoid it if you decide sensibly, don't get married, but go in for a career!"

"But surely some people must be happily married – Jackie's parents seem to get on well, and Alison's…"

"They might seem happy enough when you are there, but no-one can ever know what goes on behind closed doors. For a women, marriage is subjugation, not a partnership."

Dotey finished at the sink, dried her hands, then came and unexpectedly put her arms around Jess.

"Maybe this has been a good lesson for you to learn, Jess. Have your own job, your own money, your own life! Be independent – that's the most important thing for a woman. But one other thing I will say – whatever you choose to do – don't ever expect to be happy."

"Why not?"

"Because you can never be happy! If you read your Bible it tells you quite clearly that 'the sins of the fathers are visited on the children'. Your father and I have spoiled it for you." Dotey shook her head, sighed heavily and turned away.

Jess thought this was also unfair. It seemed an extremely daunting task to have to try to prove the Bible wrong by living a happy life, but she resolved to attempt it anyway.

Chapter 47

The annual school dance was looming – English schools had not yet adopted the word 'Prom' for such an event – and Jess had nothing suitable to wear for the occasion. Long dresses were in fashion at the time, but Jess had never possessed such an item. One of her friends, Fran, offered to lend her a spare dress, it was a full-length green and white light cotton number, with rather a daring neckline, which Dotey took one look at and declared quite unsuitable.

"You can't wear that, Jess, it'll look like you're going to the dance in your nightie! And those straps won't suit you, not with your round shoulders. You must find something else!"

"But I haven't anything remotely like an evening dress," said Jess. She told Fran that she would wear the dress, despite her mother's misgivings. However, Fran was offended because Dotey had likened the dress to nightwear. Dotey would not leave the matter alone.

"Jess, you are not to wear that dress! It may suit Fran, but on you it looks dreadful, you're such an awkward shape…"

"Well, in that case, I won't be able to go at all, I've nothing to wear!" wailed Jess. She knew other girls with cupboards full of dresses often made this claim in order to get a new outfit, but in her case it was true, and Dotey knew this. Jess's wardrobe had only a meagre supply of other people's cast-offs, none of which could possibly be worn to a dance. Nowadays, Jess lived in the jeans she had bought with her paper-round money. Sewing was never her strong point, and anyway, her earnings would not stretch to the cost of material for an evening dress. Jess felt like Cinderella.

Her mother was remembering her own dancing days, with new outfits galore provided by her indulgent parents. She deeply regretted that she had been unable to give her daughter the same, and unexpectedly proposed a solution.

"If I permit you to choose a suitable dress, one that meets with my approval, I can put it on my Bobby's budget account. As you know, I pay in eight shillings a month. I can't afford more than £3, as that would exceed my limit."

Jess was astonished and grateful. She had never previously been allowed to buy anything on her mother's account. She and Dotey took the bus to Exeter and looked in Bobby's girls-wear department. Dotey, controlling the purse-strings, insisted that the dress chosen should not be a long one, it would be far more sensible to get something which could be worn on other occasions. They eventually settled on a knee-length shirt-waisted dress in a pretty shade of blue, with a small floral design, with a discreet ruffled neckline. Jess was delighted, this was the first new item of clothing she had received since the cessation of Aunt Gladys' Canadian parcels some years ago. Dotey paid the £3, which was to Jess an enormous sum to be spending on one single item. Cinderella, you shall go to the ball…

Fran was cross. "I thought you said you wanted a long dress, like everyone else?"

"I did, but Mum wouldn't let me wear that one of yours."

"What's it got to do with her? We can wear what we like!"

"I can't really; she just won't give up if she thinks I'm unsuitably dressed. Remember the struggle I had to get my jeans for drama group? And I won't be the only one there in a short dress, some of the younger girls will have them."

"The younger girls will be in short dresses perhaps, but you're in the Lower Sixth! I was only trying to help you, Jess! It's really time you stood up to your mother, she's far too domineering and you're much too timid!"

But Jess had not yet learned to stand up to Dotey with any degree of success, since whenever she tried, her mother would skilfully deploy every tactic at her disposal to make Jess feel guilty. The sighs, the frowns, the disapproving looks, the sulks and eventually the tears, ('When I think of what I've sacrificed for you, and this is how you repay me!') The clincher was the wan smile, accompanied in a small voice by, "Of course, I won't be here for very much longer, there'll soon be no-one to advise you, and then you'll be able to do just as you please…" Jess fell for it every time, even though she was aware that this was simply another of her mother's melodramatic performances.

When it came to the subject of make-up, Dotey was as controlling as she was about Jess's clothes. It was becoming fashionable for girls to make up their eyes, with eye-liner, eye-shadow and lashings of

233

mascara. Jess had bought some blue eye-shadow from her paper-round earnings, and to her astonishment, Dotey had permitted Jess to keep a stick of mascara which fell out of a packet of Surprise Peas as a free gift. However, when Jess was applying the make-up before the school dance, Dotey insisted on supervising.

"You're really far too heavy-handed! Wipe it off! I won't have you going out looking like that, it looks tarty!"

"But you use make-up," murmured Jess.

"Yes, a little powder and lip-stick! Not that dreadful eye shadow, it makes you look like a panda. And I'm much older than you, women of a certain age need a little make-up, whereas you are still a girl, so no need for that stuff!"

Jess lacked confidence, disliked any argument, and longed for a quiet life; her mother knew this, deploying the full range of weaponry in her emotional armoury, and was thus always assured of her daughter's eventual capitulation.

The main difficulty for Jess was that she no longer had her own room to escape to. Since the family's move from The Close to the much smaller council house, Jess had been obliged to share a room with her mother. Jess's bed was in the far corner, while Dotey's was near the door. In the centre of the room were two wardrobes, one facing towards Jess's half, the other towards Dotey's, so that Jess had the back of her mother's wardrobe near her bed. She found this quite oppressive, and stuck a couple of posters donated by friends from their 'Jackie' magazines on the blank wood to cheer things up a bit. The posters featured young footballer George Best and actor Alexis Kanner. The room was not very large, and there was really insufficient space for two beds and two wardrobes, so that each half resembled a narrow cell. Every night, Dotey dragged the small chest of drawers against the door, so that Jack could not get in. This meant that Jess had always to be in bed before the barricade could be put in place, so no late nights for her. Dotey would be waiting to close the room up for safety's sake, giving Jess a good telling off if she was late, asking where on earth had she been, and why had she dilly-dallied on the way home, when she knew they must batten down the hatches before Jack returned home, drunk and disorderly.

Surprisingly, after the initial humiliation of losing his business and having to relocate to a less prestigious address, Jack seemed to have taken the move in his stride. Unlike Canal Hill, the new house was on a bus route into town, so there was no long hill to climb back home. Jack soon became friendly with all the regulars on the bus. Also, the family were now living quite close to the new Catholic church, where Bingo was held on Sunday afternoons. Jack became a devotee of the game, much to Dotey's disgust, although she did concede that it got him out of the house. Occasionally Jack would win a prize; Jess once received a dressing-table set from this unlikely source. Jess came to realise that of her parents, her mother was by far the more snobbish of the pair. Jack, who as an agricultural merchant had been used to dealing with down-to-earth old farmers and well-off landowners, could talk to anyone, whereas Dotey maintained her dislike of the 'common' people, among whom she now found herself obliged to live.

Chapter 48

Jess knew that Gilbert was coming to the Grammar School, she had heard his story from Dotey, who had got it from her friend Mary who lived in the flat downstairs from Gilbert's older sister. Following a tragic incident of carbon monoxide poisoning, when father and son had been staying in a remote caravan, Gilbert was lucky to survive, and regained consciousness to find that he had been left an orphan. He had been sent to a charitable Boarding School, but was now coming to live with his sister, who taught at the Grammar School, to study for his A levels. It so happened that the newcomer was allocated the desk in front of Jess in their classroom, he was studying Geology and Geography, as was Jess, so it was inevitable that they should spend a lot of time together. Jess suggested that he might like to come to the Friday Youth Club at the Church Hall, of which she was secretary, thinking that this would be way for him to get to know more people; and Gilbert accepted. He mistook Jess's invitation as being asked out on a date, which had not been Jess's intention, since she would never have had the confidence to ask a boy out. Drilled by Dotey, she knew that girls should never ever push themselves forward. Jess had swallowed completely Dotey's line about her being an awkward, round-shouldered, clumsy lump, so did not imagine for an instant that any boy would be the slightest bit interested in her. Yet here was this newcomer seemingly keen to spend time with her. Jess was astonished.

It was the fact that Gilbert liked Jess that attracted her to him. No-one had shown much interest in her before; Jess had had an early crush on one of the school librarians, and he had at first seemed quite keen on her, but he had then taken up with someone else. Jess had been a bit upset by this, and Dotey had asked why she was going about looking like a "Dying duck in a thunderstorm", but Jess always found it impossible to confide in her mother, preferring instead to tell the tale to sympathetic Norah next door. Then, the Sunday paper-boy, two years older than herself, had for a while been the object of Jess's silent devotion; she had gazed at him after she had finished writing her O level geography exam in the school hall, when he was doing the A level paper. A level candidates were seated on the stage, facing the main body of the hall, and Jess watched his expressive face in deep thought, possibly considering the best way to answer complicated questions about glaciation or stratigraphy; however Jess had realised all along that her admiration was hopeless, since it was well-known that he was going out with a pretty blonde sixth former, and anyway he was about to go off to college. The very idea of a boy being interested enough in Jess to invite her to accompany him bird-watching or for bike rides, or canoeing on the river, was a complete novelty and so she accepted Gilbert's invitations with pleasure.

Naturally, Dotey was dead against it all. She criticised Gilbert continually, hoping to make him less attractive in Jess's eyes, but of course, succeeded only in achieving the opposite effect. Dotey pointed out that every activity Gilbert suggested was free, whereas a proper boy-friend should be prepared to spend money on a girl. Jess protested that they were still at school, and had very little money; and anyway, she liked the bike rides and bird-watching, although she was a little unsure about canoeing, being afraid at times that they might get swept over the weir.

Dotey then commented how unchivalrous Gilbert was, refusing to walk her home, instead leaving her at the roundabout at the bottom of Canal Hill, saying that he really did not want to trail all the way up that blooming steep hill and back down again. He had done it once and wondered where on earth they were going… Any boyfriend worth his salt would be sure to see a girl safely home, said Dotey. In truth, Jess did find this rather disappointing, but she accepted that it was a long way up Canal Hill for any but the most ardent of admirers to escort her. Dotey next harped on about Gilbert's lack of stature, his status as an orphan, and how Jess was obviously a motherly type whose feelings for her classmate must surely be purely maternal; but Jess did not agree. She and Gilbert got on well, but it was an innocent boy/girl friendship. Jess knew that it was not Gilbert in particular to whom her mother would be likely to object, but any boy with whom she spent time. When she summoned up the courage to say as much to Dotey her mother protested, declaring that she would have no reservations about a nice boy – but that in her opinion Gilbert

237

was not a very nice boy. What were they doing this Saturday night? Babysitting at the Cardwells – another free activity, which simply proved Dotey's point!

Gilbert's Christmas present to Jess was a calendar, featuring an attractive photograph which he had taken of St. Peter's Church in the snow, with two little birds perched together on a branch. ("Home made – how cheap! He still doesn't want to spend any money on you!") Jess and Gilbert went to the Youth Club Christmas party together, where the band – The Caber Terrapin Quintet – comprised five of their sixth form classmates, playing their first engagement. Gilbert and Jess were still going around together the following Spring, but after a few more bike-rides and cuddles in the bracken, Gilbert wanted to take their relationship to another level, and Jess recoiled at this suggestion. She was still very naïve and not yet ready for any kind of sexual relationship. Unsurprisingly, Gilbert then complained that he found her naivety exasperating, she never understood his jokes, or maybe she was simply pretending that she did not, in order to preserve a façade of innocence. Jess genuinely did not get the jokes about nuns and candles, and she protested vehemently that she really did not understand, it was no pretence, and Gilbert must remember that she did not have a television and had been obliged to lead a sheltered life... Finally, she trod on a twig which snapped loudly, scaring away all the birds when they were in the woods looking for a lesser spotted woodpecker which had allegedly been sighted close by, thus annoying Gilbert. Jess realised that the relationship was coming to an end. An older male neighbour then took Gilbert under his wing, inviting him round to listen to classical music in his room, so Gilbert stopped coming to Youth Club, preferring the delights of Beethoven to table tennis. Dotey promptly informed Jess that the neighbour was reputed to prefer the company of young boys, and that she had of course had her suspicions about Gilbert all along...

Gilbert and Jess were both still going to Geology and Geography lessons, so bumped into each other every school day. At weekends, Gilbert could be seen riding his bike round the town, and he was also going out canoeing with other boys who were much better at managing their paddles than Jess had ever been, so no danger of going over the weir with them. Then Jess and Gilbert were due to go on a Geography/Geology class field trip to Pembrokeshire, at Easter 1968. The idea was to camp near St. David's to look at coastal landforms and search for fossils. Mr. Edwards, who taught both subjects, was to be in charge, with Mr. Gough, the R.E. teacher, providing transport with his mini-bus. Gilbert's sister was also to come along to act as chaperone for the girls. There were two large and three smaller tents, one for most of the boys and one for most of the girls; Mr. Edwards had a smaller one sharing with Gilbert, while Mr. Gough shared with his son Martin, and Gilbert's sister shared with Jess.

Dotey thought the whole scheme perfectly hare-brained; camping at Easter, when the weather was so unreliable… She was very reluctant to let Jess go, but Jess explained how important it was for her studies, and that she woud be the only one of the class not to attend if Dotey forbade it. Accordingly, they all set off, travelling in the minibus and Mr. Edwards' car, making camp at a windy cliff-top site at Carfai Bay. Unfortunately, the weather worsened durng the night and the boys' tent blew down; there was nothing for it but for them to seek shelter in the other large tent which was of course occupied by several girls. Jess was asleep in her small shared tent, and so missed all the excitement. The following day they tried to have a cliff-top walk, but the wind was still so strong that it was impossible to make proper headway. Towards mid-afternoon, the girls had decided that they had had enough and it was suggested that the party should return home. Everyone agreed, except for Mr. Edwards, Gilbert, and Martin, who elected to remain.

By the time camp had been struck and the minibus loaded, it was well into the evening, and they did not arrive back in Tiverton until late at night. Jess wondered how she would get back into the house, since she did not have a key; Dotey had said young people must be aged 21 before they were permitted to come and go as they pleased. Fortunately, Jess's loud knocking at the front door awoke Jack, who stuck his head out of his bedroom window; Jess was afraid he might decide to begin one of his serenades, but instead he came downstairs to let her in. Dotey reminded Jess that she had of course predicted that the trip would end in disater, and seemed pleased to be completely vindicated.

After this, Jess took up with a crowd of classmates who met at the town library every evening, occasionally going on to the cinema. One of the boys in the group, Richard, had a motorbike, and often gave Jess a lift home. This was in the days before pillion passengers were obliged by law to wear a crash helmet, but Richard always drove very steadily and Jess never felt that she was in any danger. Gilbert was only on the periphery of the group, so Jess did not find the situation too difficult, and in any case, she was increasingly busy with her studies and other activities.

The next boy to ask Jess out was one of a pair of twins, who invited her to accompany him to the cinema to see the film 'Camelot.' Jess arrived at the Tivoli at the appointed time, to find no sign of John. She went home feeling very let down, this was her first experience of being 'stood up'. The following day, she bumped in to John's twin, Tim, who explained that John had been very engrossed in setting up his moth trap and had consequently forgotten all about Jess. Maybe she and John could rearrange their cinema date? However, Jess did not care for the idea of playing second fiddle to a load of moths, so sent a message declining.

Dotey suspected that Jess was still holding a candle for Gilbert, and she was right. It turned out that Gilbert was also regretting ending his association with Jess; but Jess was not to discover this fact for another thirty years, when the two eventually met up again. Tim was organising a school reunion in 2002 and circulated everyone's contact details via email. Gilbert was then living in Ireland, and unable to attend the reunion, but he came the following year to visit his sister, still living in Devon. By this time Jess and Gilbert both had families and careers, and there was a great deal of catching up to be done. Gilbert had of course been very much aware that Dotey had never liked him; he recalled meeting Jess and her mother out shopping in the town, shortly before he and Jess were both due to leave for their respective universities. Gilbert told Jess that he had really wanted to talk to her at the time, but something in Dotey's stern gaze had prevented him from saying anything, and he had allowed the moment to pass.

After re-establishing contact, Gilbert and Jess remained friends, occasionally visiting each other and meeting each other's families.

It turned out that both had worked for academic institutions, Gilbert as a lecturer and Jess as a researcher. Both had travelled extensively, and had a number of publications to their credit – scientific papers in Gilbert's case, while Jess had written four novels and contributed numerous pieces to the Guardian newspaper. The unspoken question lingered – if they had stayed in touch, could it ever have worked between the two of them? After giving the matter some consideration, Jess did not think it would have, since they both had had such a lot of growing up to do when they first met; and she was quite thankful that by then it was much too late to find out.

Chapter 49

After the family had left the Close, Dotey and Jess still continued to visit it on their Sunday afternoon walks, which of course now started on the opposite side of the canal. One day they called in the see Norah, whom Dotey had heard was not well. They found her in a dreadful state, looking emaciated and gaunt, propped up in her bed against grey pillows and with the flat in complete disarray. Jess began tidying up as best she could, while Dotey looked around for anything which she could quickly prepare for Norah to eat. All she could find was a tin of Ambrosia rice pudding, so she heated it up and spooned the stuff into a tearful Norah.

"It's throat cancer, Dotey; they say the drink has caused it, so I'm dying of drink, as they always warned me I would."

"Hush, Norah; try to eat a little. When was the last time you ate anything?"

"I can't eat, only drink…"

Dotey felt duty-bound to report Norah's condition to her sister, who lived a short distance away. The sister was not especially pleased to learn of Dotey's visit to Norah, and was particularly unhappy to hear that Jess had also been present. She instructed Dotey that Jess was never to go again, giving as her reason the fact that it would be much too upsetting for her. Jess thought that the real reason might be that she was ashamed of the state of Norah's flat, how could anyone allow a terminally ill sister to live like that? However, she complied with Norah's sister's command, and never saw Mrs. O'Shaughnessy again. Dotey refused to be bound by any injunctions regarding visits, and called to see Norah several times until she eventually died. Meanwhile, Fern had moved away to a Sussex care home to be near her relatives; she survived into a grand old age, outliving Dotey by many years, and was well enough, aged 85, to write to congratulate Jess on the birth of her first son in 1978.

Jess also visited the old people in Belmont Hospital, the former Tiverton workhouse. A group of girls from the Sixth Form went once a week and chatted to the old ladies and gents sitting in the day-room. Jess found it difficult to make conversation with those who could not readily respond, there was only so much one could say about the weather or the singing of the resident budgie. Fortunately, in a side ward lay Mrs. Kingdom, who had suffered a severe stroke rendering her immobile She had been a teacher and her mind was still very alert. Jess used to have long chats with her, while the other girls made small-talk in the day-room.

Dotey once accompanied Jess on a visit to Mrs. Kingdom and shuddered at the sight of some of the Belmont patients. "I'd hate to get to that state, like a vegetable! I'd rather be dead than live like that, being a burden to everyone!" exclaimed Dotey, who could not know that a few years after this pronouncement, a sudden stroke would kill her within a few hours. There was to be no sad lingering for Dotey, and she was to have her wish granted, being at work at 11 in the morning and dead by 11 pm the same day.

Meanwhile, the new Headmaster wanted to get one of his girl pupils into Cambridge University. In 1968 only three Cambridge colleges admitted women, and competition for places was very keen. The Headmaster told six of the brightest girls to spend the summer reading as widely as possible, not forgetting a quality daily newspaper. The 'Daily Mail' was not on the Headmaster's list, and of course, Dotey and Jack would not think of changing their daily paper, or buying an extra one just for Jess, so she had to go to the library every day to read 'The Guardian'. When the time came for the special Cambridge examination, Jess and the five other candidates were closeted for the morning in the medical inspection room, writing amongst other things, the inaugural speech for the newly-elected US President. Jess liberally peppered the speech with patriotic-sounding phrases such as "My fellow Americans", ending with "God Bless America"; she also made upbeat reference to the on-going Vietnam war, despite being very much anti-war herself. She was on firmer ground when it came to the Geography paper, which asked about things with which she was familiar, such as features of glacial landscapes and the science behind monsoon climates. The university had said the interviews would be on December 6th, and every day one of the girls who had sat the exam came into school shaking her head and announcing that she had received a rejection letter. Eventually, Jess was the only one of the six candidates who had not heard from Cambridge. Time was getting short, and it was doubtful whether any letter would arrive in time for Jess to make proper travel arrangements.

"They'll telephone!" exclaimed the Headmaster. Jess reminded him that the home telephone had been cut off.

"Well, they'll phone the school! It's good to know they haven't ruled you out, they must still be considering you. Be ready to travel on 6th, they could ring as late as the 5th."

Jess thought it extremely rude of the university not to give better notice. Now complete strangers were accosting her and demanding to know if she had heard from Cambridge, seemingly everyone was following her progress. Eventually the 6th of December came, and still she had heard nothing. The Headmaster was extremely disappointed, but Jess was quite relieved, Cambridge would have been such a long and awkward cross-country train journey, and the weather was bitterly cold. Dotey had been obliged to find Jess money for the fare, which would not be reimbursed by the County Council until after the trip; when Jess was not called, her mother heaved a sigh of relief and quietly replaced the borrowed money in the 'Express and Echo' tin. The letter telling Jess she was not required did not arrive until the 7th. Jess often wondered in later life whether she would have got into Cambridge if there had been an equal number of places for men and women. Her old rival from Westfield, Jake, now at Blundells, had obtained a place – and Jess remembered she had finished the sum-book before him.

Chapter 50

By New Year 1969 Dotey and Jack were both suffering from mental illnesses. Both were depressed, Jack because of the failure of his business, and Dotey as the victim of domestic abuse. Jack was also very likely suffering from a degree of alcohol-induced dementia. However, mental illness was regarded in those days as a sign of lack of strength of character, to which no-one readily admitted, and about which no-one talked. It was rumoured that a member of the Dramatic Society had had a nervous breakdown; but unlike other pieces of gossip, this was not something Dotey was keen to discuss. Her own mother had been incarcerated in the Devon County Asylum twenty years previously, with what was then referred to as manic depression, supposedly brought on by the change of life. Dotey lived throughout her forties and fifties – as long as Jess had known her – in fear and dread that the same illness might strike her. It did not; but in Dotey's case, her appalling domestic situation was enough to send any woman spiralling into depression. The perennial financial worry caused by Jack withholding the housekeeping money, coupled with the unremitting physical and verbal assaults, were more than anyone could be expected to bear. Yet there seemed to be nothing which could be done to remedy the situation, so Dotey kept going as best as she could by taking the tranquillisers Dr. Foster prescribed, which if anything made her even more unwell, very nervy and subject to extended bouts of paranoia.

Dotey's only relative in any position to assist, her step-mother Gladys, was in Canada, married to her German millionaire husband Otto. Dotey wrote to Gladys asking for the return of her own mother's silver, because she was in such dire financial circumstances that she was unable to pay the electricity bill. In reply, Gladys sent a cheque for twenty pounds, and a letter stating that she felt quite unable to let any of her 'Dear George's' things go; this despite the fact that her Dear George's daughter was obviously quite desperate, while Gladys was comfortably off. By the time the cheque arrived, the children had clubbed together to pay the bill from their holiday job wages, so Dotey spent the money on a week's coach holiday to Folkestone and the Isle of Wight. It was to be the last holiday she ever had.

After Dotey died, Gladys sent Jess a maudlin letter, bewailing the fact that she had not 'done more' for her step-daughter. She eventually returned the solid silver cutlery to Jess on a visit to Bournemouth. It was an ugly, incomplete set, and Jess sold it to buy a washing machine, since by then everyone was using stainless steel cutlery. Jess had just had a baby, who wore terry nappies. (Disposables were yet to be invented.) It transpired when Uncle Otto died three weeks before his hundredth birthday that, despite his great wealth, he had been very thrifty, and Gladys had not had the oodles of money at her disposal that Dotey had fondly imagined. Otto had saved on household expenses wherever possible, so that Gladys had been obliged at the age of 90 to nurse her almost-centenarian husband, who was not prepared to go to the expense of employing a professional carer. Of her three husbands, her Dear George was the best, she tearfully assured Jess, on a visit too view the Book of Remembrance at Bournemouth crematorium. This was in 1989, on the anniversary of George's untimely death on a golf course. Jess's young children were also in attendance, and little Alex declared that he did not think very much of this park, and where were all the swings?

Following his business failure, Jack's state of mind had become fixated on the subject of sex. He accused Dotey of incest with her sons, and of conducting a lesbian affair with a young woman from the Dramatic Society. Jack boasted to Jeff that he had had Dotey at various sites all around Alphington village, including up against the phone-box, and that he, Jack, was also Jeff's father. (Discussing this in later years, Jess and Jeff agreed that it would have been rather awkward for anyone hoping to make a telephone call.) Jack then became obsessed with the idea that Jess was pregnant. This was actually the most interest he had taken in Jess throughout her life; her academic achievements had been scornfully dismissed or completely ignored, but the idea that she might be pregnant seemed to fascinate him. He diligently questioned Dotey as to whether Jess was getting her periods every month, despite his wife's constant assurances that Jess was a still a virgin. Jack then went on to announce that he would like to see Dotey pregnant again and they should have another child. Dotey protested this this was impossible since she was now well past the change of life. Jess, coming into the living room in the middle of this strange conversation was amazed at her father's hypocrisy; Jack was continually complaining that he had too many people to keep, that his children were still sponging on him like leeches; yet he was now proposing to add to the dependent brood. She plucked up sufficient courage to point out to Jack that he would have to apply for an increase in his Social Security payments to cover the cost of an extra mouth to feed; whereupon her father turned a dangerous shade of puce and Jess was promptly hustled out of the room by her mother. Jess had had a narrow escape, said Dotey. She must never again mention the words 'Social Security' if she valued her own safety.

During one of Jack's tirades about her living off him, Jess had asked why he had had children he was not prepared to support. Jack grinned and replied that he had very much enjoyed making her, but that was as far as it went. Dotey immediately cut in with "Jack, don't be disgusting!" but Jess realised that her father had spoken the truth. He had wanted sex, not children, and he tolerated his daughter, the unintended consequence of his actions, only grudgingly. He did not like women in general and he clearly despised Jess in particular. There was nothing Jess could do to please him apart from removing herself from his life. Jess was trapped. She felt as a wrongly convicted offender must do. The sins of her fathers were indeed being visited on Jess, just as her mother had said they would, as it stated in the Bible. God was testing her, to the limit of her youthful endurance; she could only hope and pray she would prove strong enough.

Chapter 51

During her time in the sixth form, Jess acquired a steady boyfriend. It happened much to her surprise, having been arranged between the boy, R—, and the technical drawing master, for whom Jess often babysat. This teacher lived not far from Jess and was a member of the Dramatic Society. Jess was listening to music on the gramophone – such a luxury, since her own family did not possess one – and trying to get on with some studying, when there was a knock at the door. Jess opened it to find R—, who announced that he had come to collect a record he had lent to the technical drawing teacher, "Genuine Dud". By the time Jess had found the record and made R— a cup of coffee, it was agreed that they would henceforth go out together. The teacher and his wife were of course in on the whole thing, since their first question on arriving home was to enquire innocently if anyone had called while they had been out…

Jess and R—'s first date was to Cullompton Youth Club, where Jess was surprised to be introduced to R—'s Uncle, a man of indeterminate age but hardly a youth. Uncle had several games of table tennis with his nephew, with Jess looking on, before she had to get the bus back home. Their next date was to Newton Abbot Stock Car racing. R— had borrowed his father's car to take some mates, and Uncle was of course of the party, sitting in the front with R—. As they approached the race course, where the event was to be held, R— slowed the car down and the mates jumped out, intending to climb over a fence to gain free entry. Jess was not terribly impressed with stock car racing, but felt it was good to be widening her horizons. Things did seem to be looking up a bit when R— again arranged to borrow the car to take Jess down to the coast at the weekend; but then his parents decided that they would also enjoy a trip to the sea, so Jess was obliged to squeeze in the back of the Austin Mini with Mother R—, while Father R— in the passenger seat kept exhorting his son not drive so fast on 'these old roads.'

It was very difficult to get time together, as there always seemed to be a relative in attendance, usually Uncle. They went to weekend dances and parties at Willand Village Hall or Clapps Café, and sometimes went for a walk to the park. Then, as part of a newly imposed, strict regime, R—s parents announced that he was not to see Jess any more until the A level exams were over, since she was distracting him from his studies, and they consequently forbade him the use of their car in order to meet Jess. R— sometimes managed to visit her mid-week on an old moped, especially if she was out baby-sitting and they could have some time alone together. Jess had asked her baby-sitting clients if it was all right for her to bring a boyfriend, and all had said it was fine, except one family, who cited the case of their friends' baby-sitter who had become pregnant. Jess was rather indignant at this refusal, it seemed that the family trusted her enough to look after their baby, but did not trust her to look after herself. She and R— did not sleep together, Dotey had dinned it into Jess that nice girls would never do such a thing before marriage. Jess and R— listened to music or watched television. Both had been very strictly brought up, and would never betray their respective parents' trust.

After the mock A level exams were over, with both R— and Jess achieving good marks, Jess asked Dotey if R— could stay at their house, sleeping on the settee, when there was an event in Tiverton, since it was so cold for him to be returning to Cullompton at dead of night on the moped. Dotey agreed. R— then asked his parents to return the favour, when the party or dance was in the Cullompton area. They gave their consent very unwillingly. Their problem was that they both left for work very early in the morning, Mother R— did a post round, while Father R— was the care-taker at a local school. This meant that for a few hours in the morning Jess and R— were left together, un-chaperoned, in the house until Mother R— returned from the post round. Their early start meant that both R— parents retired to bed early, but were unwilling to leave R— and Jess still sitting up. Father R— solved this problem, rather high-handedly Jess felt, by turning off all the lights and the television at 9.30pm and ordering Jess and R— to their separate beds, which in Jess's case was the settee. She lay there in the darkness, wishing she had brought a torch and a reading book. She could not even get up to make herself a cup of tea, since she knew that any sound would bring the R—s from their room in order to check what was going on.

Throughout the 1960s, the age of majority at which young people could vote and were deemed to be mature enough to make their own decisions was twenty-one. Parliament then voted to lower the age to eighteen. This change in the law did not please Dotey, or indeed the R—s, in the least. They were firmly of the opinion that no-one should be released from the yoke of parental authority until they reached twenty-one, considering that young people of eighteen were still only children. Jess and R— were both in the cohort which quietly came of age in 1970, when the new law came into effect, missing out on eighteenth birthday coming of age celebrations; by the time they reached twenty-one, this was no longer a milestone of such great significance. Dotey felt her control over Jess ebbing away, since at eighteen, Jess was now free to obtain a passport without parental consent, and she had formed the view that she was now entitled to come and go as she pleased. Dotey's mantra, "You are under my control until you are twenty-one!" was countered with "But the law says it's eighteen now!"

Jess's boyfriend's parents also insisted on maintaining the old-fashioned line. Father R— came originally from the Blackburn area, having met Mother R— when installing a milking machine on her parents' Devon farm. He was considerably younger than Mother R. A true Northerner, he always spoke his mind and laid down the law in the bluntest possible terms, leading Jess to wonder if everyone 'up North' resembled a Lancastrian version of Heathcliffe.

"Tha'll do as I say until tha's twenty-one in this house; I don't hold with this yeere 'key of the door at eighteen' nonsense! And am I not to be Maister in my own house?"

R— was an only child; he was actually a year and a half older than Jess, but so strict was the parental discipline in the household that he dared not disobey. Matters came to a head the third time Jess stayed at the R—'s house, when she awoke in the middle of the night on the settee, doubled up with period pains. She knocked gently on R—'s bedroom door, to ask if there were any aspirins in the house. R— eventually found some for her in the bathroom cabinet. The next morning Father R— announced that Jess was no longer welcome at the R—'s house, what with the two of them creeping around at night and then alone in the house for an hour the next morning; 'the entire village will be talking'. In vain did Jess try to explain that she had only needed an aspirin and had not intended to rouse the household; but it seemed that R—'s clattering about in the bathroom had disturbed his parents, who had assumed the worst. Father R— then told the pair that he and Mother had decided that they were not to see each other again. This was to be his final word, and after all, was he not Maiste…

Jess and R— both wept bitterly at the injustice of it; they had tried so hard not to offend either family, but received no thanks. That anyone should speak to two young adults in this manner would be completely risible today, and rather than provoking tears, the parents would probably be told to get lost in colourful language, but it was not in either Jess nor R—'s nature or upbringing to be rude to their parents. Nevertheless, R— refused bravely to agree to his parents' demand that he should not see Jess. He continued to visit Jess on the moped, and to occasionally sleep on Dotey's settee. Jess was relieved that Dotey had taken such a sensible attitude, and had not forbidden R— to visit, but Dotey felt that at least she knew what the pair were up to when they were under her roof. Of course they had absolutely no chance of getting up to anything, as Jess continued to share the cramped bedroom with her mother, complete with barricaded door, while R— was obliged to make do as best he could on the uncomfortable sofa.

Chapter 52

The A levels arrived, and this time it was the Geology practical that worried Jess, the necessity of having to identify several fossils and lumps of rock without the help of diagrams. Students were provided with small phials of acid, in order to test the reaction of various rocks, to help determine which type they were; and magnifying glasses in order to peer more closely at the fossils. Jess hoped she had done well enough, but expected to do better in the written exam. R— sailed through his technical drawing exam with very little effort in order to concentrate on his Maths and Physics. He was planning to train as a civil engineer.

Soon it was time for Jess and R— to leave school and get summer jobs. The Cullompton by-pass, now part of the M5 motorway, was under construction, and R— got a job as a labourer. Meanwhile, Jess was taken on at a factory on the other side of town which made such items as sponge-bags and make-up bags. She was put in the packing department. The job involved working all day in a hot shed with Radio 1 blaring away. The packers were constantly on their feet filling boxes, and the boss took the opportunity to come round and pinch the women's bottoms as they worked. This was before sexual harassment at work became a crime, and any woman who complained stood to lose her job. They all hated having to put up with it, but being powerless and part of an non-unionised work-force, could only grin and bear it. Jess quickly realised she was quite safe from the boss's wandering hands, he was a member of the Conservative Club, and Jack might well have had something to say if she had reported any assault to him. Unsurprisingly, the odious boss always made a point of behaving nicely with Jess.

It was the first time in her career that Jess had been obliged to clock in, at 8am. A works van came along Blundells Road at 7.30, picking up employees, but this was a bit far out of Jess's way. Jess discovered that a man who worked in the cutting department of the factory lived just around the corner from her, so she asked if she could travel to work with him in his van. He frowned, and said that she could on odd occasions, but certainly not on a regular basis. Jess thought this very churlish of him, since she had been more than willing to share his petrol costs; but it turned out that the man's wife did not allow him to give lifts to female colleagues. Jack was on nodding terns with this woman, whom he saw every day on his way to the bus stop. He reckoned she had previous reason to doubt her husband's faithfulness and so now kept him on a short leash. Jess was then offered the loan of a bicycle, her old one having rusted away. The borrowed machine was owned by the wife of one the Grammar School teachers, who was at the time heavily pregnant and so did not need it for the summer. Jess was now able to make her way to work independently. Dotey at first decreed that the bike be kept in the back garden, since the council house did not have an outdoor shed; but Jess was afraid that thieves might steal such a good machine, which she would never be able to replace, so insisted that she must be allowed to bring it into the kitchen last thing every night. Dotey reluctantly agreed.

Jess started to enjoy her work more when her friend Alison joined the packing staff. Originally, Alison had arranged to work at Lloyd Maunders slaughterhouse, but like Jess's brother Jeff, Alison left after only one morning, finding the conditions too harrowing. She had decided to take the job in the first place only because the pay was so much better than at Jess's factory. Jess had known all along that she herself would never have been able to cope at Lloyd Maunders, and was not really surprised when Alison gave it up. Her friend, finding herself unexpectedly jobless, asked Jess to whom she should enquire regarding employment at the factory, so Jess asked the steely personnel manager if more hands were required over the summer, and Alison was soon working on the opposite side of Jess's packing bench.

All the girls chatted about their boyfriends. Alison was going to Spain with her young man after her stint at the factory ended, while Jess and R— were planning a more modest trip to Bristol, in order that the prospective civil engineer could view the Clifton Suspension Bridge and the new Severn Road Bridge. R— had bought a second-hand car, an A30, with his wages from labouring, and he and Jess had decided that after the exams and the gruelling vacation jobs they deserved an end-of-summer treat. Unsurprisingly, Dotey was absolutely against the idea.

"But where will you stay the night?" was her chief concern.

"We'll find a B and B, there's bound to be plenty in a city the size of Bristol," said Jess. She knew what her mother was worried about. "It's OK, we'll get two single rooms!"

"Hmm, in my opinion it's extremely ill-advised, two young people going away together overnight. And I don't expect R—'s parents are very happy either. I'd be very interested to know what have they had to say about your little scheme."

"I don't think he's told them yet," said Jess. She knew of course that R— had no intention of ever telling his parents, who would raise even louder objections than Dotey if they learned of the proposed trip. R— planned to say that he was staying over at Jess's house for a couple of nights, sleeping on the settee. Luckily, neither family was on the telephone, and therefore could not check up with the other. Jess saw no reason to explain all this to Dotey, since she and R— had been working hard all summer, both earning and contributing to their respective family budgets. What they planned to do with their own leisure time was their own business, and they now had the law on their side.

"As long as you know I don't approve! If that wretched law wasn't changing I'd make you a ward of court to stop you!"

To which Jess now simply replied "Yes, Mum, I know," although she doubted the courts would have been very concerned about her; surely ward-ship was more for flighty heiresses who were planning to elope with caddish fortune-hunters rather than two very ordinary young adults on their way to view suspension bridges.

"And yet you intend to continue, despite my clearly expressed wishes? I'm so very disappointed in you, Jess!"

Jess had previously been hurt when Dotey expressed such disappointment, but she was now becoming harder of heart.

It may seem ludicrous to most modern audiences that there should be such fuss about two adults going away to Bristol for a few days. Jess's friends with more enlightened parents found it hard to understand, after all it was the very end of the swinging sixties and lots of young women were going away on proper holidays with their boy-friends, some even overseas. Dotey was horrified that any mother could permit such a thing, but of course, not only did the law of the land allow it, but the sensible parents were quite happy as well.

The sixties had seen a range of liberalisation in many areas of personal life. Law reforms concerning abortion, divorce and the decriminalisation of homosexuality had all been introduced. The arrival of the contraceptive pill meant that women no longer lived in fear of unplanned pregnancies, and could take control of their own fertility. Originally 'the pill', as it became known, was prescribed to married women only, and unmarried women wore borrowed wedding rings for their medical appointments, but soon anyone could request it. Mothers were even taking girls to clinics to have them put on the Pill, so that pregnancy would not disrupt their daughters' education. Needless to say, Dotey was not one of these women; she expressed shock on learning that a girlfriend of Jeff's was on the Pill. The young woman's mother had already seen her elder daughter through an unexpected pregnancy, and was anxious to avoid any possibility of repeating the experience with the younger girl. Then one of Jess's friends announced that she was going on the Pill prior to her impending marriage. She had been engaged to a fellow Grammar School pupil for quite some time, but was forbidden to wear her engagement ring to school, since it counted as jewellery. Dotey's lip curled on hearing of this brazen announcement, she had read about schoolgirls on the Pill in the Daily Mail. That the schoolgirls in question were young adults about to attain the age of majority, seemingly counted for nothing.

"Jess, are you quite sure R— is right for you?" mused Dotey. It seemed to her that the pair usually did the things that R— wanted to do, rather than anything Jess suggested. R— was not interested in the dramatic society or the church youth club, while Jess went to motor hill climbs and stock car racing. Privately, Jess thought that the only thing she and R— had in common was that they both came from peculiar families. She had been reluctantly allowed back to visit the R—household, where Father R— was still Maister, after the A level exams, when there was no longer any question of her relationship with R— disrupting his studies. However, since R— had now acquired a car, he always drove her back home, as she was not welcome to stay overnight, nor would she have felt comfortable doing so, with R—'s suspicious parents listening out for every sound. Meanwhile, her own father was still agog to know if she was pregnant and questioned his wife on the subject on a monthly basis. ("You'll be sure to tell me if she is, Dotey; I have every right to know!")

What with Dotey's disappointment and Jack's prurience, Jess was glad to be getting away for a few days. However, it was the height of the holiday season and all the Bed and Breakfast places had 'No Vacancies' signs. So, after looking at the two bridges, Jess and R— ended up on Clifton Downs, spending an extremely uncomfortable night trying to sleep in the cramped Austin. They awoke early, and were glad to find a transport café, where they enjoyed a full cooked breakfast for 3/6 (17½ pence in decimal money) before returning home to face Dotey, who shook her head disbelievingly. ("You don't expect me to fall for this silly story, do you? Really, Jess, I wasn't born yesterday!")

If Jess had thought her mother would be pleased to hear of the Bristol trip privations she was in for a disappointment. The very fact that Jess had disobeyed her and gone away in the first place was enough to send Dotey into one of her protracted sulks. Meanwhile, Father and Mother R— still remained unaware of the Bristol excursion. The A level results were due out shortly, and Mother R— had suddenly realised their significance, in that if he achieved his predicted good grades, her only child would soon be leaving home and going 'up country' to university. She began to cry, and would not stop; every time Jess saw her during that summer and into September she was weeping.

The R— parents now required their son's help in finding a suitable new car; given Father R—'s miserliness, this would of course be second-hand. A VW Beetle was found, at a suspiciously reasonable price. They all went to collect it one evening in R—'s A 30, with the parents returning in the 'new' VW. The Beetle conked out in a remote lane in the gathering gloom, and no-one could get it going again, so they were obliged to abandon it by the side of the road. They telephoned the vendor the following day, from the village call-box, since the R—s did not believe in being on the telephone, it was considered a wanton extravagance. The vendor told them that there was a small pedal which should be pressed to activate the emergency petrol supply, so the R— family piled into the A30 and went to retrieve the Beetle. They managed to get the car back home, but soon discovered that one of the doors had rotted away and been rebuilt from wads of old newspaper, sealed and painted to match the rest of the car. It was unlikely to pass the M.O.T. test without expensive remedial work, so was not the great bargain it had at first seemed. Eventually, Father R— was persuaded to buy a Saab from a reputable car dealer.

However, despite the bad experience with the Beetle, Father R—'s in-grained parsimony knew no bounds. Mother R— now wanted a freezer, or 'deep freej' as she called it. ("Jus' think of it – us cud 'ave fresh strawberries – Christmas Day!") Father R— heard of one for sale in someone's shed. The vendor was a retired butcher. After a short spell of price haggling, it was duly bought, delivered and installed in the R—'s outhouse, whereupon Mother R— joyfully took delivery of an entire lamb carcass, cut up into myriad joints. However, the following morning it became clear that the meat was not frozen, only chilled. An electrician neighbour was called in to look at it, and pronounced that this was only a butcher's cool cabinet, not a freezer at all. Father R— had been duped. Meanwhile, it was necessary to re-home the various joints of lamb before they went bad. All the villagers with freezers and everyone on Mother R—'s post round was pressed into taking as many joints as they had space for. Father R went round to complain to the vendor, who declared that the appliance had been 'bought as seen'. This was in the days before the Trades Description Act, and apart from suing the vendor there was nothing Father R— could do. Mother R— was still without a 'deep freej' so they had to quickly get a chest freezer from the South-Western Electricity Board. It was too big for the outhouse, being shaped like an enormous white coffin, and so took pride of place in the hall, where anyone coming in too quickly through the front door would be likely to fall over it. Luckily, at the R—s, people always used the back door. Mother R— went round the village and outlying hamlets reclaiming her lamb joints, and a quantity of strawberries was obtained from a self-pick fruit farm. Some were duly exhumed on Christmas Day, only for the R—s to discover, disappointingly, that fresh strawberries did not freeze particularly well, and the defrosted strawberries tasted more like tinned fruit rather than fresh. Meanwhile, back at Jess's house, she was still jamming blackberries before going away to university, since of course Dotey still did not possess even a fridge, let alone a freezer.

Chapter 53

The A level results confirmed Mother R—'s worst fears, her son was indeed going to Leeds to study civil engineering. In the days before Skype and the Megabus, students often disappeared in September and were not seen at home again until Christmas, which seemed an unbearable length of time to many doting parents. Jess was going to Leicester. Her lack of confidence had led her to accept the lowest university offer she had received, a B and 2 Es. She actually obtained an A and 2 Bs, but by then it was too late to change her mind. She and R— worked out that Leicester and Leeds were about 100 miles apart, so R— would visit her every weekend in the A30.

Jack of course had other ideas. "She might as well get it into her silly head as soon as possible, she's not going to any university, because I shall refuse to fill out the forms!"

Jack thought he had played his trump card; the policy of Devon County Council, clearly stated on the student maintenance grant application forms, was that the applicant's father should complete the forms, giving full details of family income. Jess was obliged to get in touch with the Head Master, and explain her predicament. He then contacted Devon County Hall, where a special dispensation was issued, so that Dotey could fill in the forms. This was actually quite a simple matter in the end, because Jack's business had gone into liquidation, and the family's income consisted solely of Social Security benefits. Dotey obtained a letter of confirmation from the relevant government department to send off with the forms, and in due course Jess was told she would receive the full grant, then £360 per year, paid in three termly instalments.

R—s family were planning a get-together of their various friends and relatives one Sunday afternoon before R— left, and Jess was invited. Dotey was upset and annoyed.

"You and I have always gone out together for our walk on Sunday afternoons, Jess; but of course, I can see that I don't matter now you have all these other new interests…"

Jess said this was easily solved, she would get Dotey an invitation to the R— family soirée. This was not the solution that Dotey wanted, she would have much preferred for Jess to miss the R—'s party and to accompany her on their usual walk; in her heart of hearts, Jess would have preferred that too, but she felt duty-bound to accept the invitation. Dotey reluctantly agreed to go with Jess to the R—s; she did not think much of the R— family, and had only met them once, after which she had told Jess that Mother R— was such a dumpy little woman who should really do something about her facial hair, and as for Father R—, that cast in his eye made it difficult to work who he was speaking to, you or the man next door... Dotey sat all afternoon in an armchair chair, with a teacup balanced on her lap. Jess could see that her mother was ill at ease. She clearly did not care for R—s relatives with their broad Devonshire accents, she did not know what to make of the garrulous Uncle, who insisted on trying to tell her some incomprehensible tale, and she took an especially dim view of the exuberant dancing of one cousin; although luckily Dotey saved her critical comments for the journey home.

"She's nothing but a little tart! That skimpy dress! And she obviously wasn't wearing a slip! I didn't know where to look! I'm surprised at you, associating with such people..."

Jess knew that Dotey was upset at the prospect of her own imminent departure, even if she was not constantly in tears like Mother R—. Jess pointed out that she would be back at Christmas, the university terms were quite short, and anyway, Peter was still at home. Dotey gave a wan smile.

"Of course, I shall have to start doing things on my own; it's a mother's penance, we bring up our children only to send them out into the world without a backward glance..."

"But you wanted me to go to university! You've always encouraged me, and I'm very grateful for that."

"I hoped you might decide on Exeter, then you could have travelled every day, rather than go so far away..."

Jess wondered whether she should change her plans. Then she remembered something. "If I give up the idea of going to university, Dad will be pleased; he's always saying he'll make sure I can't go. And we can't let him win, can we?"

Dotey sighed. "You're quite right, Jess, we don't want the old man to get his way. At the moment he doesn't know I filled in those grant forms, he thinks you'll have to stay here. It will be a big surprise for him when you leave."

The following Monday, Jess was packed and ready. R— was collecting her, and would drop her off at Leicester on his way to Leeds. Dotey had been obliged to tell Jack the night before that Jess was going away, although Jess had been all for not telling him and quietly slipping way when her father had left for town. However, Dotey still deferred to Jack as head of the household, saying that Jess's departure might affect his benefits payments. Jack had scoffed at the very idea that she might actually be going off to university.

"I just don't believe this university nonsense. Now, tell me the truth – she's going away to have an abortion, isn't she!"

Jess had loaded her belongings into the car and was preparing to leave. Her father had not emerged from his room, and Jess thought he must be planning to stay there sulking, when Jack suddenly put his head round his bedroom door and shouted down the stairs after her.

"Well, wherever it is that you're off to, I hope they can teach you how not to hate!" He then retreated back into his room and slammed the door. He did not wish her luck, or come down to see her off, or even wave from the window. Jess was defying him by going to study at university, and he would never forgive her. Nor did he forget or forgive Dotey's complicity in Jess's escape, by secretly filling out the grant forms behind his back, when only the fathers of prospective students were supposed to do this. This had been Jack's trump card, he was not used to being outwitted by women, and he especially did not appreciate being out-manoeuvred by the very women whom he had for so many years striven to keep firmly under his financial, physical and emotional control. He found it impossible to accept, and consequently never again spoke a kind word to Jess as long as he lived, indeed he hardly spoke to her at all. Dotey was left to bear the brunt of his hatred, desperately maintaining the bedroom barricades, swallowing her daily dose of tranquillisers, and even in her darkest hours, contemplating suicide. Only the thought of leaving poor Peter behind prevented her from that drastic course of action.

Chapter 54

The A30 chugged its way northwards, and Jess soon found herself in the strange environment of a university Women's Hall of Residence. This was presided over by a Warden known as Mildred, who was in the habit of patrolling the corridors after the eleven o'clock curfew, looking for any young men who might be hiding in broom cupboards. Jess was allocated a ground floor room, facing a courtyard. She kept the window open slightly, in order to ventilate the stuffy room, and one night awoke to find a young man climbing in, "Don't worry, I'm on my way to see Louise on the third floor, I'll just let myself out into the corridor…"

Jess thought the atmosphere of the Hall of Residence was quite like that of a boarding school, and she found it very difficult to settle, although there were several pleasant young women with whom she made friends. Jess noticed that those who seemed happiest were the girls who had actually attended boarding school. To make matters worse, Jess was not enjoying her course; the first term's work was proving to be very mathematical. R— was finding it tiresome driving down the motorway to see her at the weekends, but when she suggested that they have a break one weekend, he became distraught and accused her of wanting to finish their relationship. He phoned from a public call-box in Leeds to Jess's Hall of Residence Junior Common Room, where the only telephone available for students' use was located; but by the time someone had fetched Jess, R—'s money had almost run out. He insisted that they should continue to see each other every weekend, so Jess found a lift going to Leeds the following Friday night. She could not stay at R—'s lodgings, since he was in a shared room in a house full of people, but some Tiverton friends had relatives in Leeds, who kindly allowed her to stay.

R— took Jess to the Students' Union, where by chance they bumped into Carol, another girl from Tiverton, who told them she was about to transfer from her current university to Leeds in order to be with her fiancé. Jess wondered if transferring might be a way forward for herself. Carol warned her not to leave it too long before making her decision, since if she stayed a whole year at Leicester she would lose an entire year's grant when she started at Leeds. If she left after one term, she would lose only a single term's grant when starting afresh, since under normal circumstances it was possible to have a grant for only three undergraduate years in total. Jess realised that she would have to make a decision about her future quite quickly.

When it came to the return journey on Sunday evening, it was snowing heavily, the first snowfall of the winter, so that the driver could scarcely make out where he was going. He had to lean out of the open window of his old Riley to knock lumps of snow from the windscreen, since the wipers were unable to cope. One of the four scared passengers began composing an unhelpful news bulletin,

"Five people identifiable only by their Leicester University scarves were discovered in a snow drift on the M1 tonight."

The Riley slipped and slid the thirty miles from Leeds to Sheffield, when the snow unexpectedly turned to rain. Jess was very relieved to be back, just before Mildred's curfew.

On top of everything else, Jess was receiving weekly letters from Dotey, telling her how miserable she was, how beastly Jack was being, and that she was considering taking her own life, since she had nothing now to live for. Jess should realise that any problems with her course of study were as nothing compared with what she, Dotey, was now obliged to endure. Naturally, Jess was alarmed and wanted to go straight home, even though the university did not have a mid-term break; however Mildred the Warden advised her not to give in to what sounded like emotional blackmail. Dotey was not of course on the telephone, so the Warden suggested that Jess should try to contact one of her mother's friends. Jess gathered up a bagful of shillings and went to the call-box to ring Helena Hake to ask how Dotey seemed to her. Helena reported that she thought Dotey was just about coping, and it would do no good for Jess to come home mid-term; but that it had not helped Dotey when Jess had written to say that she was not enjoying her course.

Jess resolved to try to make her letters more cheerful in future, but it was very difficult, there really was very little to be cheerful about. R— had recently issued her with an ultimatum: either Jess must leave

Leicester and come to Leeds, or he would throw in his engineering course and move to Leicester. This was definitely not the personal freedom and independent adult life of which Jess had long dreamed. She imagined the reaction of R—'s parents if he gave up his course; and then she thought of Jack's glee and Dotey's disappointment if she gave up hers. She knew she was damned either way. However, even at the very end of the 1960s, it was still generally considered that a man's career was more important than a woman's. Also, R— was enjoying his course of study whereas Jess did not like hers.

Meanwhile, Jess was surprised to receive a letter from Mrs. Steele, the mother of Peter's friend, Hedley, enclosing a newspaper cutting from the 'Tiverton Gazette'. It was from the letters column, and contained a piece written by Jack in response to the debate about whether smoking was bad for health. Jack wrote that he had smoked all his life, man and boy, and that the argument that passive smoking adversely affected the health of children was utter nonsense, since his children of an age were mostly at the university. Jess was astonished that he should boast of her academic success in a letter to the paper after having done all within his power to prevent her attending university in the first place. She wrote back to thank Mrs. Steele, and sent the cutting on to Dotey who usually bought the paper but had apparently not done so this particular week. Her mother was equally astounded and annoyed that Jack could brag about Jess's academic achievements to the readership of the local paper but had never once praised her to her face.

Some of her friends in Hall were reading Sociology, and since Jess had a free period, she went along to one of the lectures, a fascinating presentation on Durkheim's classic study of Suicide. Who would have thought that suicide rates were higher in the summer than the winter, when it could perhaps be expected that the poor weather would make people even unhappier? No, it turned out that during the winter, when everyone stayed indoors, unhappy people did not feel they were missing out on anything. It was when the sun shone and everyone else could be seen out and about enjoying themselves that unhappy people felt even more isolated, thus increasing their tendency to suicide.

Another Sociology lecture introduced Jess to Marx's idea of the patriarchal family, where the father is in a position to completely dominate and exploit his wife and children. Jess immediately recognised this description of her own family.

Her continuing anxieties about Dotey and R— and her course caused Jess to come out in red blotches all over her body. The doctor at Student Health Services ruled out any physical ailment, and said the rash had a psychological cause. He referred Jess to a helpful counsellor. She listened to Jess's account of Jack and Dotey's unhappy married life, and eventually told Jess in reassuring tones that it was really no wonder she was ill; after all, not many teenagers were in the difficult position of sharing a small bedroom with a depressed mother, having to barricade the door every night to forestall the entry of a violent alcoholic father. And now this additional pressure from the boyfriend was clearly unhelpful. Jess had been through too much, and would clearly benefit from a break from academic work until the rest of her life was calmer. To Jess, this made perfect sense, and confirmed that what she now intended to do was indeed the right course of action. She would leave Leicester, the Hall of Residence and the disappointing Geography course, and go to Leeds. She did not feel that she could return to Tiverton, to have to listen to the recriminations of her depressed mother, and to endure her father's constant inquisitive staring at her abdomen. Leeds had a big university, and she would enrol there to study Sociology. With her unexpectedly high A level grades, she felt she would stand a good chance of obtain a place.

Jess gave notice to Leicester University that she would be leaving at Christmas. However, the fact that she was going on medical advice cut absolutely no ice, either with the disapproving Warden or her disappointed mother. Mildred wrote coldly to Jess, saying how surprised she was that Jess was giving up her place so soon; while Dotey wrote a long letter composed in equal measures of sorrow and anger, saying that Jess had let her down so very badly, and she really should have stuck it out; Dotey concluded by saying that everyone in Tiverton was extremely disappointed in her, including it seemed all the Grammar School teachers. As for Jack, he was of course jubilant, since this simply proved what he had known all along, that Jess would never cope at university; and just when was the baby due?

Chapter 55

The only person who was pleased that Jess had decided to leave Leicester was R—, since he would no longer have to drive two hundred miles every weekend. However, once her decision had been made, Jess knew it was right for her. She found a temporary job as a clerk in an insurance office in Leeds, and quickly obtained a place on her new chosen course, Geography and Sociology Joint Honours. The lecturer interviewing her said there was no problem with her A level grades, but expressed anxiety as to whether she might throw up another place. However, he was soon satisfied with Jess's explanation that she had left Leicester on medical advice, but was now recovering and happily settled in Leeds. The interviewer confided that something similar had happened with his own wife, in that she had transferred universities to be with him. He understood!

Jess now had several months in which to prepare for her new course and to do some advance reading. She gave Dotey the news that she had been accepted for a place on a more interesting course, at a Russell Group university, so her mother need no longer worry on that score. Jess knew that Dotey would be less than impressed with any description of the accommodation Jess had found. This was a furnished flat rented for £3 per week, hot water included, comprising two shabby attic rooms in a terraced house, with a kitchenette located in a cupboard; it was imperative to remember to duck when entering or leaving this kitchen or risk suffering a knock on the head. Electricity came via a meter which took sixpences and shillings. The bathroom and toilet on the floor below were shared with all the other occupants of the house, including Indian and Swiss gentlemen in bedsits on the first floor, a West Indian family on the ground floor, and an Irish couple in the basement. It was in an area of Leeds spoken of as being 'multi-cultural.' The landlord, Frankie, was an Italian ice-cream man, who came round on Saturday lunchtimes to collect the rent. The chimes of his approaching van spurred the tenants either to go out and pay him, or to hide, depending on whether they had the money to hand. In return, Frankie handed out '99's.

Of course, no sooner has Jess settled into the flat than R— wanted to leave his lodgings and move in with her. Jess thought it might be better for R— to stay on at his landlady's house for the time being, but R— wanted to be in the flat with Jess, after all, as the popular saying of the time went, two could live as cheaply as one; so they had better get married, then no-one could object. Jess knew that Dotey and the R— family would be horrified at any 'living-in-sin' arrangement. So on their next visit to Devon, Jess and R— announced they were getting married at St Chad's Church Headingley, not far from R—'s digs, where Jess was now on the electoral roll. Mother and Father R— begged the pair to consider marrying in Devon, so that all R—'s many relations could attend, they even offered to pay for a posh reception at the Fisherman's Cot Hotel; but Jess was adamant. She wanted a quiet wedding, far away from Jack, so that he could not spoil her day. She showed Dotey the white lacy mini-dress she had bought for £3 in a sale. Dotey realised that there was nothing she could do, because of the new 'wretched law' relating to the age of majority. She wept.

"But what about all your plans? It would be a crying shame to waste that good brain, and you said all along you were going to be a Head Mistress! You've never wavered!"

"Mum, that's not true! YOU always TOLD me I was going to be a Head Mistress. Now I'm going to be a Sociologist!"

To which Dotey could make no reply, since she was not at all certain what a Sociologist did. Jess was not entirely sure either, but she was looking forward to finding out.

Dotey had a valid point. Married women still suffered discrimination in the workplace, many people continuing to believe that women in the fortunate position of having husbands to keep them should not be competing for jobs which by rights belonged to men. Jess frequently heard other women grumbling about the glamorous young Head of Accounts in the insurance office where she was working.

"She's keeping a man out of a good job, is that one; and what can her husband be thinking of, allowing her to go out to work looking like that?" Susan wore fashionable dresses, and was faultlessly made up. She had a stylish hair cut and red nail polish, and a very charming manner. Susan was in the vanguard of the feminist movement, achieving the hitherto almost impossible combination of holding a responsible job, being married, and still looking good. But it was her female colleagues who judged her most harshly.

Then there were those who said "No woman can do two jobs," since of course housework and childcare was still regarded as women's work, and the poor husbands of working women were thought to be returning home to chaotic households, with unruly children, and worst of all, with no tea ready. The majority of men still seemed to expect their evening meal to be on the table the minute they walked in the front door, after a hard day's bread-winning, just as Jack had always done. The law was soon to change, allowing men and women equal opportunities, but it took a long time for peoples' mindsets to alter.

In the meanwhile, Jess herself was soon to find herself the victim of sex discrimination when she applied for a student grant, only to discover that a married woman's grant was £85 per year less than that of all other students, including married men. She wrote to complain to the Secretary of State for Education (at the time, Margaret Thatcher) saying that the effect of this discrimination was to encourage students to live together rather than to marry, in order not to incur any financial penalty. She received a reply from one of Mrs. Thatcher's assistants, stating that it was the policy of the government not to encourage students to take on family responsibilities while dependent on public funds. Jess was annoyed that her comments had not been properly addressed, and the fact that the system promoted sex discrimination had also been overlooked, since married men students were still entitled to the full grant of £360 while married women had to make do with only £275p.a.

For many years after the equal opportunity laws had been enacted, and despite the best endeavours of the feminist movement, Jess and other women like her still had to face intrusive questions at job interviews, about marital and family status. After her marriage ended, Jess always replied to such questions simply with "I'm not married."

"Yes, but does that mean single, widowed or divorced?"

"It simply means I'm not married."

There were often further questions as to whether she was planning to start a family in the near future; and after her sons were born, it was common for interviewers to ask exactly what arrangements she had made for their care. Interviewing panels still demanded to know numbers and ages of any female candidates' children, and sometimes whether there were any dependent elders for whom a woman was caring. It was common for people to check a woman's left hand to see if she was wearing a wedding or engagement ring, so anyone not wanting to answer illegal questions about family circumstances had to always remember to remove their jewellery. Jess was frequently tempted to say that she would always lock her boys in a broom cupboard before coming to work, just to see what reaction she provoked; but of course, she never did.

R—'s parents, with Dotey and Jeff arranged to drive north for the wedding; miserly father R— of course refused to fill up with expensive petrol from the motorway service station, and consequently ran out of fuel on the M1, necessitating Jeff to run back down the hard shoulder with a can. Several friends who lived in daily travelling distance also came, including Jackie, Jess's great friend from the Grammar School Domestic Science classes, now living with her family in Bury, and R—'s friend Anthony from Birmingham. R— and Jess happily paid for everything themselves; it was all done on a shoe-string, even the cake was reduced in price because an icing flower was slightly damaged, although it still tasted fine. The reception was held at Jess and R—'s attic flat, Dotey wincing at the poverty and multiculturalism of it all. It appeared that R—'s parents' offer of paying for the reception had applied only if the wedding was held in Devon. Their gift to the bride and groom, who was their only child, was a £5 note. Dotey was absolutely disgusted. She herself had spent an equivalent sum providing Jess with various items of baking equipment from Woolworths, but she had spent as much as she could afford. R—'s parents had sold a small-holding, they owned their own house, and were both working, so were well-off in Dotey's opinion, and she felt that they could have done far more to lessen the austerity of the occasion.

Jess's new life in Yorkshire was certainly not what Dotey would have chosen for her, and she continued to express her regret at Jess's early marriage, dingy flat and northern location; but Jess was at last enjoying her life. She began her new course, quickly settling in, and achieving good marks for her assignments, although she had to be coaxed into contributing to tutorial discussions, since it took some time to banish her mother's opinion as to the 'unseemliness' of young girls expressing views on any subject. It also took Jess some time to get used to Yorkshire folk, whom she first regarded as being overly inquisitive. "What do your parents think about you moving so far away from home?" her boss at the insurance office has asked. Jess merely said that they were OK with it, not wanting to go into details about her odd family with a stranger. In the summer, the boss's daughter, who was Jess's age, came to work in the office and the two women became friends; Jess realised that what she had initially taken to be nosiness sprang from genuine interest and concern. That's what Yorkshire people were like, they would rather ask outright than silently wonder, and Jess soon found that she preferred it this way.

Chapter 56

Throughout her childhood, Jess had noticed that her mother was a different person out of the house, temporarily away from her personal and financial worries. The anxious expression disappeared, she laughed and cracked jokes, and was more like the Dotey Jess could just about remember, pre-marriage to Jack. It was impossible for her to relax at home, since even when Jack was out, she was all the time tense, listening for the rattle of his key in the lock, starting at the slightest sound. "Was that him?" "No, just the cat…"

Dotey's main means of escape was her membership of the Tiverton Dramatic Society, and for as long as Jess could remember her mother had been the secretary. She was also a frequent performer, mainly in comedy roles but also in what were known as 'straight plays'. Jess particularly remembered Dotey as the dotty archaeologist in "Wild Goose Chase" and as flirty barmaid Lottie Grady in "When We Are Married." Her mother also gave a very moving performance in "A Letter from The General" as elderly nun Sister Magdalene, who gives up her safe passage out of a war-torn Far Eastern land to a young priest. He disguises himself in Sister Magdalene's habit in order to effect his escape, while the nun calmly awaits what will be her inevitable end once the cruel general reaches the convent.

Dotey went on to produce several plays, when women producers in Tiverton Dramatic Society were still relatively rare. Her most difficult challenge was 'Barefoot in the Park', where everyone had to speak with New York accents. The press reviews were excellent, and the cast presented Dotey with a lovely bouquet after the final performance. Dotey returned home, tired but happy, to a house in darkness. She let herself in, not knowing that Jack was waiting in the gloom behind the front door, ready to knock Dotey and her bouquet to the floor. He too had read the reviews, and was consumed with jealously. His wife may be utterly downtrodden at home, but she had dared to find a place where she was appreciated and Jack was unable to control her; and this he just could not allow.

Jack had threatened several times to join the Dramatic Society, so he could keep an eye on Dotey, but she insisted that if he did,

271

then she would immediately resign, pointing out that Jack had the Constitutional Club and she had the Dramatic Society, and it was better to keep their social lives entirely separate. Jack raged that she must be having an affair with fellow actor Derek; she had played the part of his wife in a production which Jack had attended, and he had seen the way Dotey looked at him... Dotey protested that she had of course been acting! However, Jack's jealously knew no bounds, and he then suggested that Dotey was having a lesbian affair with the young woman who had taken the leading role in 'Barefoot in the Park'.

Jack's completely unfounded accusations were possibly a sign of alcohol-induced dementia, but all his family knew was that his rages were making it intolerable for Dotey to live with him. After Jess had left home for university, and with Peter out with his friends much of the time, Dotey was alone in the house most evenings, wondering nervously when Jack would return and what state he might be in. She still barricaded her bedroom door every night, but there was no Jess in the other bed to keep her company, or to help if Jack attacked, so she began seriously to look for somewhere to escape. She needed two bedrooms for herself and Peter, and such a rental property was not easy to find.

Dotey now worked part-time in the offices of Whitbread Brewery, which had taken over Starkey, Knight and Ford; but few people would be happy about renting a property to a married woman, even if she had her own income, since many contracts required a male guarantor. The search for a safe home had to be carried out under conditions of great secrecy, since if Jack realised that she was planning to leave him, Dotey believed he might kill her. A few trusted friends were asked to help; they were eventually successful in finding an attic flat in the town centre. A removal date was set, and a furniture van booked to come from Exeter.

Dotey knew that if she engaged a local removal firm, the news would undoubtedly get back to Jack, via his cronies at the Conservative Club, and that would be the end of her plans, possibly even the end of her. She simply could not risk discovery, and did not even tell Jess her plans until Jess arrived to stay for two weeks at the end of the summer vacation, having finished her holiday job working in an insurance office. Jess was of course pleased to hear that her mother was leaving Jack, but wondered how the removal bill might be afforded; the quotation given was for £27! Dotey simply shook her head and said she had not the least idea how she would pay, at the same time fixing Jess with a steely gaze which immediately left Jess in no doubt that she was expected to pay out of her summer earnings. She was happy enough to do this, in fact she would willingly have paid any price to get Dotey safely away from Jack. Dotey said she would repay Jess at the rate of ten shillings a week, and she kept to this arrangement, posting Jess a pound note every fortnight until her death, by which time there remained only a few pounds outstanding.

Meanwhile, Jack remained oblivious to the removal plan, and was still serenading the neighbours from his window:

"He stood in a beautiful mansion, surrounded by riches untold; and gazed at a beautiful picture, which hung in a frame of gold. 'Twas the picture of a lady, so beautiful young and fair; to the beautiful child-like vision, he mourned in sad despair -

If those lips could only speak! And those eyes could only see! If those beautiful golden tresses were here in reality! Could I only take your hand, as I did when you took my name; but it's only a beautiful picture, in a beautiful golden frame!"

Chapter 57

The day of Dotey's removal dawned, and the van was expected at ten o'clock. Jack usually left for town on the 9.45 bus, but today of all days, he contrived to miss it. It appeared that Dotey's escape was threatened, but luckily Jess's husband R— came to the rescue, offering to drive Jack into town, saying that he was going anyway to meet some old school friends. Jack still did not have had any idea of what was about to take place, and eagerly accepted R—'s offer. Immediately he had left, the removal plan swung into action. Dotey had been unable to pack anything much for fear of arousing Jack's suspicions. Seeing Jack and R— depart, two trusted neighbours rushed to help, turning out cupboards and filling boxes and suitcases. Peter had taken the day off school; he was in charge of re-homing the cat at his friend Hedley's, since it was not possible for Felix live in an attic flat. Unfortunately, the boys met one of the more officious teachers as they were approaching Hedley's house, and were told to report to the Head Master the following day. Hedley's mother then took the teacher aside and quietly explained just what Peter had had to put up with in his sixteen years – an alcoholic bullying father who inflicted mental and physical cruelty on his family – but that today was the clandestine removal which must be accomplished before Jack returned home. The teacher looked abashed and accepted that Peter was not truanting.

The van arrived on time, R— later reporting that he and Jack had passed it coming up the hill as they had been on their way down. It had been a close-run thing. The strong men of the removal team made short work of loading the numerous boxes, and Dotey cleared up the final odd bits and pieces. Her last act before leaving was to throw her tranquillisers into the dustbin. "I won't be needing these any more!" Jess put some old shoes on top and the bin was full. The house looked very empty, with just Jack's solitary armchair, the paraffin heater and a few pots and pans left downstairs.

The unloading took several hours at the other end, because it was necessary to haul everything up two flights of stairs to Dotey's attic. Of course, the baby-grand piano presented the worst difficulty, and the removal men had to use a special piano shoe. Dotey had not wanted to dispose of the instrument, which she still occasionally played, and which was a bequest from her beloved father. Then there were the carpets, two beds, the cooker, the settee and chairs, the dining room suite and a seemingly endless number of boxes, bags and suitcases. Eventually, Peter returned from Hedley's house (where his friend's kind mother had insisted he have dinner) having left Felix tucking into a plate of Kit-e-Kat. By a stroke of unfortunate timing, Jack, on the homeward bus at tea-time, spotted Peter bringing a box from the removal van; at the time, he thought Peter was helping a friend move, but on reaching the empty house, the reality of the situation immediately became evident. After brewing tea on the paraffin stove, Jack appeared at his bedroom window and serenaded the astonished neighbours, in a show of studied unconcern.

"Just a song at twilight, when the lights are low;
And the flick'ring shadows softly come and go.
Tho' your heart be weary; sad the day and long,
Still to us at twilight comes love's own song;
Comes love's old sweet song."

"Ramona, when day is done I hear you call; Ramona, we'll meet beside the waterfall; I dread the day when I awake, to find you gone. Ramona, I made you my own."

The newly removed family were having a late tea. Dotey had sent Peter out to buy everyone fish and chips, while Jess had thankfully located the kettle. Suddenly, a gasping sound was heard at the door and an extremely breathless Jack appeared, having tried every other flat in the building before being directed to the attic. Jess at once tried to close the door but Jack had his foot in it and refused to move.

"But why, Dotey, why?" Jack sounded quite maudlin, maybe the paraffin stove-brewed tea had been laced with something a bit stronger, and after all, he had had a shock.

"It's better this way, Jack," cried Dotey. Jack was by now too overcome to continue the conversation; not for nothing had his estranged wife settled on an attic flat, and she felt that it was unlikely that Jack would struggle all the way up those stairs again very soon, since a lifetime of smoking had rendered him short of wind. It was left to R— to escort Jack back down to the ground floor and off the premises.

However, Jack was not to be their final visitor that evening. Just as Dotey and Jess were making up the beds, a loud knock was heard at the door. Fearing Jack had returned, R— opened it cautiously, only to find a police officer asking to speak to Dotey. Jess thought for a wild moment that the policeman was going to order her mother to return to Jack, maybe there was some archaic law that compelled a wife to reside under her husband's roof still on the statute book and enforceable in Tiverton. However, the policeman began speaking sternly to Dotey about a little girl who had been taken to hospital, having swallowed tranquillisers retrieved from Dotey's dustbin. Jess sprang to her mother's defence.

"Officer, surely it's not my mother you should be talking to, but parents who let their daughter rummage around in other people's dustbins! I put some old shoes in on top of the tablets, so she must have had to reach right in to get at the pills. Of course I'm sorry to hear that she's ill, but really it's not Mum's fault!"

"Yuu 'ave likely bin just as naughty when yuu was a maid."

"No, indeed not, I was properly brought up…"

"Well, the way to get rid of pills is to flush 'em down the toilet, so 'ee must remember always to do that in footure."

A chastened Dotey agreed. Fortunately, the child survived. R— went to Woolworth's the next day and bought a security chain, which he fitted to Dotey's flat door. Dotey and Peter soon settled in, able to be relax for the first time in years.

Jack, meanwhile, stayed on in the council house despite the fact that it had been in Dotey's name, and she had of course relinquished the tenancy. The council naturally allocated the house to a new family. However, Jack had no intention of moving out until it suited him, so the unfortunate new tenants were obliged to move in around him. Dotey heard all about it from her friend Mrs. Wally, who knew someone who was related to the new tenants. The story went around Tiverton of the family who had been given a lovely council house only to find that there was a dreadful old man in residence refusing to move out, occupying the bedroom which the little girl of the new

276

family was supposed to have, and whose disreputable habits included getting blind drunk every night, belching and farting… This bizarre situation continued for several weeks, until Nicholas, Jack's son from his first marriage, found his father a cottage to rent in the town, in a courtyard just off St. Andrew Street, so Jack and his meagre effects were finally ready to be moved, leaving the new tenants to heave a sigh of relief.

After Dotey's move she was finally away from the malign atmosphere of the marital home, living nearer her work and many of her friends, and so her mental health improved. She was cheered by Jess's reports of her course and the encouraging remarks of her tutors. In 1971 Peter left home for Teeside Polytechnic, where he was to study maths. With two children in the North, Dotey was persuaded to have a short holiday in Leeds. Jess and R— came to fetch her, and she booked the return journey by coach. Jess and R— had moved to a much nicer flat, with a large front room where Dotey could sleep on the couch. They went to Harrogate, where they admired the display of autumnal colours in the Valley gardens, calling for a fish and chip meal at the original Harry Ramsden's on their way home. The next day they visited Saltburn, where Peter was in digs. He had just celebrated his nineteenth birthday, and they all went out for tea and cakes. On Dotey's final day in Yorkshire, she and Jess looked around the shops in Leeds, and to her daughter's astonishment, Dotey actually tried on a pair of cream trousers in C&A, although she did not go so far as to buy them… it seemed that such 'masculine' garb was still not for her, although by the 1970s women's slacks were widely worn and were far from being regarded as the Biblical abomination they had once been deemed…

Chapter 58

One evening in early February 1972, a policeman knocked on the door of Jess's flat in Leeds, saying that her mother had been taken into hospital. He had no further details. The country was in the grip of a postal strike, so Jess had not been able to write her usual weekly letter home. Dotey was not on the telephone at her flat, so Jess had been calling her mother's place of work, the accounts office at the brewery, during her free period every Thursday morning. Dotey's colleagues in the office knew that Jess's call would be coming at this particular time, and Jess always got straight through to her mother. They could not talk for more than a few minutes, since a long-distance call at peak time simply gobbled up the florins (ten pence coins.) It was Thursday, so Jess had spoken to her mother that very morning, when everything had seemed perfectly normal; Dotey had not complained of feeling unwell, but had used the brief time available to ask Jess what special item she might like for her forthcoming twenty-first birthday. Would she perhaps wear a signet ring? Jess had protested that twenty-one was not really significant these days, when young people came of age at eighteen, and she really did not want her mother to spend much on her birthday present. Dotey had of course replied that the age of majority would always be twenty-one in her book, and Jess had better let her know soon what she wanted as a gift. The discussion ended inconclusively when the pips sounded and Jess ran out of money. Yet now here was this policeman just a few hours later, telling her that Dotey was in hospital. An alarmed Jess assumed her mother must have had an accident on her way home.

Jess's problem was to now find a public telephone in working order, and to obtain a fresh supply of ten pence pieces. She managed to get some coins from the neighbours, and set off through the dark streets to find a working telephone. The first one she tried had been vandalised, but she discovered one in working order next to the cemetery. Dialling the hospital number with shaking fingers, she heard that her mother had been admitted at five o'clock with a severe stroke and was not expected to live.

R— drove her the 300 foggy miles through the February night

in the trundling A30. It was dawn when they finally arrived at the hospital, and as Jess entered the lobby, she saw Jeff with a nurse. The nurse was handing Jeff a bag; Jess recognised it as the brown shopping bag from Timothy Whites which she had once given Dotey as a Christmas present. In that instant, Jess realised that her mother was dead. Jeff turned and embraced Jess, tears streaming down both their faces. The nurse explained that Dotey had died late the previous night without regaining consciousness, at about the time when Jess was setting off from Leeds and Jeff from London. They were then offered a cup of tea and a visit the morgue; Jess accepted the tea but declined to visit the morgue, preferring to remember her mother as last she had seen her, waving from the gable end window of her flat when Jess left for Leeds after the Christmas holidays.

Jeff, Jess and R— went round to Dotey's building and roused the landlord, who lived on the ground floor, since of course they did not have a key. It seemed that Dotey had actually gone downstairs to pay her rent the previous afternoon, when she had been taken ill. It was fortunate that she had been with someone, and not alone in her attic, since the landlord had been able to ring for the ambulance and tried to make Dotey comfortable on the sofa. The stroke had immediately rendered her unable to speak and she lost had consciousness. The landlord had no idea of the addresses of Dotey's children, so had looked in her handbag, and finding some old letters from Jess and Jeff, he had contacted the police. He had then gone up to the attic and packed a few things, such as Dotey's flannel and toothbrush, into the shopping bag, and taken them round to the hospital.

The weary trio entered Dotey's flat to find a mug and cereal bowl in the sink, unwashed after Dotey's final meal. A pair of her stockings were drying in the bathroom, and it looked for all the world as though she had simply popped out for a few minutes, as of course she had intended. Jeff and Jess and R— tried to sleep, but Jess could only catnap. The street below was filling up with the noise of clinking milk bottles and early morning traffic. She was in deep shock, but knew there was so much that must be done. Terry and Peter must be informed; Terry was working at a branch of WH Smith in London, while Peter was studying at Teeside Polytechnic. A funeral must be arranged, and twenty-year-old Jess had not the least idea how to go about it. She was vaguely aware that there was a state death grant – it was about £30 – so she supposed they would have to try to find a funeral director who would be prepared to accept this amount, since she knew her mother had no savings, and her three younger children had no resources other than student grants. Then someone would have to go and tell Jack. He was after all, still her legal next of kin. After all the cruelty and suspicion heaped upon Dotey, and indeed herself, for so many years, Jess did not feel prepared to do this, but luckily Jeff volunteered to go. He found Jack at home in his cottage in a tiny courtyard off St Andrew's Street. Jack's reaction on learning of his wife's death was to exclaim that it would never have happened if she had stayed with him.

Jeff had then to go to the brewery and inform Dotey's shocked colleagues what had happened. Since Dotey had died in hospital there was no requirement for the coroner to be informed or for a post mortem. She had been treated for high blood pressure and had smoked most of her adult life. This was apparently sufficient to explain the sudden fatal stroke. However, Jess knew that the years of stress, the physical and mental cruelty, the violence and verbal insults she had suffered at the hands of her alcoholic bullying husband, must certainly have taken their toll. Jess herself had become stressed and ill simply by having to helplessly watch while Dotey suffered, as the counsellor at Leicester had observed; how much worse must it have been for her mother. If a manslaughter charge had been brought against Jack, Jess would happily have given evidence against him.

Chapter 59

Jeff and Jess knew that they must quickly get advice on how to arrange a funeral, and being quite clueless about the matter, they went to find Helena and Roland Hake, Dotey's friends and her first sub-tenants at The Close. Both the Hakes were teachers at the Secondary Modern School, and were sitting in shock in the staffroom, having just learned of Dotey's death through the Tiverton bush-telegraph. Someone at the hospital must have told someone from the Dramatic Society, who had told everyone they knew, and so the news was spreading. Helena and Roland were aware of a local burial charity, so an arrangement was made for Jeff and Jess to meet the administrator that afternoon, at his offices in the old Belmont Hospital, the former workhouse.

Meanwhile, Jess and Jeff had to gather as many ten pence coins as they could muster for all the necessary phone calls. Jess's first thought was to telephone her godparents, Phyllis and Cecil, in Exeter. It turned out that fortunately Dotey had made a Will, and Cecil was the executor. Cecil told her not to pay any bills, since he would come straight there to begin sorting out Dotey's finances. Jess was very relieved, as she knew her mother had a couple of outstanding Hire Purchase agreements, one for the electric cooker and another for an electric fire. Meanwhile R— had to return to Leeds, where he had a job interview the following day. Jess felt very sad as the A30 chugged off around the corner; she had no idea when she would be returning home. She had left a message with the university to say that she had been urgently called away, to explain her unauthorised absence, and had also asked her friend Susan, who was doing the same course, to duplicate all the lecture notes.

On learning that the deceased's children sitting in front of him were both students, the kindly administrator of the burial charity said that the charity would see to everything, which was a tremendous weight off Jess and Jeff's shoulders. Then Jess remembered that her mother had expressed a preference for cremation. It had come up in conversation during one of their Sunday afternoon walks, when they were passing a cemetery, and Dotey had shuddered at the idea of rotting in the ground, saying that she considered cremation a better option. The administrator explained that while it was usual for the charity to fund an interment, in this case it would indeed be a cremation, in accordance with the deceased's expressed wishes.

Jess could not get used to this talk of 'the deceased' in relation to her mother, it was like some sort of horrible nightmare, and she kept expecting Dotey to come breezing in, explaining that it had all been a dreadful mistake. After all, on the morning before her death she had had nothing more troubling on her mind then what to give Jess for a twenty-first birthday present. There had been no suggestion of any ill health, no reference to aches and pains, no hint that anything was wrong. Was it really possible for anyone to die quite so suddenly? Meanwhile Jeff had to go and register their mother's death while Jess returned to the flat, where she discovered a posse of Dramatic Society ladies with suitcases going through her mother's wardrobe. They immediately sat her down and began bombarding her with questions as to which items of clothing and jewellery she wanted to keep and which she was happy for them to dispose of. No doubt these kind souls meant well, but it was all too much for Jess, who found herself unable to speak. She began trembling violently, so the ladies stopped their rummaging and questioning to make her a cup of tea.

"Take it all!" said Jess, when she had recovered her voice. The ladies demurred, saying that this was a pretty little brooch, and wouldn't Jess like to wear it in remembrance of Dotey, and what about this pink jumper? Jess, who was in deep shock and had had very little sleep, was simply not well enough to attend to such matters, and repeated that they should take everything. The ladies eventually left, with their suitcases full of items for the WRVS, leaving Jess to contend with the next episode of her ordeal. This was the landlord, who appeared menacingly, wanting to know just how long it was likely to be before the flat was cleared out. Jess said she had no idea, whereupon the landlord squeezed her arm threateningly, announcing that he already had someone lined up to take over the tenancy, so she had better be quick, and what about the rent? Dotey had not actually managed to hand over the money before she was struck down, so was technically in arrears. The landlord was evidently terrified that Dotey's children might remain in the flat as squatters, but Jess assured him that she was as anxious to return to university as the landlord was to see her leave. However, she could hardly wave a magic wand and dispose of her mother's entire household at a stroke, and meanwhile she had to see a house clearance man. Jess told the bullying landlord that her mother's executor had advised her that he would see to all outstanding financial matters when he settled the estate in due course.

The landlord retreated crossly to his ground floor lair, and Jess sat in a daze, surrounded by her mother's possessions. There was so much to be dealt with. Dotey's baby grand piano, for instance – who could possibly take such an awkward piece of furniture? Then she remembered R—'s parents' bungalow, with its large front room. Maybe they would store it for her until she could get it to Leeds. When Uncle Cecil and Auntie Phyl arrived Jess was very relieved to see them. Cecil went to have a word with the landlord while Phyl made tea and helped Jess with the sorting out. The house clearance man came and looked around disdainfully, obviously unimpressed with Dotey's effects, and offering only a modest sum; but since he was the only local man available, Jess was obliged to accept his offer.

Peter arrived from Middlesbrough, and had to be given brandy when he learned that Dotey was dead. The college had simply passed on the message that his mother was in hospital. In many ways it was hardest of all for him, since he was just nineteen and had left home only a few months previously. He was the only one of the children who had actually lived with Dotey in the flat, and so it was doubly shocking for him to lose his home as well as his mother at such a young age. Terry, the oldest of Dotey's four children and the only one working, sent a message that he would travel down from London for the funeral on Tuesday.

The chapel at Exeter crematorium was full with Dotey's many friends and colleagues from the Dramatic Society, the Townswomen's Guild, and the Brewery Accounts office. Of Dotey's few remaining relatives, the cousin from Dartmoor, who had recently declined to guarantee Dotey's television rental, was there with his family; but cousin Barbara was living in Gibraltar, where her husband was stationed, and of course Aunt Gladys was in Canada, so neither were able to attend. Some of the men present were wearing black armbands, on loan from the Air Training Corps. Jess was told that she and Terry must lead the mourners, as Dotey's eldest son and only daughter, with Jeff and Peter following behind. There was no sign of Jack, until, when everyone was seated, Jess spotted him right at the back, in a new coat, not the awful old tweed-belted-with-baler-twine garb. He was keeping a taxi waiting, and left immediately after the service, speaking to no-one. Someone said he had come up on the pools, yet he made no offer to contribute any of this largesse towards the cost of his wife's funeral, which was paid for by the kindness of strangers, the unknown contributors to the Burial Charity. This was the last time Jess was ever to see the man whom she had always been told was her father, although she was shortly to discover her hitherto concealed birth certificate, naming an entirely different man, Dotey's first husband Albert, whom Jess had met only in passing, once in her life.

The Vicar of St. Peter's Church, where Jeff had been a choirboy and Jess a Sunday School teacher and distributor of parish magazines, gave the funeral address; he commented on the large number of friends present at the service, on Dotey's service as secretary of the Dramatic Society since 1954, and her pride in the academic achievements of her children, three of whom were presently studying at college, university and polytechnic. He recalled how she had stepped forward to take over Jess's parish magazine duties when Jess had left for university, and how older people on the round had looked forward to her monthly visits. However, Jess, although appreciative of this eulogy, was dreading the moment when the curtains would close around her mother's coffin, and she would have to say a final farewell, so could not really take in all that was being said. Finally, after the service was over and everyone was leaving, she had to stand at the door of the chapel and shake everyone's hand, and thank them for coming, trying all the while to be brave and not to cry.

The afternoon brought a bizarre contrast to the solemnity of the morning's proceedings, when a cattle truck arrived to remove the baby grand piano and a few other pieces of furniture to R—'s parents' house. Now that the Tuesday livestock market was over, the driver, Mr. Ellison, had finished his cattle moving duties, and had volunteered the use of his vehicle to assist the children. His daughter Heather had been a school classmate of Jess's, and like many other

Tiverton residents, he had been moved by the plight of the young people. A posse of Peter's friends were on hand to shift the furniture, and once they had loaded the piano, they all piled into the truck so as to be available for unloading duties at the other end. The vehicle was still full of straw and a lingering bovine aroma, so the lads began mooing. Jess, sitting in the cab, did not know whether to laugh or cry. She could imagine how Dotey would have felt, seeing her prize possessions being carted away in a cattle truck; it was rather *infra dig,* but still quite funny.

With the furniture out of the way, the clothes gone to the WRVS and the remnants of Dotey's effects taken to the tip, there was nothing more for the children to do, and so they made their way back to their respective places of education. Uncle Cecil was able to pay the landlord and settle all the outstanding bills, leaving a total residue of £50, which he divided between Jess and Peter, according to Dotey's will. The amount was so little that a grant of Probate was not required. Dotey had long known that her legacy would not be financial, but that she would live on through the achievements of her children, and later, the four grandchildren, whom sadly she was never to meet.

Jess and her brothers were naturally very badly affected by their mother's sudden death. After all the years of stress, it had seemed that Dotey had finally recovered from the depression which had haunted her for a decade. After a lifetime of insistence that Jess should never marry, she seemed to have eventually become reconciled to Jess's choice of R—; and after all the fuss about Jess leaving Leicester and transferring to Leeds, Dotey had recently been pleased to hear of Jess's progress in her Sociology studies, and the praise her essays had earned from tutor. On her last trip to Leeds, Dotey and Jess had done mother-and-daughter things together, such as going shopping, without any hint of pursed lips or criticism of choices. They had gone to the cinema to see 'Love Story' with no mention as to the unsuitability of the film. Jess felt that only recently had she been able to get to know her mother as another woman, rather than as the controlling parent with subjugated daughter, which had characterised their relationship throughout her childhood. Jess had waited for so long to have this more equal relationship with Dotey, to get to know her as others did:

the witty and charming woman from the Dramatic Society, the caring person who had time for the elderly parishioners on her magazine distribution round; and now this mother had been suddenly snatched away, just a few weeks before her daughter's twenty-first birthday. It was so hard for Jess to bear, but with her usual stoicism, born out of years of having to live with Jack and his bullying, bear it Jess knew she must. There was simply no alternative.

Chapter 60

Back in Leeds, Jess was in trouble. The message she had left explaining her unauthorised absence had been received by her Sociology tutor, but for some reason not reached the Geography Department (Geography was the other subject she was studying) and now her name was included in a list of those who had failed to hand in their migration project data. Each student had been allocated raw data from a different county to analyse the previous week. Jess had been given Northamptonshire; she had actually done the work before being called away, so now she hurried to Dr. Morgan's room to hand in the results.

Dr. Morgan's study door was slightly ajar, and he could be seen sitting at his desk, wearing his old red jumper – by the 1970s only a few of the staff still wore academic dress. Jess knocked, hovering in the doorway, clutching the foolscap sheets containing her assignment. Dr. Morgan looked up.

"Ah, Jess, come in; and I see you've brought the migration data, but you know it was meant to be handed in on Tuesday morning! How can we possibly hope to complete the project if students cut class and don't hand in their work? And it's so unlike you, Jess, you are usually so reliable. What was so important that you couldn't get to class on Tuesday, anyway? Where were you?"

"I was attending my mother's funeral."

Dr. Morgan and Jess stared at each other across the room for a few seconds, until Jess realised that his red jumper was becoming pink and blurred. She knew she was about to cry, something she had scarcely done since Dotey's death, apart from a few tears shed at the crematorium and a few more in the cattle truck. However, this felt like a torrent that had been pent up for ten days, a dam that was about to give way in spectacular fashion, and here in Dr. Morgan's room of all places. Jess sank into a chair and sobbed, the Northamptonshire migration data paperwork cascading onto the floor around her. Dr. Morgan, probably wishing that he was in Northamptonshire with the data, handed Jess a large white handkerchief, then hurried away to make her a cup of strong, sweet tea; it tasted horrible, but Jess drank it anyway, and dried her eyes, while Dr. Morgan hastened to the notice-board to cross her name off the list of shame.

This was the end of the rainy season for Jess; the long and anxious time which had begun on the chilly landing at The Close finally ended in Dr. Morgan's study thirteen years later. It would no longer be necessary for Jess to worry about her parents' criticism and to seek lonely solace in tears every time she was deemed to be wanting; thanks to the opportunity of a university education, she quickly grew in confidence and found her voice. Of course, as the years went by, there were plenty of incidental tears – of delight when she gained her BA, and then later her Masters degree; of sorrow when relationships broke down, of joy when her sons were born, and later, of grief when close friends died. However, tears were no longer her only recourse. Jess was finally free to speak her mind. There was no stern parent to remind her that she was only a little girl, who should know better than to answer back or contradict her elders, or that it was unseemly for her to express her views. Jess was now finally a young woman with a mind of her own. Whenever anyone – and always it seemed to be a man – attempted to disparage her, as a surprising number over the years tried to do, belittling her achievements, criticising some aspect of her appearance or emphasising her weaknesses rather than her strengths, she came to realise that the only thing to do was to leave these negative people behind. Jess knew now that there was absolutely no requirement for her to be what anyone else wanted her to be; and no-one had any right to demand more of her, so long as she was doing her best.

Jess did not weep for Jack, whose death occurred in 1976, in his seventy-eighth year. Mrs. Steele posted her the announcement from the local newspaper, which stated that Jack's funeral was to be the very next day. Nicholas, Jack's son by his first marriage, had never even acknowledged Jess's existence, but she obtained his number from directory enquiries and telephoned him, asking him to kindly send on anything of Dotey's he might come across when sorting out Jack's effects. Nicholas replied coldly that he had cleared out Jack's cottage, and had found nothing whatsoever relating to his father's second wife; not a single letter or photograph. It was as though Jess's mother had played no part at all in Jack's life. In the circumstances,

Jess felt that it would be inappropriate for her to attend Jack's funeral, since she clearly would not be welcome; and anyway, Jack was not the man named as her father on her newly discovered birth certificate. Jess felt that it would be hypocritical to pretend to mourn the passing of a man who had made her mother's life a misery and caused herself such heartache. When she rang Peter, he said did not want to go either; and Jeff was at the time working overseas.

Everything which had constrained Dotey and her female contemporaries throughout their lives began to change over the ensuing years, with reforms bringing in sex equality in the fields of education, employment and the provision of goods and services. (One reform which came too late for Jess was that Oxford and Cambridge universities, which had for years had only a limited number of colleges for female undergraduates, began to admit women on equal terms with men.) The long-held notion that women were to be regarded simply as providers of domestic services, dependent on men for their keep, was swept away during the last quarter of the twentieth century, and a reform was passed ushering in separate taxation, so that a married woman's income was no longer classed as belonging to her husband. Domestic violence came eventually to be treated seriously, and a countrywide network of women's refuges opened. Rape within marriage was at last deemed a crime.

Mortgages and all other services were made available to women on the same terms as they were to men, and male guarantors were no longer required in order for a woman to rent a television set. Jess had heard of a woman with a well-paid and responsible job in the Probation Service who had been obliged by the building society to get her less well-paid younger brother to guarantee her mortgage, but thankfully this requirement was finally abolished. Married women entered the workforce in increasing numbers, and were legally obliged to receive equal treatment; the hitherto commonly-held idea that they were working simply for 'pin-money' disappeared. Workplace harassment was eventually taken seriously, so that the bottom-pinching factory owner (whose attentions Jess's co-workers had been obliged to endure or else risk losing their jobs) would now be taken to court. The elbow-tugging shop manager at WH Smith's would also now have to be made aware that such inappropriate behaviour could not go unchallenged; and the potato digging women would naturally expect to receive the same wage as their male colleagues, rather than a fifth less, for an afternoon's work.

No-fault divorce, abortion more or less on demand, and reliable contraception became available, and sex education was introduced into state schools when Jess was a Parent Governor at her sons' primary school, so that children could be taught the facts of life in a sensible manner, and young girls were no longer shielded from something coyly referred to as 'unpleasantness,' as Dotey had successfully striven to shield Jess for so many years.

Throughout her professional life as a university researcher, interviewing people all over the country on all manner of topics, and particularly when collecting life stories of older people, Jess heard again and again from women who had been denied opportunities afforded to their brothers, simply because of their gender. In Care Homes and Women's Institutes and University of the Third Age meetings Jess met intelligent women who had been obliged to leave school at the earliest possible opportunity, without any qualifications, in order to get work and contribute to the family budget. Jack had been far from being alone in his opinion of the irrelevance of educating girls. Women also told her how they had been made to stay home in the evenings and at weekends, helping with household chores, while their brothers were allowed to come and go as they pleased; and how, when they were occasionally permitted to go out, the girls had to be back home at a specified time, and were obliged to account for every detail of their whereabouts; Dotey had not been at all unusual in her double standard treatment of her sons and her only daughter. Thankfully, nowadays most girls are no longer expected to be simply dutiful and submissive, but are encouraged and expected to be as confident as boys.

However, Britain is still far from being a perfect society, with shocking accounts emerging of the grooming, exploitation and trafficking of young girls by sexual predators, indicating that, even in the twenty-first century some people continue to treat girls and women simply as commodities. Contempt for females is shown not only by the criminal gangs who exploit them but also the authorities whose duty it is to protect children. Police forces and Local Authority

Social Services departments have been shown to be failing in their statutory duty, often dismissing sexual exploitation as the 'life-style choices' of vulnerable teen-and pre-teenage girls, and using this as an excuse not to take action against criminals operating in towns and cities throughout the land. While legislation exists to protect the vulnerable, the fact that it is on the Statute Book is almost irrelevant if the laws are not enforced. Controversy has arisen about the unequal treatment of girls in some state schools; while the internet has provided new opportunities for misogyny, where women who speak out can find themselves attacked by so-called internet 'trolls', denigrating their appearance or opinions. Examples include remarks made against those campaigning for women to be depicted on new banknotes, and women speaking out against a convicted rapist being re-employed as a professional footballer. There have even been death threats against a woman TV presenter thought to be about to replace a man on a popular motoring show. Jess herself was denigrated as an 'old hag' when she appeared on a TV teatime quiz show in 2015. Of course, it is impossible to legislate for beliefs; and it seems that re-education of half the population cannot be achieved in a single generation.

The progress regarding the status of women achieved over the past fifty years must never be taken for granted, but must be carefully guarded. Women of Jess's generation, where girls were paid threepence less per hour in wages than boys, want such discrimination to be recorded, so that there can never be any complacency and no thought of going back. No-one should ever have to live like Dotey, subservient to a cruel husband – yet it has been recently recorded that incidents of domestic violence increase markedly when the England football team lose a match. Women seem to be judged more than ever on how they look, having to conform to a notional standard of glamour, daily reinforced by the publication of photos of topless models in a popular newspaper; until the time of writing in 2015, when thankfully, the practice appears to have ceased. Cosmetic surgery has boomed, indicating that many women still lack confidence in their natural appearance. In many ways, thanks to the explosion of social media, there is more pressure than ever on young women, despite the reams of equality legislation intended to widen their opportunities.

As Dotey had insisted throughout Jess's childhood, "A mother knows best!" and Dotey was proved correct in her opinion of Jess and R—'s marriage. They were not really well suited, and after four years, with their student days finished, their marriage ended, (although as it turned out, Dotey was never to know this.) It did not help that bean-pole R—'s pet name for Jess was "Tub-Tub", even though Jess had at last 'fined down' to a size 12, the slimmest she would ever be. R—, who was in the fortunate position of having been taught to drive by his parents at age 17, was very disparaging about Jess's efforts to learn to drive the A30. ("You'll **never** pass your test!) although Jess actually went on to pass at her very first attempt, some time after she and R— had separated. Her partner at that time, with only a motorbike licence, complained that Jess's driving test examiner really must need his own head examining, fancy passing Jess! Jess began to wonder what it was with these exasperating men, who appeared to regard driving as some sort of divine right bestowed upon the male sex, not to be extended to women except in certain limited circumstances, for example, those working as district nurses, and then of course such women should be suitably grateful for the privilege… Jess blithely took no notice of her partner's remarks, and purchased her first car, a second hand green Ford Anglia. When the Harry Potter films came out many years later, she wished very much that she had kept it. Meanwhile her partner borrowed the Anglia to take his driving test, in order to up-grade from the motorbike licence; inexplicably, he failed, giving as an excuse the fact that Jess's car was too high-geared and anyway the test examiner had clearly been hungry and in need of his lunch.

It dawned on Jess in middle age that while she had never succeeded in living up to her mother's expectations – in that she had not stayed long in teaching and had therefore never become a Head Mistress- she had actually exceeded every expectation of all the men in her life, starting with Jack and continuing with husband, partners and boyfriends. Each and every one of them had informed her categorically that she 'would never' do something – go to university, learn to drive, be happy, write a book, be successful; Jess wondered how they could all have been so wrong; and, more importantly, why they had all wanted so much to be right…

The women of Jess's generation, the post-war 'baby-boomers,' have lived through and contributed to an extraordinary social revolution which, to her daughter's great sorrow, Dotey did not survive to witness.

Other books by Jill Robinson.

Berringden Brow: Memoirs of a single parent with a crush
Introducing Jess and her friends, the struggling yet still optimistic women of a Pennine village, coping with stroppy kids, bizarre job interviews, ageism, lookism, sizeism, sexism... scanning the personal columns in search of that rare eligible man without hypochondria, a live-in mother, multiple allergies, a penchant for playing with toy soldiers or sex in public places. But when it all gets too much for Jess she can always escape into the library...

Sons and Lodgers
All Jess wants is a quiet life. All her friends want is somewhere to stay. Jess feels her serenity slipping as she struggles with teenage tantrums, men's mid-life crises, dope, dogs, refugees, rampant plants, rough sleepers in the shed, bureaucrats on the doorstep – and she is rapidly running out of floor space.

A Place Like This
So many people find their way to Jess and Nick's advice centre – asylum seekers, a trafficked young woman, a heart-broken husband, a man with evil spirits in the house... Jess tries to help everyone, with varying degrees of success. Meanwhile, why is widowed Norah living in a dog kennel, who has stolen the office aspidistra, and will Nick really be sent to prison for conspiring to make a false passport?

Life's Rich Tapestry
While working on a research project collecting the life stories of Care Home residents, including the Yorkshire Ripper's former newsagent and Nell, the proud 'resident from Hell', Jess reflects on how her own life has led her from running round the Wishing Tree to chasing peacocks down the back streets of Berringden Brow. Then she finds herself at a Folk Week chaperoning a troupe of 46 Koreans.

An entertaining series of small-town oddness...